BIRDS OF THE PACIFIC STATES

MOBBING A PYGMY OWL

The nearer birds, reading down and left to right: Chestnut-backed Chickadee, Red-breasted Nuthatch, Oregon Chickadee, Golden-crowned Kinglet ♂ and ♀, Pygmy Owl, Oregon Junco, Ruby-crowned Kinglet ♀ and ♂.

BIRDS OF THE PACIFIC STATES

CONTAINING BRIEF BIOGRAPHIES AND DESCRIPTIONS OF ABOUT FOUR HUNDRED SPECIES, WITH ESPECIAL REFERENCE TO THEIR APPEARANCE IN THE FIELD

BY

RALPH HOFFMANN

Member of the American Ornithologists' Union
Director of the Santa Barbara Museum of Natural History

WITH TEN PLATES IN COLOR AND OVER TWO HUNDRED ILLUSTRATIONS IN BLACK AND WHITE

BY

MAJOR ALLAN BROOKS

Fellow of the American Ornithologists' Union

BOSTON AND NEW YORK
HOUGHTON MIFFLIN COMPANY
The Riverside Press Cambridge
1927

The Riverside Press
CAMBRIDGE · MASSACHUSETTS
PRINTED IN THE U.S.A.

TO

IRENE AND BERNHARD HOFFMANN

THIS BOOK IS AFFECTIONATELY

DEDICATED

PREFACE

In the preparation of this book I have received generous assistance from many people. Mr. H. S. Swarth has given me much help and advice, especially on questions of nomenclature. Dr. Joseph Grinnell has given me every facility at the Museum of Vertebrate Zoölogy and Mr. L. E. Wyman has been equally hospitable at the Los Angeles Museum of Science. I owe thanks to the Bureau of Biological Survey and to its chief, Dr. E. W. Nelson, for permission to use Dr. W. P. Taylor's notes on distribution for Washington and Mr. S. G. Jewett's for Oregon, and to Dr. Taylor, Professor W. T. Shaw, and Mr. Jewett for the loan of their notes. Mrs. Florence Merriam Bailey has kindly allowed me to use the figures for the length of the species given in her *Handbook of Birds of the Western United States*, taken from Mr. Robert Ridgway's *Manual of North American Birds*. Commander H. E. Parmenter and Dr. C. W. Townsend have read most of the manuscript and made valuable suggestions. Dr. T. I. Storer has read parts of the manuscript and made helpful comments. Mr. J. Hooper Bowles has very kindly checked over the descriptions of nests and eggs. Mr. F. H. Allen has not only helped to correct the proof but has also made valuable suggestions as to the text. I desire to express my gratitude to Major Brooks for his constant coöperation in the preparation of the illustrations; if the text is as good as the illustrations I shall feel assured of the worth of the whole. Major Brooks has also supplied the colors of bill and feet for a few birds; these are indicated by the initial (B).

In the use of scientific names I have followed the A.O.U. Check-List, but have added in brackets certain species and subspecies not yet adopted by the committee, but constantly referred to in the publications of the Cooper Ornithological Club. The arrangement of families and subfamilies is that of the new Check-List, not yet published; thanks are due to Dr. A. Wetmore for assistance in making this arrangement. In the matter of popular names I have tried to bring out the fact that in the field species and not subspecies are important. The descriptions are based on field notes checked by skins. The distribution for California is based on Grinnell's Distributional List with whatever additional data I have been able to secure, the distribution for Oregon on Mr. S. G. Jewett's notes, and that for Washington on Dr. W. P. Taylor's and Professor W. T. Shaw's notes.

I have tried to make the book readable as well as accurate, and have depended as much as possible on my own field observation; in the relatively few cases where I have compiled from other observers, I have given credit.

Ralph Hoffmann

Carpinteria, California
January, 1927

CONTENTS

COLORED PLATES

INTRODUCTION

Cicero in a famous passage in one of his orations extols the delights of the study of literature, asserting that it forms the taste of youth, delights old age, is an ornament in prosperity, a solace in adversity, accompanies us to the country, and travels with us to foreign lands. We might easily paraphrase the orator's words and apply them to the study of birds. It develops keen observation in youth and is a resource in old age, even for the invalid if he can but have a porch or a window for a post of observation. Birds become the companions of our work in the garden and of our walks; martins and nighthawks or a gray-winged gull sail across the sky even opposite a dentist's window. Birds in a new region are simply birds to the uninitiated; to one who has known the birds at home, a journey offers an opportunity to make new friends. If a parent wishes to give his children three gifts for the years to come, I should put next to a passion for truth and a sense of humor, love of beauty in any form. Who will deny that birds are a conspicuous manifestation of beauty in nature?

The time to begin the study of birds is when the impulse first comes to the individual. Each season has its attractions and its difficulties. Let us assume that the student has begun his study in the winter, not the eastern winter of snow and leafless trees which we on the Coast must go into or across the mountains to experience, but the winter which is marked in the life of a bird by the freedom from family cares. Birds have their homes in winter as well as in summer. In the case of resident birds, House Finches, Jays, and Chickadees, for example, the winter and the summer homes are often the same. Let the student who begins his study of birds in December or January make a list of fifty common resident birds that he may expect to find; if he lives on the Pacific slope of California he will have for neighbors such varied examples of bird life as the Valley Quail, the Flicker, the Black Phœbe, the House Finch, the Brown and Spotted Towhees, the Wren-Tit, the Bush-Tit, and the Mockingbird. In Oregon and Washington Chickadees, Kinglets, Woodpeckers, and Jays are common in the winter woods. Let him read in this or any other book (one cannot have too many good bird books) the account of any one of these birds. If he wishes to begin with the House Finch, he will learn that the bird frequents the weedy borders of roadsides or perches in long rows on telephone wires; that the male has a crimson head and breast; that the female is gray and much streaked below. He will read that the bird is talkative; that its notes are often harsh, but that the song of the red-breasted male is a vigorous succession of warbled notes. He will expect the bird to roost at night in the vines on his porch. If he begins his search for a House Finch with these facts in mind, he will have no difficulty in finding a bird that fits into his mental picture. Then let him compare with his supposed House Finch the detailed description given in this book, and if it checks, he should feel satisfied that he has made the bird's acquaintance. Let him, however, read carefully in the discussion of the House Finch the paragraph dealing with the other birds with which it might be confused, to make sure that he has not mistaken the Purple Finch for the House Finch. The distribution given for each species directly after the description is also an important check. If the House Finch is not supposed to occur in the region where the student thinks he has found it, in Tacoma, for instance, he should assume that he has made a mistake.

When the mysterious urge impels some of the winter birds to leave a land of plenty and return to the grove or field or rocky islet in the north where they were bred, new birds appear along the whole coast, often announcing their arrival by song. If the student has become fairly well acquainted during the winter months with the common resident birds, the first Bullock Oriole with its striking black and orange markings and its distinctive high-pitched song will attract his attention. A student can easily secure or prepare for himself a list of common migrants; by reading over the accounts of each of these the student should have no difficulty in determining the identity of such a strikingly marked bird as the Bullock Oriole. Care must be taken, of course, by a careful study of the description of the bird to guard against mistaking the Arizona Hooded Oriole of southern California for the Bullock Oriole. An earnest student will read up beforehand and store his mind in migration time with mental pictures of what he may expect to see or hear.

In nature one season runs imperceptibly into the next; not all birds mate on Saint Valentine's Day. Before the student has made the acquaintance of the last of the migrants, he will be astonished to find some of his acquaintances of the winter, the resident birds, feeding half-grown young. Particularly in southern California, where spring comes not by the calendar, but whenever winter rains descend, nesting begins early. Anna and Allen Hummingbirds, California Thrashers, and California Horned Larks have generally laid their eggs by the middle of March. Nesting time offers the best opportunity to become intimate with a bird. The song or courtship performances of the male, the selection by the business-like female of a nesting site, the feeding of the young and their first entry into the world of the air, all make up a drama which one can sometimes follow from a rocking-chair on the porch, a drama in which tragedy and comedy occasionally darken or relieve the sober course of everyday events.

The song of birds is one of the hardest things to indicate or describe on the printed page. The tempo, the pitch, and the quality of tone are all such important factors in characterizing a song that syllables of human speech fall far short of giving a close imitation. The best that such syllabification can do is to suggest enough to make the student reasonably sure that he has attributed the notes he hears from a given bird to the right species, especially if he himself has a good ear. If the book says that the song of the Cassin Vireo is a series of detached phrases with rising and falling inflection, a careful student should not confuse the song with that of the Warbling Vireo, described as a continuous warble with very little range as to pitch. If the student will make his own transcriptions, after he has identified the singer, they will be a great aid in remembering the song.

Midsummer is the poorest season in which to study land birds in the lowlands, but it is the best time to observe shore-birds. The Sandpipers and Plover that breed in the tundras beyond the Arctic Circle remain in the North only long enough to hatch out their young and then begin their long southward migration. As early as July they appear on the mud-flats of estuaries and lagoons, or along sandy beaches. They are protected by law against hunters and have become so tame that close observation is frequently possible.

Many sea birds also breed in the Far North and migrate southward in winter. Our harbors and beaches are visited from October to April by cormorants, gulls, loons, grebes and sea ducks. Farther offshore other diving birds may be observed about the rocky shores of islands or on the ocean itself. Gulls become very tame, roosting on piers, following ferry-boats or gathering along the beaches for refuse cast up by the tides. There are a number of species of gulls and several plumages of each species, representing different stages of maturity. They therefore offer an excellent opportunity for careful study and training in accurate observation.

Ducks have of late years resorted to lakes and ponds in city parks and have become very tame; geese are harder to observe, keeping to wide-open spaces and made wary by hunting.

After a student has become acquainted with the birds commonly found within a short radius of his home, he longs for new worlds to conquer. If he is at all interested in natural history, he has already become aware that climatic conditions greatly affect the animal and vegetable life of different regions, that the plants and animals of the desert are very different from those of the humid northwest coast or of the high mountains. Scientists have studied these different associations in which life is grouped, and have divided the coast regions into distinct life zones which have received names. The student is referred to an excellent treatment of these life zones in Grinnell's Distributional List of the Birds of California (Pacific Coast Avifauna No. 11). If a student becomes familiar with the significance of the terms Upper and Lower Sonoran, Transition, Canadian, Boreal, and Arctic he will gain a much clearer notion of the birds that he may expect to find in his own region and when he travels. There is no part of the United States where touring is easier or more alluring than on the Pacific Coast, and there is no greater thrill to which a bird student can look forward than his first trip to the tree yuccas of the desert, the sugar pines and firs of the Sierras, or the sagebrush east of the great mountain divides. If he is genuinely interested in bird study and has carefully prepared himself to recognize the new birds that he will meet, a trip to any of these regions cannot fail to add largely to his list of bird acquaintances.

This book is intended as a guide to the study of birds, but, by its nature it is far from being as helpful as a living guide would be. If the student can find among his acquaintance some one who can help solve his puzzles or direct him to the favorite haunts of this or that species, he will make much greater progress. At the same time it is a general experience that what one learns in an easy fashion from a more experienced person often goes in at one ear and out at the other. If the student solves his own puzzles by hard work, he will never forget what he has learned. The best use to make of a teacher is to confirm or correct the results of the student's own careful work. All of us have profited again and again by a bit of help from a more experienced person given at the moment when it bore directly on what we had already worked out for ourselves. If there is a local bird club or class, a student should if possible become affiliated with it. If there is a museum he should visit it again and again. In the national parks, local museums, lectures and guides are being provided of which the tourist can take advantage.

Feeding tables outside a window and bird baths will attract many birds to our homes and give us opportunities to observe the same bird over and over again. If a student knows some one who has been allowed to band birds, he can see a wild bird in the bander's hand and by a close study learn characteristics that he will later recognize at a distance when the bird is free.

There are as many types of students as there are habits of mind. The hasty and inaccurate will ignore the clearest descriptions and rashly put down on their lists birds that it is extremely unlikely or impossible that they should have seen. The careful and accurate student will catch something of the scientist's attitude toward evidence and proof, will check up his identification in every possible way and will prefer for his own satisfaction to enter many birds in his list with a question mark, or await more evidence before coming to a decision. Perhaps the best lesson a beginner can get from a trained observer is to discover how the latter discriminates between favorable opportunities for definite identification and hasty glimpses which he at once declares are insufficient to enable him to come to a conclusion. The student with a field glass should take a lesson fron the gunner, who will not waste a shot on a bird that is out of range. A course in mushrooms should be prescribed for the rash bird student; if mushrooms are identified as edible on insufficient evidence and then eaten, the accuracy of the identification may be tested in an extremely convincing manner. There are many birds which cannot be identified in the field by a beginner. Each year as his knowledge and skill increase the number diminishes, but even after years of field work, the most experienced observer will not venture to distinguish between the small flycatchers or identify a too distant hawk.

It is assumed that any one seriously taking up the study of birds will provide himself with a pair of field glasses of six or eight power. The descriptions of plumage of birds given under each species and the color of bill and feet are based on the appearance of the bird under favorable circumstances as seen with such a glass. Such circumstances do not come every time the bird is seen, but sooner or later a favorable opportunity will reward patient study. The most prominent or characteristic field marks, those that serve best to distinguish one species from others closely resembling it have been italicized; those that may be seen only under exceptional circumstances have been enclosed in parentheses.

There has been no attempt to give a full biography of each bird; the limits of space would not permit it. The characteristic haunts of each species have been mentioned in the general picture with which the account of each bird opens, and those habits and tricks of behavior have been described which serve best to identify the species. The writer has included very little material compiled from other authors, believing that the book would gain in freshness and force if he confined himself to his own observations.

The descriptions given of the nests and eggs of such birds as breed in the Coast States is not intended to be full or minute. If a student has reason to suppose that a given bird is nesting in a certain spot and wishes to hunt for the nest, the descriptions given will give him a fairly good notion of where to look and what to look for. Or if he has found a nest, which he supposes to belong to a pair of birds that he has observed frequenting the neighborhood, the descriptions will go a long way to confirming or correcting his belief. Unless he has seen a parent bird on or near a given nest, even a minute description of the nest and eggs would often be insufficient to establish their identity without question.

The preparation of the book has entailed a great number of happy hours spent in field observation and repeated trips to the characteristic regions up and down the Coast. The book must now prove its worth by actual use. If it becomes a stimulus to bird study and a help to those who have already begun it, it will pay in part the debt of gratitude which the author owes to the long list of people who have helped him in many ways.

BIRDS OF THE PACIFIC STATES

• •
•

LOONS: *Order Gaviiformes*

LOONS: *Family Gaviidæ*

Common Loon. *Gavia immer*

On mountain lakes from northeastern California northward, particularly in Washington, the long quavering cry of the Loon is a not infrequent sound. The common calls are a long-drawn wailing *oo-ah-ee,* higher pitched in the middle than at the beginning or end, and a sound like maniacal laughter; the former is often given at night or at the approach

COMMON LOON (Breeding)

of a storm. In winter the Loon is for the most part silent. The Loon is often found in comparatively shallow water near the shores of bays or estuaries, peering down with bill and forehead under water or diving with a leap. The flight of the Loon is very swift and direct; it is notorious for its ability to dive instantly and to swim long distances under water. It is unable to rise from the water except against a wind.

Birds in adult breeding plumage are easily recognized, the *black head and neck* with its *white collar* contrasting with the white under parts. Most of the Loons seen along the coast in winter are immature birds or adults in winter plumage; these can be distinguished from Pacific and Red-throated Loons only by size. The two smaller species are much commoner than the so-called 'Common' Loon, and a student must become familiar with the relative size of the smaller species before attempting to identify the larger one in winter plumage.

28–36 Bill 3

Ad. in breeding plumage. — *Head and neck greenish black; white streaks* on the throat, and *on the side of the lower neck;* rest of *upper parts black, thickly marked with white spots,* especially prominent on the back; under parts white. Bill black. **Ad. in winter and Im.** — Top of head and hind-neck brownish black; rest of upper parts blackish, waved with light gray; under parts white. Bill, top dusky, sides whitish.

Dist. — *Cal.* Rare S.V. on elevated lakes in northeastern California; fairly common W.V. (Oct.–May) along the coast and on large inland bodies of water.

Ore. Common M. and W.V. along the coast (Oct.–May); occasional on the ocean in summer.

Wash. S.V. (Apr.–Oct.) on lakes both west and east; common M. and W.V. along the coast and in the Sound region.

Nest, a mass of decayed reeds, moss, etc., either on the shore close to the water, or on small islands or floating logs. *Eggs,* generally two, olive-brown, rather sparingly marked with blackish brown.

Pacific Loon. *Gavia pacifica*

An observer, a mile or so off the coast in April or May, will pass through endless lines of sea birds that are on their way to their breeding grounds on the tundras of the north. Flock after flock of Pacific Loons rise from the water and fly swiftly northward, their long necks and legs bent slightly downward, giving the body a slightly bow-shaped outline. Their rapid wing-strokes, long slender necks, and *pure white under parts* distinguish them from cormorants; the contrast of their *black throats* and *gray napes,* and the *conspicuous white spots on the back* identify them as Pacific Loons.

The Pacific Loon when swimming in winter in calm water near shore often thrusts the fore part of its head under water to peer for fish. It shares with other sea birds the habit of turning over on its side, showing its white under parts, preening itself meanwhile with one leg often out of water. Pacific Loons are silent along our coast in winter; only in late spring, birds in breeding plumage occasionally utter a guttural *owk* and a long wailing *aa-ick.*

In the winter plumage the Pacific Loon may be distinguished from the Red-throated Loon at close range by the absence of white spots in the uniformly dark back; in the first winter the feathers of the back are edged with whitish, giving it a slightly mottled appearance, but it is never thickly speckled with white like the back of the Red-throated Loon. When only the side view of a Loon is seen, the trained observer can generally tell the Pacific Loon from the Red-throated by the bill; the bill of the former is straight while that of the latter is apparently slightly

PACIFIC LOON (Breeding)

upturned. Its smaller size distinguishes the Pacific Loon from the Common Loon in winter.

23 Bill 2–2$\frac{1}{5}$

Ad. in breeding plumage. — *Top of head, nape* and *hind-neck gray,* — deepest on forehead and palest on nape; rest of *upper parts black,* marked on the *middle of the back with rows of large, square white spots*; *throat and fore-neck black,* purplish in strong light, streaked with white on the sides; under parts white. Bill black. **Ad. in winter.** — Hind-neck grayish brown, back blackish; under parts white. Bill dusky above, bluish gray on sides and below. **Im.** — Similar but feathers of back edged with light gray, but not spotted with white.

Dist. — *Cal.* *Ore.* *Wash.* } Common M. and W.V. (Sept.–May) along the coast and in estuaries, and in the Puget Sound region of Wash.; a few remain off the coast in summer.

Red-throated Loon. *Gavia stellata*

A Loon riding lazily the calm water of a harbor seems only a picturesque bit of a marine landscape. Let it approach close to the pier on which the observer stands and dive for its prey directly below in the clear water; then in an instant its latent speed and dexterity are revealed. Propelled by powerful strokes of its webbed feet, it follows every dart or winding of its victim till it seizes it in its bill, rises to the surface, and swallows it. The Red-throated Loon has a strong swift flight, and shows against the sky the slightly bow-shaped outline, the narrow wings and the snowy white under parts which distinguish loons in flight from cormorants. It dives, fishes and preens its plumage in much the same manner as the Pacific Loon. The writer has never heard any sound from the bird off our coast.

When directly below the observer, the *round white spots on the dark back* distinguish the Red-throated Loon in winter from the Pacific Loon. When seen from the side, the *bill* of the Red-throated Loon, owing to the curve of the lower mandible, seems slightly *upturned*, while that of the Pacific Loon looks straight. In April birds are not infrequently seen

RED-THROATED LOON (Winter)

with the *rich chestnut patch* in the *gray throat* characteristic of the breeding plumage. At close range the Red-throated Loon in breeding plumage can be identified in flight by the general gray appearance of the neck, which lacks the contrast of black throat and light gray nape characteristic of the Pacific Loon in breeding plumage. The back of the Red-throated Loon also lacks the large white spots that mark the Pacific Loon in breeding plumage.

24–27 Bill $2\frac{1}{4}$

Ad. in breeding season. — *Top of head dark gray;* back of neck blackish, streaked with white; *sides of head and neck clear gray;* rest of upper parts brownish; *a chestnut patch on the fore-neck;* rest of under parts white. Bill black, *apparently slightly upturned toward* the tip. **Ad. in winter and Im.** — Upper parts brownish gray; *back everywhere marked with small white spots;* under parts white. Bill dark above, lighter below.

Dist. — *Cal.* Common M. and W.V. (Sept.–Apr.) along the coast.
Ore. Common M. and W.V. (Nov.–June) along the coast.
Wash. Fairly common spring M. and W.V. (Nov.–June) along the coast and on the Sound.

GREBES: *Order Colymbiformes*

GREBES: *Family Colymbidæ*

WESTERN GREBE. *Æchmophorus occidentalis*

If one stands in winter on any wharf that runs some distance out into the harbor, or watches the calm sea off the beaches, here and there on the surface a white breast appears, above which extends a *very long and slender neck, pure white in front* and bearing a *black-topped head* and *long, slender yellow bill.* Presently the bird leaps forward and disappears; in a moment or two the water breaks near by and out of the ripples shoots the stately head and neck of the Western Grebe. Western Grebes spend much time on the ocean sleeping with the neck drawn back between the wings, the head pointing forward but turned slightly to one side with the bill concealed in the plumage. They are rarely seen in flight, but when they do fly, it is with very rapid strokes of their small wings, the long, slender neck stretched out in front and feet behind.

WESTERN GREBE

The Western Grebe breeds in many large lakes from northeastern California through eastern Oregon to Washington. Along the shores of such lakes, pairs of Western Grebes may be seen floating well off shore, or where not alarmed, diving in the shallow water close to the beach. Their rasping notes, *kerr kree,* sound all day and most of the night from every part of the lake. In the mating season a pair of Grebes go through an extraordinary performance. They swim side by side and repeatedly throw the head backward with a quick motion as if throwing something away. After working their emotions up to the requisite pitch, both birds suddenly stand upright with head and neck erect and wings held stiffly against the body, and rush forward on the water. In the breeding plumage the Western Grebe, though without a distinct crest, shows from the front or rear a puffy, slightly triangular effect on the sides of the head, both the black crown and the white cheeks being fuller at this season.

There is no other bird with which the Western Grebe can be confused, except the Holboell Grebe in winter; the former is much commoner in winter south of San Francisco Bay. The bill of the Western Grebe is longer than its head, more slender and straight than that of the Holboell. The *neck* of the Western Grebe is longer and more slender, and is *pure white* in front.

24–29 Bill $2\frac{3}{4}$–3

Ad. — *Top of head* and back of long neck *black;* back gray; white patch in extended wing; sides of neck and *under parts silvery white. Bill long and slender*, dusky along the top, *sides yellow* or greenish yellow.

Dist. — *Cal.* S.V. on lakes and ponds northward, chiefly east of the Sierras; abundant W.V. (Sept.–May) on the ocean, a few remaining on the ocean through the summer.

Ore. Common S.V. (May–Sept.) east; common W.V. (Sept.–Apr.) along the coast.

Wash. Not common S.V. east; common M. and W.V. (late Sept.–Apr.) on the Sound and along the coast.

Nest, a floating structure of reeds or other water plants, in or near aquatic vegetation. *Eggs*, 3–5, bluish white, soon stained darker.

Holboell Grebe. *Colymbus holbœlli*

From Monterey northward a student soon discovers among the birds that ride the ocean in winter a Grebe intermediate in size between the large slender-necked Western Grebe and the smaller Horned and Eared Grebes. The Holboell Grebe has a bill nearly as long as the head, much longer and heavier than that of the Horned and Eared Grebes, stouter even than that of the Western Grebe, and often giving the effect of curving slightly downward. The neck is distinctly longer than in the Horned Grebe, but is not slender and 'swan-like' as in the Western Grebe, and is gray in winter, not pure white as in the Western Grebe. Toward spring, particularly in April and May, the Holboell Grebe assumes the breeding plumage and is then unmistakable; it shows at this season a conspicuous *whitish cheek* between the *black top of the head* and the *reddish brown neck*. When seen from directly in front or behind, two low black tufts are evident on the sides of the head.

On the many arms and passages of Puget Sound and neighboring waters Holboell Grebes are common and are easily distinguished, both in the dull winter plumage and in the brighter breeding plumage, from the smaller Horned Grebes; south of Monterey, Holboell Grebes are rare.

Holboell Grebes dive for fish like their relatives, feeding commonly along the shore. They are not often seen in flight, except when migrating. They are silent in winter.

Left to right: HORNED GREBE, WINTER; HORNED GREBE, BREEDING; HOLBOELL GREBE, WINTER; HOLBOELL GREBE, BREEDING; EARED GREBE, BREEDING; EARED GREBE, WINTER

18–20½ Bill 1¾–2⅓

Ad. in breeding plumage. — *Top of head black*, with a short crest at the back; rest of upper parts blackish; *sides of head and throat ashy*, separated from crown by white line back of eye; *neck* (except down the back) *brownish red;* upper breast tinged with brownish red; rest of under parts white, dappled with dusky; white patch in extended wing. Bill stout, slightly decurved, upper mandible black, lower yellow, especially toward the base. **Ad. in winter and Im.** — Upper parts blackish brown; *throat and sides of head white;* neck ashy or ashy brown; rest of under parts whitish. Bill mostly yellowish, dusky above.

Dist. — *Cal.* W.V. (Oct.–May) along the coast, south to Santa Barbara, commoner northward; occasional on inland lakes.
Ore. Fairly common M. and W.V. (Oct.–May) along the coast.
Wash. Common M. and W.V. (Oct.–May) along the coast and on the Sound; not common S.V. on lakes in north-central region.

Nest, a floating structure of reeds, etc., in reedy lake borders or sloughs. *Eggs*, generally 4 to 5, pale bluish white, soon stained darker.

Horned Grebe. *Colymbus auritus*

The long piers that extend into the harbors of the Pacific Coast, harbors often only by courtesy, are excellent observation points for the student of wintering birds. A stout-bodied, slender-necked bird, dark above and white below, is frequently seen from such a post of observation, disappearing with a clean forward leap to emerge again in half a minute, perhaps with a small fish in its bill. The top of the head is *blackish, sharply separated from the white cheeks.* In this winter plumage the Horned Grebe is extremely hard to distinguish from the Eared Grebe. After much careful observation a student will note that some of the birds seen in the ocean itself have a more *clearly defined white cheek*, a stouter bill and a thicker neck than most of the birds seen in small inland ponds or lagoons; these are Horned Grebes. From Monterey southward the Horned Grebe is less common even on the ocean than the Eared Grebe, and great care must be taken even by a trained observer in identifying the species. North of Monterey the Horned Grebe becomes commoner, and in and about Puget Sound it is the only small Grebe commonly observed in winter. In April and May from Monterey northward, Horned Grebes are seen in breeding plumage; the *red neck* then distinguishes them readily from the black-necked Eared Grebe. The black top of the head, moreover, is not raised in a pointed crest as in the Eared Grebe.

Horned Grebes have a strong, vigorous flight with necks outstretched like small loons; they show *white wing-patches* in flight or when flapping their wings. They are practically silent in winter.

12½–15¼ Bill .85–1

Ad. in breeding plumage. — *Top and sides of head black*, forming a ruff on the sides; reddish brown area between eye and bill, a *brownish yellow stripe back from eye*, widening behind into a crest and deepening in color; rest of upper parts brownish black; white patch in extended wing; *neck, upper breast* and sides rich *brownish red;* rest of under parts white. Bill black, tip yellow; iris red. **Ad. in winter and Im.** — Top of head and back of neck blackish; rest of upper parts grayish black; chin, throat and *sides of head* *white,* white sides of neck almost meeting on nape; fore-neck washed with gray; rest of under parts white. Bill dusky, lighter beneath.

Dist. — *Cal.* } Fairly common M. and W.V. (Sept.–May) along the coast;
Ore. } M. on large inland lakes.
Wash. Common M. and W.V. (Sept.–May) along the coast and on the Sound; occasional on large inland lakes. A few non-breeding birds in summer.

Eared Grebe. *Colymbus nigricollis californicus*

Among the wintering ducks and mudhens on ponds and estuaries or off beaches and wharves one notes a smaller bird, *dark gray above* and *white below,* with slender neck and a broad, high stern. Suddenly it leaps forward and disappears head first, rising later a short distance off. The Eared Grebe in winter rarely flies, but occasionally it flaps its wings, showing white patches. In spring the birds acquire the breeding plumage; the entire neck becomes *black,* a *black crest* adorns the head, and *yellowish brown feathers* extend backward in silky tufts on *the sides of the head;* the flanks are now *reddish brown.* In this striking plumage Eared Grebes are found breeding in colonies in shallow lakes chiefly east of the Cascades and Sierras.

A morning spent in watching a breeding colony in June or early July will disclose a fascinating variety of activities. Here a pair are diving and coming up with masses of green weed, with which they are building up their floating nest. Males are rushing at each other with lowered heads, or diving and reappearing near the female. Other pairs are engaged in striking courtship performances, swimming side by side, throwing back their heads and suddenly facing each other with their bodies erect, or in the same upright position rushing side by side along the water. Here and there females are standing on the nest platform in a curious posture, with neck bent downward and head pointing forward, or a female returning to her nest is removing the weed with which she has covered the eggs. From all parts of the marsh comes a chorus of cries, sounding at a distance like the peeping of frogs. The commonest note is a drawled *whoo-eek;* other notes are a long-drawn *whee* and a rapidly repeated *wheek wheek wheek.*

The beginner will find it almost impossible to distinguish the Eared Grebe from the Horned Grebe in winter plumage. The bill and neck of the Eared Grebe are more slender, and the whitish sides of the head are *less clearly marked off from the dusky top* and less extensive. The body of an Eared Grebe often has a more dumpy appearance, the back ending in a high stern. The Eared Grebe is much the commoner species in southern California, often abundant in spring and fall. There should be no difficulty in distinguishing the two species in the breeding plumage; the Eared Grebe has a *black neck* and upper breast and a *black crest;* the Horned Grebe has a reddish neck and upper breast and the black feathers on the top of the head lie flat.

12–14 Bill 1

Ad. in breeding plumage. — Head, *slender neck and upper breast,* including the crest, *black;* tufts of somewhat fan-shaped yellowish feathers extending back from the eye; back blackish; white patch in extended wing; *flanks brownish red;* rest of under parts silvery white. Bill slender, black; iris red. **Ad. in winter.** — Top of head, hind-neck and back black; cheek whitish; front and sides of neck gray; throat and under parts white. Bill dusky above; sides lead gray. **Im.** — Back browner; sides of head more tinged with dusky.

Dist. — *Cal.* Common S.V. on shallow lakes, chiefly east of the Sierras, as far south as Bear Lake; common M. and W.V. (Sept.–May) along the coast and on inland bodies of water.

Ore. Common S.V. on shallow lakes in southern Ore. east of the Cascades; M. and W.V. (Sept.–Apr.) along the coast.

Wash. S.V. on shallow lakes east; fairly common M. and W.V. (Sept.–early May) in the Sound region.

Nest, a floating structure of reeds, etc., in lake borders and sloughs. *Eggs*, generally 4 or 5, dull bluish white, soon stained darker.

Pied-billed Grebe. *Podilymbus podiceps*

In all the bays and estuaries along the coast, as well as in tule-bordered

PIED-BILLED GREBE (Adult)

inland ponds and sloughs, a brown bird, smaller than a Coot, with slender arching neck and narrow snake-like head, floats lazily on the water, or, when feeding, dives with a forward leap. There is no bird more expert than the Pied-billed Grebe in disappearing under water when it believes itself better off out of sight. It often simply submerges, the body going down first while the head is still above the water. Seen from behind, the stern is broad, the tail is so absurdly short as to appear lacking, and a white area is apparent under the tail. In winter the general color is brown, paler on the under parts. As spring approaches, the top of the head and the back become blackish, a small *throat patch of black* appears, and the *light-colored bill* is circled with a black band.

The Pied-billed Grebe breeds in any body of water where tules afford protection. Here the loud cuckoo-like call of the bird may be heard from March till July, — *cuck-cuck-cuck-cuck-cow-cow-cow*. A rarer note is a loud *wáh-hoo, wáh-hoo* suggesting, in the quality of the tone, the call of the Loon. The Grebe also has an alarm note, *toot, toot, toot*. In the breeding season, when a mated pair are swimming close together, they utter a call like the syllables *kek-kek-kek-kek*, etc., so rapidly repeated that the notes seem to be shaken out of their bills. Very young birds have the head and neck striped with black and white; when alarmed, they mount on their parent's back, where they ride while the latter swims off.

The Pied-billed Grebe may readily be distinguished from the Eared Grebe with which it is often associated by its brownish under parts and its short, blunt bill; its head is flat, suggesting a reptile's. The Pied-billed Grebe occurs commonly on salt-water estuaries but rarely off shore.

12–15 Bill .85

Ad. in breeding plumage. — Top of head, back of neck and top of back blackish brown, rest of upper parts brown; eye-ring white; small area of *black on throat;* rest of under parts white mottled with dusky. *Bill* shorter than head, *light colored,* crossed near the middle *by a black band;* iris brown. **Ad. in winter and Im.** — Black of upper parts replaced by brown; throat-patch concealed or lacking. Bill dark above, sides yellow, without a black band. **Im. when first hatched.** — Upper parts blackish with four whitish stripes; head and neck streaked with white.

Dist. — *Cal.* Common R. More widely distributed in winter.
Ore. / *Wash.* } Common S.V. (Apr.–Oct.); a few winter.

Nest, a floating structure of decayed weeds, etc., generally in or near reeds. *Eggs,* 5–8, dull bluish white, soon stained darker.

TUBE-NOSED SWIMMERS: *Order Procellariiformes*

ALBATROSSES: *Family Diomedeidæ*

Black-footed Albatross. *Diomedea nigripes*

It is perhaps just as well not to inquire too closely why a bird of such romantic associations as an Albatross should generally be seen in the wake of a steamer. Let us forget why it settles on the water for a few moments well back of the stern and rather watch for the crescent of its *long narrow wings* when it begins again to follow the steamer. Its flight is the characteristic soaring and gliding of its smaller relatives the Shearwaters, sweeping upward till it is silhouetted against the sky, then downward till it is lost for a moment against the dark waves. Occasionally one passes close enough to show the *brown upper parts*, the *whitish head* and *rump*, and the *pale spots* toward the *tips* of the *saber-shaped wings*. The flight is accomplished by a few strokes which bring the wings well below the body, followed by a masterly gliding; the bird can rise from the water far behind the steamer directly into the wind and without a single stroke overtake the vessel. Like the Shearwaters, the Black-footed Albatross comes boldly about the boats of deep-sea fishermen far off shore to feed on refuse fish.

28½–36 Wingspread 7 ft.

Ad. — Upper parts brown except *whitish head, whitish* rump and light gray spots near the tips of the *long narrow wings;* under parts whitish. Bill dark reddish brown (Coues); feet black. **Im.** — Uniformly dark sooty.

SHORT-TAILED ALBATROSS. *Diomedea albatrus*

The Short-tailed Albatross was formerly not uncommon at all seasons off the coast, but has rarely been seen of late years. Its manner of flight resembles that of the preceding species, from which the adult is readily distinguished by its nearly uniform white color, only the wings or tail being dark or blackish. It is said to be much shyer than the Black-footed, not following so freely in the wake of vessels. (Nelson.)

33–37 Wingspread 7 ft.

FULMARS, SHEARWATERS, etc.: *Family Hydrobatidæ*

PACIFIC FULMAR. *Fulmarus glacialis glupischa*

On the fishing banks well off shore or even in Monterey Bay where fishermen are baiting hand lines, *stocky gray or whitish* birds about the size of a small gull gather about the boats as confidingly as chickens, waiting for fragments of bait or rejected fish to be thrown overboard. When they fly, Fulmars take a few strokes, not so rapid as a Shearwater's, and then, setting their wings stiffly in a slight curve, sail now with one wing inclined toward the water, now with the other. In a breeze they sail upward till their outlines cut the skyline, then down into the next trough of the waves. When sitting on the water, their short thick necks and the *stout deeply hooked bill* distinguish them from gulls. Occasionally Fulmars come close in to a pier, but for the most part they are birds of the open sea, to be observed only from a boat.

The Fulmar has many phases of plumage, ranging from one that is uniformly sooty gray to one with a white head, nearly white tail and white areas in the forward part of the wing. The heavy body and lighter color of the upper parts distinguish a Fulmar from any Shearwater. Fulmars, moreover, are commonest in winter, Shearwaters in summer and early fall, though a few of each overlap. If seen at close range, the stout, *light-colored bill* distinguishes the Fulmar from any other winter sea bird.

17–19

Ad. in light phase. — Head, neck and under parts white, mantle light gray; wings dusky at tip and with a whitish area toward the tip. *Bill stout,* hooked, dull orange at tip, *greenish yellow on sides* and black about the nostrils; feet whitish. **Ad. in dark phase.** — Whole plumage dark gray; light-colored patch in wing evident but not conspicuous.

Dist. — *Cal.* Common W.V.; a few occur in summer and fall.
Ore. / *Wash.* } Probably common M. and W.V. (Oct.–Apr.) off shore.

Rodgers Fulmar. *Fulmarus rodgersi*

A Fulmar mottled with white on the upper surface of the wings has been considered a distinct species but may prove merely a color phase of the Pacific Fulmar.

Pink-footed Shearwater. *Puffinus creatopus*

Among the Sooty Shearwaters off our coast in summer one often sees Pink-footed Shearwaters, slightly larger and with nearly uniform *white under parts.* Their flight and feeding habits are very much the same as those of the Sooty Shearwaters. The Black-vented Shearwater also has white under parts and can be distinguished from the Pink-footed only by its smaller size. The latter is slightly larger than the common Sooty Shearwater; the former is considerably smaller.

19

Ad. — Upper parts dark brown; light areas showing in the outspread wings; *under parts chiefly white.* Bill dark at tip, pale flesh-color on sides and below; feet flesh-colored.

Dist. — Common off our coast in summer and fall; occasional in winter.

Black-vented Shearwater. *Puffinus opisthomelas*

When gulls and cormorants are hurrying toward a spot in the ocean, and pelicans begin to strike with a splash, it means that a school of herring are swimming so near the surface that even the non-diving gulls are able to scoop them up. A close scrutiny of the busy throng will occasionally reveal birds with long, narrow wings flying with rapid wing-strokes low over the water, then sailing with wings stiffly set or flopping suddenly into the water. The Black-vented Shearwaters appear in summer, having moved northward from their breeding grounds in Lower California, and remain off our coast through the fall and early winter. They are noticeably smaller than the Pink-footed, and have a slightly different flight, flapping more and sailing less. When they light on the water, their *white under parts* show prominently. They stay for the most part several miles off shore but are occasionally seen from some projecting point of the mainland, following a school of herring.

$12\frac{1}{4}$–15

Head, sides of breast and upper back dark grayish brown; wings, lower

back and tail black (at a distance whole upper parts apparently black); under side of wing white; *under parts white;* area under base of tail black; bill blackish above, sides lead gray; feet, outer face dusky, inner very light flesh-colored.

Dist. — Common off the coast of southern Cal. as far north as Santa Cruz in late fall and early winter; a few occur nearly throughout the year.

Sooty Shearwater. *Puffinus griseus*

When the smaller fish are driven to the surface by the barracuda and the albacore, Brown Pelicans plunge into the swarming mass and splash the water high into the air. At the same time a flock of dark-bodied, long-winged birds circle over the water, the foremost lighting and seizing their prey, the rear of the line passing over the van and alighting in turn. At times the ellipse thus formed extends along the coast as far as one can see, the birds streaming past in close formation.

SOOTY SHEARWATER

On any trip off shore in summer Sooty Shearwaters are met singly or in small flocks gliding close to the water, holding their wings stiffly extended and inclining them so that first one wing and then the other just grazes the surface. When the wind is fresh, they soar upward till their forms are outlined against the sky. They often alight on the water, getting up again with some difficulty in calm weather but easily against a wind; after a few strokes of the wings they begin to sail, rising over the crests of the waves and disappearing from sight in the troughs between. Ordinarily Shearwaters keep more than a mile from shore, where their forms are sometimes just visible from the beach against the skyline, but when small fish are running close in shore they may sometimes be seen from the beach. The Sooty Shearwater can be distinguished from any of our other species except the Slender-billed by the dark gray of its under parts. It is larger than the Slender-billed but unless mixed flocks afford some criterion of size the two species are almost impossible to distinguish. The Sooty is by far the commoner species, and is abundant in spring and summer; the Slender-billed occurs chiefly in the late fall.

16–18

Entire plumage dark gray, except for the whitish lining under the wings; light areas near tips of long narrow wings. Bill, upper mandible dusky, lower bluish gray; feet, outer face dusky, inner bluish gray.

Dist. — Occurs in great numbers off the entire coast from Apr. to Oct. and less commonly at other seasons.

Pale-footed Shearwater. *Puffinus carneipes*

The Pale-footed Shearwater, a native of the islands off New Zealand and Australia, has been taken off Monterey. The bird resembles the Sooty Shearwater but might be distinguished by a trained observer under favorable conditions by the absence of any light color on the under sides of the wings and by the *light-colored bill.*

Slender-billed Shearwater. *Puffinus tenuirostris*

At the end of their breeding season Slender-billed Shearwaters migrate from the South Pacific northward, apparently keeping to the west Pacific on the outward journey and returning south through the east Pacific; they appear off our coast in the fall and winter. The Slender-billed Shearwater has dark under parts like the Sooty Shearwater but might be distinguished by a trained observer under favorable conditions by its smaller size.

14

Upper parts sooty black; under parts dark gray.

Dist. — Common in fall and early winter (main flight in Nov. and Dec.) off the coast.

New Zealand Shearwater. *Puffinus bulleri*

The New Zealand Shearwater has been taken in winter off Monterey. It is a white-breasted bird but it would be rash for any but an experienced collector to attempt to distinguish it from the commoner, larger Pink-footed Shearwater.

16½

Head and tail black; *back gray in marked contrast;* lower parts white.

LONG-LEGGED STORM PETRELS: *Family Oceanitidæ*

Fork-tailed Petrel. *Oceanodroma furcata*

The Fork-tailed Petrel, if encountered on the ocean by day, will be easily recognized. Its plumage is bluish ash instead of the sooty black of its relatives.

8–9

General plumage bluish ash. Bill and feet black.

Dist. — S.V. on islands off Humboldt and Del Norte Cos., Cal., and on Three Arch Rocks, Ore., but not known to breed in Wash. Recorded from Wash. along the coast (occasional in the Straits) from Oct. to Mar.; M. and W.V. as far south as San Pedro, Cal.

Nest, a burrow scantily lined with grasses and rootlets. *Egg,* one, dull white, unspotted or finely spotted with lilac.

BEAL PETREL. *Oceanodroma leucorhoa kaedingi* in part [*Oceanodroma leucorhoa beali*]

From the deck of a steamer plying between San Francisco and Seattle one can observe in May the northward migration of *white-rumped* petrels. The birds fly steadily low over the water, occasionally turning quickly to one side or the other but keeping easily abreast of the boat. The white rump is often hidden by the angle at which the bird flies, but sooner or later comes into view. During the breeding season the Beal Petrel is rarely seen by day even in the vicinity of its breeding ground.

BEAL PETREL

An island occupied by Beal Petrels is honeycombed by hundreds of burrows. Shortly after dark the petrels begin a wild nocturnal flight, issuing from their burrows and circling to and fro, in and out, with such abandon that two often strike each other in mid-air. From the air and from the ground their crowing note is constantly repeated, *kick-era-rick-oo,* very rapid and vigorous. Besides this note a soft crooning issues from the burrows *crrr-oooo-kuck* or *ooee-crrr.*

8

General plumage sooty black at long range; *rump white;* wings long, showing silvery gray under surface; tail forked. Bill and feet black.

Dist. — Common S.V. (May–Aug.) to the islands off northern California, sparingly on the Farallon Is., and northward on Arch Rocks, Ore., and the islets off the coast of Wash. Recorded from Wash. from Apr. to Oct.

Nest, eggs laid at the end of burrows extending two or three feet under turf on islands. *Egg,* one, dull white, unspotted or finely spotted with lilac about the larger end.

Black Petrel. *Oceanodroma melania*

In May and June Black Petrels nest in loosely piled rocks or in crevices on the Coronados Islands off San Diego. At night they celebrate an aerial dance; their notes at this time have been described by A. W. Anthony as 'a loud *tuc-a-ree, tuc-tuc-a-roo,*' harsher than those of the Socorro Petrel. Like the rest of the family they feed and fly chiefly at night, but may occasionally be seen after the breeding season flying low over the open sea.

9

General color sooty black above, paler below. Bill and feet black.

Dist. — Breeds on the Coronados Is. off San Diego. Occurs in summer off the coast as far north as Monterey Bay.

Nest, eggs laid in crannies or crevices or at the end of burrows. *Egg,* one, dull white, unspotted or finely spotted with lilac about the larger end.

Ashy Petrel. *Oceanodroma homochroa*

The name Ashy is misleading for this petrel, and would be more appropriate for the Fork-tailed Petrel. The Ashy Petrel appears black at a distance, so that the bird is practically indistinguishable on the ocean from the Black Petrel except by its smaller size. It is the smallest of our petrels, considerably smaller than the Black Petrel, but unless the two species are seen together recognition by size alone is very difficult. It is occasionally seen off shore feeding over the surface of the waves with the easy flight characteristic of its family.

$7\frac{1}{4}$

General color grayish black; no white on rump. Bill and feet black.

Dist. — Abundant S.V. to the southeast Farallon I. and sparingly to Santa Cruz I.

Nest, eggs laid in crevices or under boulders. *Egg,* one, dull white, unspotted or finely spotted with lilac about the larger end.

Socorro Petrel. *Oceanodroma socorroensis*

During migration in April and May, and in late summer when the young are ready to fly, Socorro Petrels are occasionally seen flying low and gracefully over the ocean off San Diego. The Socorro Petrel is generally as black as the slightly larger Black Petrel; unless the two are together, it would be impossible to distinguish them.

$7\frac{3}{4}$–8

General color sooty black. Bill and feet black.
Dist. — S.V. to the Coronados Is. off San Diego.
Nest, eggs laid at the end of a short burrow. *Egg*, one, dull white, unspotted or finely spotted with lilac about the larger end.

PELICANS, CORMORANTS, etc.: *Order Pelecaniformes*

PELICANS: *Family Pelecanidæ*

White Pelican. *Pelecanus erythrorhynchos*

If one visits the irrigated cattle country in the San Joaquin Valley, or the lake region of eastern Oregon, a far-off line of snow-white resolves itself on nearer approach into large white birds riding rather high on the water, with large heads, short necks, and huge yellow bills drawn down close to the breast. When startled they rise with a noise of wing-beats against the water, and with each flap shove backward with their legs. When at last under way they fly with great ease, flapping a few times rather slowly and then sailing. They fly in line and follow the line taken by the leader, not only horizontally but vertically; if he rises, the whole line rises as if over an imaginary hurdle. The *long black tips* of the *wing feathers* make a sharp contrast to the snow-white body. When migrating, a flock often spiral upward to get the direction, and then, forming an irregular V, stream off over some mountain-range. In summer a flock often circle at a considerable height, one half in shadow, the other showing snow-white in the sunlight. White Pelicans secure the fish on which they feed, not by diving from a height as the Brown Pelicans do, but by a quick thrust from a sitting position on the water.

The only other bird that could be mistaken for a White Pelican is the Snow Goose, which has the same pattern of white and black. The Pelican is much larger, the neck is shorter, and head and bill much more prominent, and the wing-stroke is slower. Pelicans, moreover, alternate flapping with a long interval of sailing, while geese sail only when about to alight. Pelicans are silent in flight, geese generally noisy.

5 ft. Wingspread 8–9 ft.

Ad. in breeding plumage. — *Entire plumage white*, except the *black primaries* and the short tuft of pale yellow feathers at the top and back of the head. Naked skin around eye yellow; iris bluish. Bill reddish yellow in the breeding season, with a horny protuberance on the upper mandible; pouch under bill yellow, orange at base; feet orange-red. **Ad. in winter.** — No protuberance on bill, no yellow on head. **Im.** — Top of head brownish gray. Bill yellow; feet reddish orange.

Dist. — *Cal.* Common R. on large bodies of water inland, from the Salton Sea through the San Joaquin and Sacramento Valleys to Lassen and Modoc Cos.; M. in central and southern Cal.
Ore. Common S.V. (May–Aug.) on lakes in Klamath, Lake and Harney Cos.
Wash. S.V. (May–Dec.) on large bodies of water east.

Nest, a depression in the earth with a rim of weed stalks, rubbish, etc., generally on islands in lakes. *Eggs*, 2–3, dull white, stained and soiled.

California Brown Pelican. *Pelecanus californicus*

Above the other sea fowl gathered on some sandy beach or rocky point, the Brown Pelicans' *whitish heads* are noticeable. When the birds are at rest, their *huge bills* point downward and are held close to their breasts. When the birds are fishing, or flying about singly, the great expanse of wing, the scanty tail, and the long bill carried straight ahead give the bird the appearance of a huge mosquito. The head is pulled in close to the body, as the bird flaps heavily and then sails. When a fish is espied, the bill is pointed straight down, the wings are turned so as to offer the least resistance, and the bird plunges into the water heavily enough to splash it several feet into the air. Then the bird rests a moment on the water riding high, until it rises, kicking backward with each wing-stroke, and resumes its flight. Occasionally, over shallow water, Pelicans drop from a height of only a few feet, and when riding the water over a school of small fish, they scoop them up from a sitting position. When fishing, the Pelican commonly flies at least twenty or thirty feet above the water, but when traveling up or down the coast, a line of Pelicans often fly steadily along close to the surface just inside the last wall of breaking surf. Then this awkward fowl becomes a miracle of ease and power, gliding easily with outspread wings. When the wave breaks, the birds shift to the next oncoming wave and continue their even course. Pelicans seize a fish crosswise, then throw it into the pouch lengthwise before swallowing it; while it is held for a moment crosswise, gulls which have followed the diving Pelican to the water attempt to rob it of its catch.

Brown Pelicans come into the larger bays and estuaries, but are practically never seen on bodies of fresh water. Immature birds are common in fall and winter. They are to be distinguished from adults by the light *under parts* and the *dark head.*

$4\frac{1}{2}$ ft. Wingspread $6\frac{1}{2}$ ft.

Ad. in breeding plumage. — Forehead and *top of head cream-color*, a small tuft on back of head; iris white, bare space around eye brownish; neck black with a chestnut crest down the nape, and long white stripe down the sides; *upper parts gray, streaked with brownish*; under parts brown. Bill, upper mandible straw-color, lower gray, tip of bill and edge of lower mandible pinkish red; pouch reddish; feet slaty gray. **Ad. in winter.** — Hind-neck white. **Im.** — Head, back and wings brown; under parts whitish; white stripe along middle of under surface of wing. Bill and pouch dark; feet light gray.

Dist. — *Cal.* Common R. along the ocean. Breeds on Coronados Is., Santa Barbara, Anacapa, Santa Cruz and San Miguel Is. Wanders northward after the breeding season.

Ore. }
Wash. } Casual fall visitant along the coast from Aug. or Sept. to Nov.

Nest, bulky structures of sticks, etc., on the ground or on bushes on slopes of islands. *Eggs*, 2–3 (4 or 5), dull white, soon stained.

CORMORANTS: *Family Phalacrocoracidæ*

DOUBLE-CRESTED CORMORANT. *Phalacrocorax auritus* subsp.

Among the Brown Pelicans or gulls that fly or soar over the ocean off our shores, large black birds are constantly flying low over the water, their thick necks and long bills extended far forward and slightly upward, their broad wings beating much faster than those of the gulls. When their goal is reached, they either splash into the water and sit with neck up and bill pointing at an upward angle, or light on a buoy, a boat or a rock among a row of their erect black companions. If the *sides of the bill* and the *pouch at the base* are *yellow*, the birds are readily identified as Farallon (or, in Washington, White-crested) Cormorants. Among the black-bellied birds in winter are many immature birds with brownish white lower parts. When perched, Cormorants often sit with wings spread, occasionally shaking them. When feeding, they leap forward and disappear under the water.

FARALLON CORMORANT (Immature)

The Farallon Cormorant occurs at any season on large inland bodies of water; many colonies breed on inland seas and lakes, either in trees or on low islands. Along the coast they breed on outlying rocks, either apart or in colonies with the Brandt Cormorant or Brown Pelican. In late winter they begin to acquire above and behind each eye the two tufts of delicate white feathers which characterize the breeding plumage. These are so quickly lost that many breeding birds lack them, and show only black crests. In the breeding season a mated pair stretch their heads and necks up, with the orange pouch conspicuously displayed, and bring them down and forward together, uttering a loud snoring grunt.

The Farallon Cormorant may always be distinguished from the Brandt, which is of about the same size, by the *orange patch at the base of the bill,* and from the smaller Baird Cormorant both by the orange patch and by the difference in size. Any adult Cormorant may be distinguished from any loon, if they are riding the water, by the dark breast, or even when the color of the breast cannot be detected, by the upward angle at which the bill is generally held; a loon's bill and head are usually held parallel to the surface of the water. In flight an adult Cormorant shows no white under surface; moreover, the *wings are broader* and less pointed than a loon's, and the body from bill to tail does not as a rule form the slightly curved outline characteristic of the loon in flight.

Ad. — Entire plumage black (head, neck and under parts showing greenish in strong light); *throat pouch orange;* an orange line from eye to bill; in breeding plumage crests of delicate white feathers above and behind eye, soon falling and revealing black crests below. Bill blackish along top, *sides yellow;* iris bluish green; feet black. **Im.** — Upper parts brownish, lighter on throat and breast, whitish on belly.

Dist. — Farallon Cormorant. 30 inches. *P. a. albociliatus:*

Cal. Common R. along the seacoast and on large bodies of water inland.

Ore. Common R. along the coast and S.V. (May–Nov.) on large lakes in Klamath, Lake and Harney Cos.

Wash. Probably casual off the coast, replaced by *P. a. cincinnatus.*

White-crested Cormorant. 36 inches. *P. a. cincinnatus:*

Wash. Common R. off the coast. Breeds on the rocky islands off shore.

Nest, of seaweed along the coast, on the ground on islands or isolated promontories; inland high up in trees generally close to water, of pondweed and sticks. *Eggs,* 3–4, rarely more, pale blue or bluish white, more or less concealed by a white coating and soon stained or soiled.

BRANDT CORMORANT. *Phalacrocorax penicillatus*

If the broken face of a sea cliff or some outlying pinnacle of rock is scanned through a glass, the black forms of Brandt Cormorants are often seen standing on every available niche. From the rocks individuals or groups are constantly flying into the swirling or surging water, to dive for fish and reappear, riding easily in the dangerous eddies. *Across the throat there is a buffy band,* and in breeding season the bluish pouch is conspicuous. Cormorants often gather in a compact body over their feeding ground, riding so low that only the head and neck and a portion of the back are above the water. When they leave the water, they splash for some distance along the surface before getting under way. In the breeding season the birds dive into the eddies, to reappear with masses of seaweed in their bills, with which they fly to the rocks, where the nests are placed. When a pair are mating, the head is thrown upward and then forward, displaying the blue pouch under the bill. At this season long, slender white or cream-colored feathers adorn the sides of the head and middle of the back. The bird's note at this season is a low piglike grunt.

BRANDT CORMORANT (Winter)

For the distinction between the Brandt and the Farallon Cormorants, see preceding species. The size of the Brandt Cormorant distinguishes it from the Baird Cormorant, and in the breeding season the absence of the white patches on the flanks.

33

Ad. — Entire plumage black, showing in sunlight purplish reflections on head and back, and greenish on under parts. In breeding plumage, *throat pouch blue, brown band across throat* below the pouch, long white or yellowish filaments extending back from sides of neck and from the shoulders over the back. Bill dusky; iris green; feet black. **Im.** — Plumage brown, under parts paler.

Dist. — Common R. along the whole coast.

Nest, chiefly of eelgrass or seaweed, on shelves, niches or sloping sides of rocky islands or headlands. *Eggs*, 3–6, pale blue or bluish white, more or less coated with white, soon stained or soiled.

Baird Cormorant. *Phalacrocorax pelagicus resplendens*

An ardent bird student will not rest till he has visited some 'bird rocks,' where the perpendicular cliffs are the home in the breeding season of gulls, cormorants, murres and puffins. As the boat nears the rock, the black forms of cormorants are seen riding low in the water, diving for fish or flying to and from their nests on the cliffs. Often there are three species of cormorants nesting on the same ledges, but after a very little practice the beginner learns to distinguish them even at long range. The Baird Cormorant is smaller than either of the two other species, with a very slender bill, and in the breeding season, from February till June, shows *two conspicuous white areas on the flanks*. These white areas are prominent as the bird leaves the water and flies away from the observer, or when the bird sits on its little niche of rock with its back to the ocean. The old birds on the nest utter a low droning note suggesting bullfrogs.

BAIRD CORMORANT (Adult, breeding)

In winter the Baird Cormorant often comes into bays and harbors but never like the Farallon Cormorant to bodies of fresh water. In the fall and winter it lacks the white patches, but at all seasons it may be distinguished by its very slender neck and bill and its brighter iridescence if in good light. Occasionally it may be found perched on a buoy or piling about a wharf near enough to display in strong light the purple or violet of the neck and the glossy green of the head and body. Its feeding habits, attitudes and manner of flight are similar to those of the other Cormorants.

25½

Entire plumage glossy black (body greenish in strong light, neck with violet or purple reflections); *white patches in the breeding season on the hind flanks* and loose, white, thread-like feathers on the neck; pouch dull coral-red. Bill blackish gray (B.); feet light gray.

Dist. — R. from Santa Barbara I., Cal., to northern Wash.

Nest, of dry grass, on niches on steep cliffs of rocky islands. *Eggs*, 3–5, rarely more, pale blue or bluish white, more or less concealed by a white deposit, soon stained or soiled.

MAN-O'-WAR-BIRDS: *Family Fregatidæ*

MAN-O'-WAR-BIRD: FRIGATE-BIRD: *Fregata aquila*

On rare occasions a wanderer from Lower California, a large black sea bird with long pointed wings and a tail over a foot long, forked for half its length, is seen off the coast of southern California. In spite of the ease with which it could reach our shores, its occurrence is only accidental. There are less than a dozen records from San Francisco Bay to San Diego. The black upper parts, the white which generally shows on the breast, the long, narrow wings and *long, forked tail* are all unmistakable characteristics. The Man-o'-war-bird is about three and a half feet long with a wingspread of from seven to eight feet.

HERONS, STORKS, IBISES, etc.: *Order Ciconiiformes*

HERONS, BITTERNS, etc.: *Family Ardeidæ*

HERONS: *Subfamily Ardeinæ*

GREAT BLUE HERON. *Ardea herodias* subsp.

In marshes, on the beaches or even in dry fields, the tall, lean figure of the Blue Heron either stands motionless or advances cautiously one slow step at a time. When near its prey, a lightning-quick forward lunge of the long neck and bill ends the patient waiting. Even on the

GREAT BLUE HERON

bed of kelp which fringes the shore of southern California, the solitary figure of a Heron is often seen, apparently waiting idly in this security. When a Heron flies, the neck is pulled in with a noticeable kink, the legs are held out straight behind and the bird is carried with slow strokes of the broad wings either to some other feeding ground or to the top of a tall tree, from which the neck emerges and the bill and head point forward at right angles. When flying a short distance only, a Heron holds its long, snaky neck downward and just before alighting throws its legs suddenly forward. When startled, the Blue Heron rises with a series of hoarse, often violent croaks, lower and less melodious than the cry of a goose.

A Blue Heron either at rest or in flight should be readily distinguished from any other bird. Even at a great distance the slow wing-strokes and the long legs stretched out behind are unmistakable; there is a greater length of leg behind than of neck and head in front. The chief amount of *blue* is *on the wings* and is evident only in flight or against the sides of the lean body. Young birds are gray, but both young and old have a large area of *black* on the *outer portions of the wings*.

42–50 Bill $4\frac{1}{2}$–6 Wingspread nearly 6 ft.

Ad. — Top of head white, sides black, continued in the breeding season in two long black feathers; *back, wings and tail slaty blue; terminal portions of the wings black*; long neck lavender-gray; long, loose feathers on sides of neck and upper back; under parts streaked, black and white. Bill dusky along the top, yellowish on the sides and below; feet black. **Im.** — Top of head black; no loose feathers on sides of neck and upper back; upper parts darker. Bill darker; feet blackish.

Dist. — California Blue Heron. *A. h. hyperonca:*
Cal. Common R. throughout Cal., chiefly west of the mountains.
Pallid Blue Heron. *A. h. treganzai:*
Cal. Common R. along the Colorado R. and on Salton Sea, probably also in Owens Valley and about Mono L.
Ore. Common R. east, winters south.
Wash. Status of Blue Herons from southeastern Wash. not yet determined.
Northwest Blue Heron. *A. h. fannini:*
Ore. } *Wash.* } Common R. west, southern limit in Ore. not yet determined.
Eastern Great Blue Heron. *A. h. herodias:*
Wash. S.V. (Mar.–Nov.) in eastern Wash., and apparently R. south.

Nest, a rude platform of sticks, generally in trees, often at a great height, sometimes in tules or on the ground. *Eggs*, 3–6, dull greenish blue.

Egret. *Casmerodius egretta*

In sloughs along the coast of southern California or in the irrigated portions of the interior valleys, the tall snow-white figure of an Egret is frequently seen far off on the marsh or conspicuous against the green foliage of a tree. When the bird flies, the broad snowy wings are extended in slow easy strokes. The Egret feeds, like the Blue Heron, with slow forward steps, or leans stiffly forward till a fish is near enough to be speared with a sudden lunge. When resting, it often stands erect with the neck withdrawn in a hump. The note is a harsh low *corr*. There is no bird with which an American Egret can be confused except the smaller Snowy Egret: the yellow bill and greater size distinguish the former; the latter has a black bill.

37–41 Bill $4\frac{1}{2}$–5 Wingspread $4\frac{1}{2}$ ft.

Ad. — *Entire plumage white;* in the breeding season, long plumes of loose, finely divided feathers from upper back to beyond tail. Bill yellow, often blackish at tip; feet black. **Im.** — More black on bill.

Dist. — *Cal.* S.V., breeding locally in the San Joaquin and Sacramento Valleys; irregular W.V. along the coast from Watsonville south.

Ore. R. about Malheur L.

Nest, a platform of sticks, in trees or in bushes. *Eggs*, 3–5, light greenish blue.

Snowy Egret. *Egretta candidissima candidissima*

The Snowy Egret is occasionally seen, either alone or in company with the American Egret, in the marshes of southern and central California. Its small size and above all its *black bill* distinguish it from the American Egret.

24 Bill 3

Plumage white throughout. In breeding season long plumes of loose, finely dissected feathers from upper back curving upward over end of tail. Bill black, yellowish at base; feet black, webs yellowish.

Dist. — Rare and irregular in southern Cal., occurring chiefly in late summer, fall and winter. A few breed in the San Joaquin Valley.

Nest, a platform of rushes in tules or of sticks in bushes. *Eggs*, 3–5, light greenish blue.

Anthony Green Heron. *Butorides virescens anthonyi*

When startled from a reedy pool or ditch, a Green Heron flies off with legs dangling, head and chestnut neck up and the blackish feathers of the crown all on end. When it lights, if it feels safe, it stretches up to its full height and watches an intruder. If on the other hand it feels the need

ANTHONY GREEN HERON

of concealment, it crouches till the whole neck disappears, and bill, head and back make one continuous curve. The short tail, almost concealed by the wings, is jerked nervously when the bird is alarmed. When a startled bird flies from cover, it utters either a series of protesting *kuks* or a very penetrating *kyow*. The name Green Heron is misleading; an adult bird shows in good light a bluish cast on its dark wings. The Green Heron is usually solitary, feeding at the marshy edges of ponds, along irrigation ditches or sluggish streams.

16–18½ Bill 2½

Ad. — *Top of head* apparently *black* (greenish black); feathers of head long and loose, often raised and spread; line of greenish yellow from eye to bill; *back and sides of neck chestnut; back and terminal portions of wing greenish mixed with bluish in strong light;* fore-neck streaked with white and dusky; rest of under parts brownish gray. Bill dark above, yellowish on the sides; iris yellow; legs greenish yellow. **Im.** — Head brown, the feathers shorter; upper parts browner; under parts white, heavily streaked with brown. Bill yellower; legs more greenish.

Dist. — *Cal.* Common S.V. along rivers, lakes and irrigation ditches; a few winter as far north as Santa Barbara.
Ore. Rare S.V. (Klamath Falls).

Nest, a platform of twigs in trees or bushes. *Eggs*, 3–6 (9), light bluish green.

Black-crowned Night Heron. *Nycticorax nycticorax nævius*

As twilight comes on along the bays and estuaries of the ocean, or in marshy or irrigated country inland, a hoarse short *qua* drops from the darkness overhead, another sounds a little farther off, and indistinct forms of large birds pass overhead. These are Night Herons which have passed the day in thick trees or in the tangled tules and are on their way to the mud-flats or irrigation ditches to feed. Occasionally they feed in the daytime and are seen scattered over the marsh or flat. They are much shorter than the Blue Heron and have a squat appearance, little of the neck being visible. The adults are *light gray*, with a conspicuous *black crown* and a *black area down the back*. Young birds are grayish brown, streaked with dusky below and spotted with whitish on the back. Night Herons breed either in dense tules or in trees. If one visits a heronry in mid-

BLACK-CROWNED NIGHT HERON (Adult)

summer, scrawny young Night Herons are everywhere, clambering along the branches, standing motionless on large limbs or stalking along the ground. Young Night Herons have been mistaken for Bitterns, but they lack the tawny and blackish colors and the slimness of the Bittern.

23–26 Bill 3

Ad. — Forehead white, rest of *top of head* and *middle of back black;* wings and tail bluish gray; *under parts whitish;* in the breeding season two long, narrow white feathers extend from the back of the head down the back. Bill black; iris red; legs yellow, webs orange. **Im.** — Upper parts grayish brown, head and neck narrowly, back and wings broadly streaked with white; terminal portions of wings dusky; under parts whitish, streaked with brown. Bill dusky greenish yellow; iris amber; legs dusky greenish yellow.

Dist. — *Cal.* Abundant S.V. throughout; winters less commonly as far north as Marin Co.

Ore. Common S.V. east; a few winter. Casual west.

Wash. Not common S.V. (Mar.–Aug.) in eastern Wash.; probably casual M. in western Wash.

Nest, of reeds or sticks, in tules or in trees. *Eggs*, 3–6, pale bluish green.

BITTERNS: *Subfamily Botaurinæ*

Bittern. *Botaurus lentiginosus*

When one walks through marshy land in winter, a large brown bird may suddenly rise from a clump of dried tules just ahead, either silently or with a low hoarse croak, and after a moment straighten its dangling legs behind it, and fly off with slow beats of its *rich brown, black-tipped wings*. Very rarely a sharp eye will detect the bird before it flies, standing motionless with bill pointed upward, the *long stripes of buff and brown along the neck and sides and under parts* matching the pattern of the reeds. When it lights in tules, it grasps separate stalks with its greenish feet, elongates its body, and blends with its surroundings. Unlike the Herons it is rarely seen in the open. In spring on its breeding grounds, especially in the early morning, late afternoon and eve-

BITTERN

ning, the male Bittern gives its curious mating call. Standing in some open spot in the marsh or wet meadow, it utters at intervals a series of two or three guttural notes, which sound either wooden, like the blows of a mallet on a stake, or liquid like the gurgling of a pump. The notes have been variously transcribed; perhaps *ploõm-púdd'n* or *oong-ká-choonk* will suggest the sounds. A Bittern in the mating season, if seen in short grass, may display a patch of downy white feathers on each side of the breast.

24–34 Bill 3

Ad. — Upper parts brown (speckled with blackish, tawny and whitish); *long neck, sides, and under parts streaked with brown and buff;* throat bordered by a black line; *tips of wings black.* Bill greenish yellow; legs and feet yellowish green.

Dist. — *Cal.* Common R. in swampy areas in the interior valleys and south to Los Angeles Co.; M. and W.V. west of the Coast Range.

Ore. Common S.V. in the lake country of eastern Ore.; a few may winter.

Wash. M. and S.V. (Apr.–Aug.); a few may winter along the southern border, east.

Nest, on the ground, usually in marshes, of grasses, reeds, etc. *Eggs*, 3–6, brownish drab.

Least Bittern. *Ixobrychus exilis*

Except for some of the Rails there is probably none of our birds that succeeds better in avoiding publicity than the Least Bittern. It spends its life in thick growths of cat-tails or tules, feeds in the stagnant pools beneath their shelter, and steals out occasionally along their margin. If a student forces his way through the obstructing tangle, he may get a glimpse of a small *rich-colored body, black, chestnut and buff,* with the long neck and head of the heron family, flying for a moment above the reeds or straddling the tules with bill pointed directly upward in a successful effort to simulate its surroundings. The bird when startled occasionally utters a 'harsh sibilant note' (Abbott). It also gives from the depths of the reeds in the breeding season a 'mellow cuckoo-like call *coo-coo-coo*' (Eaton). A Green Heron might be mistaken by a beginner for a Least Bittern; the Bittern is a much lighter colored bird, showing in flight a buffy or yellowish wing-patch instead of the bluish or greenish wing of the Heron. The Least Bittern never ventures into the comparatively open situations in which the Green Heron is often seen.

12–14¼ Bill 1¾

Ad. ♂. — *Top of head and back,* rump and tail glossy *black;* sides of head and *back and sides of neck chestnut;* wings pale buff, tipped with black and chestnut; throat and under parts white. Bill black above, pale yellow below; legs greenish yellow. **Ad.** ♀. — Black of male replaced by light brown; under parts more or less streaked with buff.

Dist. — *Cal.* Fairly common S.V. (Apr.–Sept.) in suitable localities in southern Cal. near the coast, in the San Joaquin and lower Sacramento Valleys and in Lassen and probably Modoc Cos.

Ore. Has been taken in Klamath Co. and reported as a rather common breeder at Malheur L. (Willett).

Nest, a platform of tules, placed in living tules, which are arched over it. *Eggs*, 3–6, white, faintly tinged with bluish.

STORKS AND WOOD IBISES: *Family Ciconiidæ*

Wood Ibis. *Mycteria americana*

Along the Colorado above Yuma are shallow lakes filled by the river in spring floods. Here in summer tall white birds with heavy bills feed in the shallow margins or soar with black-tipped wings far overhead. The square-tipped tail shows in flight, extending for a short distance above the legs. When the bird is standing, the long heavy bill, decurved toward the tip, is pointed downward, its tip reaching below the bird's breast. When feeding, the Wood Ibis keeps the head and neck constantly down, only lifting it slightly to swallow each capture; as it moves forward in the shallow water, it stirs the water by wiggling the toes of each leg in turn. In flight the Wood Ibis sails and flaps alternately, or, mounting to a great height, soars like a Turkey Buzzard. When startled it utters a hoarse croak. From June to August, Wood Ibis, usually immature birds, wander irregularly northward into the marshes of southern California. The Wood Ibis is readily distinguished from the Egret by the black tail and wing-tips, and when in flight from the White Pelican by its long neck and legs, and black tail.

40–45 Bill 9

Ad. — *General plumage white; wing-tips and tail black;* head and upper neck bare, dark colored (dusky bluish). Bill long, stout at base, slightly curved downward at tip, dull yellowish; legs bluish. **Im.** — Head and neck feathered grayish brown, except a naked area on forehead and about base of bill.

Dist. — Not uncommon in summer along the lower Colorado R.; occasional in southern Cal.

IBISES: *Family Threskiornithidæ*

White-faced Glossy Ibis. *Plegadis guarauna*

On the west side of the San Joaquin Valley in summer above the bending cat-tails from almost any quarter of the sky one sees lines of Ibis appear, their long necks and curved bills straight out and their feet extended well beyond the tail. Their lines tend to form a V but constantly break and re-form. As they prepare to alight, they tumble and dart downward, swooping suddenly this way and that. After alighting they often stretch their wings over their backs; then they fringe the edge of the shallow water, standing in the same attitudes that the Egyptian artists portrayed thousands of years ago. When they feed they often walk steadily forward, thrusting the whole head and neck under water. In flight they flap till they get under way and then flap and sail alternately. The head makes a curious knot-like effect in the outline of a flying bird, thicker than the bill in front or the neck behind; the slender legs project beyond the square-tipped tail and then broaden out into the feet. The birds when startled or when calling to one another utter a low *cruck, cruck*. The *general color* at a distance is *black*, but a close view in good light brings out the *rich chestnut of the neck and under parts*, and the *purplish bronze green of back and tail.* The white about the base of the bill is only noticeable when a bird is facing the observer at fairly close range.

WHITE-FACED GLOSSY IBIS

19–26 Bill $4\frac{1}{2}$–$5\frac{1}{2}$

Ad. — *Head, neck and under parts rich purplish chestnut;* most of *wings and tail bronzy green;* narrow border of white encircling naked red space about the base of the bill. Bill, long, curved, slaty blue (reddening toward tip); feet varying from dark reddish purple to grayish brown. **Im.** — General plumage grayish brown, no chestnut or purple.

Dist. — *Cal.* S.V. in swampy areas in southern Cal. and in the interior valleys; M. along coast from Watsonville southward. Winters occasionally as far north as Los Baños.

Ore. S.V. in Harney Co.

Wash. One specimen taken near Spokane.

Nest, of dry tules, placed in growing tules, a foot or more above water. *Eggs*, 3–4 (5), dark blue.

DUCKS, GEESE and SWANS: *Order Anseriformes*

DUCKS, GEESE and SWANS: *Family Anatidæ*

SWANS: *Subfamily Cygninæ*

WHISTLING SWAN. *Cygnus columbianus*

No sensitive observer will ever forget his first sight of a flock of Swans, whether swimming in single file with arched necks from the tules bordering a pond, or floating across the sky on broad wings with necks outstretched. When Swans feed in shallow water, they extend the head and neck under water like 'dabbling' ducks with the rear of the body up; when they feed on firm ground, the middle of the long neck is arched. When standing at ease, their necks are arched but when the birds are vigilant, they are held erect. They fly in either V-shaped or diagonal lines, with a stroke that gives them the appearance of floating. The common note is a soft *hoo*, low and almost whistled, but when excitedly calling to a flock among which they intend to settle, the note becomes more nasal and resonant, a more goose-like *quow*, often uttered in two different pitches. Occasionally a slight whistled *whée-i* is uttered in flight.

$4\frac{1}{2}$ ft. Wingspread 6-7 ft.

Ad. — Entire plumage white, sometimes tinged with rusty; (an oblong yellow or orange spot in front of the eye). Bill and feet black. **Im.** — Head and neck pale gray.

Dist. — *Cal.* Fairly common W.V. (Nov.–Apr.) on lakes, bays or marshes.
Ore. Common W.V. (Oct.–Apr.) in the lake region of eastern Ore., less common elsewhere.
Wash. Rare M. and occasional W.V. (Oct.–Apr.) along coast and on Sound; also east.

TRUMPETER SWAN. *Cygnus buccinator*

There are no recent records of the Trumpeter Swan in the Coast States, but the species occurs each year in the region about Okanagan Lake, B.C. (Brooks), and should be looked for on migration in eastern Washington. It is practically identical in appearance with the Whistling Swan but is larger, and has a deeper, more sonorous note.

GEESE: *Subfamily Anserinæ*

SNOW GOOSE. *Chen hyperboreus hyperboreus*

A fringe of distant white on a green marshy meadow in winter may be a line of White Pelican or a flock of Snow Geese. If through a glass we see birds moving forward, cropping the grass with necks bent, we can decide at once that they are geese. When we approach, the long necks are raised, the birds stand watchful or rise with much flapping of wings and a jangle of discordant cries like the yelping of a pack of hounds.

Often there are brown birds mixed with the white ones, White-fronted Geese or the black-necked, white-bibbed Hutchins or Cackling Geese. In flight the Snow Geese show the *conspicuous black tips of the outspread wings.* The notes, while resembling in quality those of the White-

WHITE-FRONTED GOOSE; SNOW GOOSE; HUTCHINS GOOSE

fronted Geese, are generally a single nasal *kerr* or a lower *karr* often followed by a low *kuk, kuk, kuk;* the White-fronted Goose has a double note *toll-luk.* The habits of Snow Geese in winter are much like those of their associates the White-fronted Geese. (See p. 33.)

23–28

Ad. — Plumage *white* except the *black tips of the wings.* Bill red, the edges of the mandibles black; feet dark red. **Im.** — Head, neck and back pale gray, tinged with brownish; under parts usually tinged with yellowish brown.

Dist. — *Cal.* Abundant W.V. (Oct.–Apr.) in the interior valleys, less frequent near the coast.

Ore. Common M. east, less common along the coast.

Wash. Spring and fall M. and W.V. (Oct.–May), more sparingly in east.

Ross Snow Goose. *Chen rossi*

In a mixed flock of wintering geese in the interior valleys of California, two sizes of Snow Geese can often be distinguished, one about the size of the brown White-fronted Goose, the other distinctly smaller. The smaller bird is the Ross Snow Goose; its habits and probably its notes are practically the same as the preceding species, from which it can be distinguished only by its size as compared with the other geese with which it is associated.

20–26

A smaller edition of the Snow Goose, not much larger than a Mallard. Bill (when seen near to) lacks the black edging of the mandibles.

Dist. — Common M. and W.V. to the interior valleys of Cal.; one record for eastern Ore.

White-fronted Goose. *Anser albifrons* subsp.

From far off in the sky one hears in fall and spring a chorus of jangling cries, made up of high-pitched notes alternating with deeper ones. Then a line of dark bodies comes into view, often in wedge formation, flying with rapid wing-strokes with a little sailing at long intervals. If one is concealed near the feeding or sleeping ground, and the flock pass close overhead, the fore-neck looks dark but not black, the under parts light with bands of dusky color across the lower belly. If the birds come head on and are near, they show *pink bills and white foreheads.* When the flock are about to light, they settle slowly down with outstretched wings, and then suddenly individuals begin to twist, turn or gyrate. When a few feet above the ground, the orange-yellow legs are thrown forward, the bodies kept nearly perpendicular, the tail is spread and wings are fluttered to break the descent. When seen from behind, the tail shows a conspicuous *white crescent, edged with brown* toward the tip. This is the best field mark, if the birds are flying away. The cry is made up of two or three notes *tóll-luk, tóll-la-luk,* with the throaty quality of all geese but less deep and resonant than the *honk* of the Canada or the Hutchins Goose. The White-fronted is the commonest and most wide-spread goose on the coast, and may be seen in migration anywhere.

27–30

Ad. — General color *brown; narrow border of white around base of bill;* a gray area toward the tip of the brown wing; upper surface of *tail brown with crescent of white*; belly marked with broad black bands; *area under tail white.* Bill yellow or orange, tip whitish; feet orange-yellow. **Im.** — **Lacking** the white forehead, and the black bands on the belly. Bill dusky at **tip.**

Dist. — *A. a. gambeli.* [*A. a. albifrons.*]

Cal. Common W.V. (Sept.–Apr.) throughout, most abundant in the interior valleys.

Ore. Common M. (Sept.–Nov.; Apr. and May).

Wash. Spring and fall M. (Apr. and early May; Sept. and Oct.) along the coast; a few doubtless remain on the Sound in winter.

Tule Goose. [*A. a. gambeli.*]

Darker and larger. Reported only from the upper Sacramento Valley near Butte Creek.

Canada Goose; Honker. *Branta canadensis canadensis*

The deep sonorous *honk, ka-hónk* from a wedge-shaped line of geese, the military precision of their flight, and their rapid passage from full view overhead till they vanish as mere specks in the distant sky, never fail to stir one's blood. In winter in the interior valleys of California where there are extensive grain fields near bodies of water, Canada Geese fly each day back and forth from their feeding grounds in the fields to the water. Unlike ducks they feed at some distance from water, bending their long necks down to pick up the scattered grain or to pluck the springing wheat or grass. They are extremely wary; at the approach of an intruder the long necks are raised, the birds stand watchful, honking in low tones, or if too closely approached take a short run and are off with powerful strokes and a full bugle blast of notes. Canada Geese as a rule do not mingle with the other species but feed more on the uplands and spend the night and the middle of the day on ponds or lakes.

Canada Geese breed from northeastern California (Lake Tahoe) through eastern Oregon and Washington. Here a pair may be seen convoying a line of downy goslings across open water, or their harsh but sonorous calls are heard from the marshy borders of lakes. The Canada Goose is the only goose that breeds in the Coast States, but two other forms, smaller but otherwise similar, which breed farther north are migrants and winter visitants, generally associating with the White-fronted and Snow Geese. There is no difficulty in distinguishing the Canada Goose and its two smaller forms from the White-fronted and Snow Geese; the *black head and neck with the white 'bib'* extending from back of the eye across the throat characterize all three. To distinguish the three members of the Canada Goose group from each other, one must have other species near by to furnish a criterion of size (see the following species).

35–43

Head and neck black, except *large white patches on the cheeks,* meeting on the throat and forming a bib; back brown; *tail black enclosing a white crescent-shaped area;* under parts gray, becoming white under the tail. Bill and feet black.

Dist. — *Cal.* Common M. and W.V. (Nov.–Mar.); S.V. in the northeastern portion of the State.
Ore. Common S.V. about the lakes of eastern Ore., common M., and sparingly a W.V.
Wash. Common M. throughout; S.V. east, less common in winter.

Nest, on the ground, built up of grasses, weeds, twigs, etc. (occasionally in a tree in an old nest of some other species), lined with down. *Eggs,* 5–7, dull white.

Hutchins Goose. *Branta canadensis hutchinsi*

The Hutchins Goose is a smaller edition of the Canada Goose, about the size of the White-fronted Goose, with which it is often associated in grain fields, on hilly slopes or in marshy lowlands in the interior valleys. Its notes resemble those of the Canada Goose and may be readily distinguished by their lower pitch and resonant quality from those of the Snow and White-fronted Geese. They suggest the syllables *kyónk*, or when uttered in a higher pitch, *kyánk*. Only the relative size of the bird when seen with other species can serve to distinguish it from the larger Canada Goose.

25–34

Similar to Canada Goose; a narrow white collar around the base of the neck may or may not be present.

Dist. — *Cal.* Common W.V. throughout (Oct.–Apr.), most abundant in the interior valleys.
Ore. Common M.
Wash. Doubtless a spring and fall M. along the coast and inland, a few wintering.

White-cheeked Goose. *B. c. occidentalis*

35

Wash. (Nov. to Mar.) principally in the Sound region.

Cackling Goose. *Branta canadensis minima*

Among the large flocks of geese that gather in winter in the interior valleys of California, there are three distinct types, the pure white Snow Goose with black-tipped wings, the brown-necked White-fronted Goose, and the black-necked forms with white bibs, smaller editions of the Canada Goose. The latter again come in two sizes, the Hutchins Goose, about the size of the White-fronted, and the Cackling Goose, not much bigger than a Mallard. The note of the Cackling Goose is higher-pitched and more rapidly repeated than either the Hutchins or the Canada, resembling the syllables *lyuk-lyuk-lyuk*. Its habits are similar to those of the other species with which it associates; it feeds on the sprouting grain or on the young grass of hilly slopes, spending the night and the middle of the day in the marshy borders of ponds or sloughs.

23–25

Similar to Canada Goose; a narrow white collar about base of neck often present.

Dist. — *Cal.* M. and W.V. (Oct.–Apr.).
Ore. } *Wash.* } Probably regular spring and fall M. and W.V.

Black Brant; Sea Brant. *Branta nigricans*

In large bays and estuaries during the winter months a long line of dark birds, riding with head and neck well up and showing white along the flanks and under the tail, utter when disturbed a low *cronk*, or take wing and fly in lines to a safer part of the bay or out to sea. If a shot is fired, the calls become an uproar as flock after flock rise from all parts of the bay, till the air is filled with black lines and masses. If the bay becomes unsafe, Brant ride by thousands in the ocean outside the surf, waiting to return to the beds of eel-grass in the quiet waters where they feed. In flight the Sea Brant shows the ordinary outline of a small goose, head and neck extended, plump body and short tail. The wing-stroke is rapid, without intervals of sailing. The *head and neck are black;* a *white collar encircles the neck;* the tail as the bird flies from the observer appears *white with a small black edging.* When the bird is standing on the exposed flats, the whitish flanks are conspicuous.

The only birds with which the Sea Brant could be confused are the Hutchins and the Cackling Geese, neither of which are often found on salt or brackish water, while the Brant is practically confined to the sea coast. The Brant has *black cheeks* and *a white collar,* while both the Hutchins and the Cackling Geese have white cheeks.

22–29

Ad. — *Head and neck black,* a *white band around neck;* wings dark brown; *tail black with white coverts;* breast black; flanks whitish; area below tail white. Bill and feet black. **Im.** — Lacking the white collar; white bars on the wings.

Dist. — *Cal.* Common M. and W.V. (Oct.–Apr.) on large bays; occasional elsewhere.
Ore. Probably common M. along the coast, and W.V. (Oct.–Apr.) on large bays.
Wash. M. and W.V. (Sept.–May) along the coast, in the Straits and on the Sound.

Emperor Goose. *Philacte canagica*

The Emperor Goose breeds and winters far north; only stragglers reach our coast. In 1918 there were ten records of its occurrence in California, two in Oregon and one in Washington.

26

Head and hind-neck white; chin, throat and forehead blackish brown; back, sides and breast bluish ash barred with black; tail white-tipped. Bill chiefly white; feet orange-yellow.

TREE-DUCKS: *Subfamily Dendrocygninæ*

Fulvous Tree-Duck; Mexican Duck. *Dendrocygna bicolor*

The name Tree-Duck is misleading for this species. In its breeding haunts in central California it frequents the grassy margins of wet sloughs and the borders of ponds and lakes, nesting and feeding in the marshes. It feeds both by day and at night either in dense masses of reeds or in high marsh grass, but is often seen resting in small ponds in the marshes. It may be easily recognized by its comparatively long legs and neck, which give it on the ground a goose-like appearance. When alarmed, it raises its head and neck, so that these are often evident above the long grass in which it is sheltered. When in the open, the *pale cinnamon-colored under parts* readily identify it; the color is paler than in the Cinnamon Teal, the legs and neck much longer. When flying, the legs extend well beyond the tail and the head and neck are often held at a downward angle. The note, constantly uttered in flight, is a squealing whistle.

FULVOUS TREE-DUCK

20–21

Ad. — Top of head reddish brown, black stripe along hind-neck; back and tail brownish black; *white bar across base of tail;* sides of head yellowish brown; throat buffy white; wings chiefly blackish brown; rest of *under parts yellowish brown.* Bill bluish gray; feet long and stout, apparently black (bluish gray in strong light). **Im.** — Paler below.

Dist. — *Cal.* Common S.V. (Apr.–Sept.) in marshes in the interior in central and southern Cal.; M. along the coast (Apr. and Sept.) from Monterey Co. southward. Occasionally winters.

Wash. One record.

Nest, on the ground in marshy situation, of grass sparsely lined with down. *Eggs*, 12–17, white.

RIVER DUCKS: *Subfamily Anatinæ*

Mallard. *Anas platyrhynchos*

In the grassy margins of lakes and sloughs from Washington to southern California in the breeding season the *green head* and *chestnut breast* of the Mallard drake may be seen above the grass, the white ring round the neck conspicuous as the bird stretches up its head; in winter flocks gather in inland lakes and ponds, brown females mixed with the handsome males, both sexes showing orange-red feet as they dabble head down for food in the shallow water. Toward evening the loud *quack, quack, quack* of the female sounds from the reeds with the same cadence as in the barnyard; the quack of the male is much lighter in volume. It is difficult for a beginner to distinguish the female Mallard from some of the other female ducks; the yellow in the bill, the shorter neck, the *white under surface of the wing*, and in flight the lack of a white border on the inner edge of the outspread wing distinguish her from the female Pintail. She should be readily distinguished from the female Baldpate, even if the dull orange of the Mallard's bill cannot be seen, by the coarsely mottled flanks; the female Baldpate shows an unmottled pinkish brown flank. The female Mallard lacks the heavy, broadened bill of the Shoveller and the light blue patch near the bend of the wing. The female Gadwall (usually much less common than the Mallard) most nearly resembles the female Mallard, but if the wing can be observed at close range, the Mallard shows *two narrow white bars* bordering the blue speculum fore and aft, while the Gadwall shows both when on the water and in flight one small white patch.

20–25

Ad. ♂. — *Head and upper neck glossy green;* narrow white collar around neck; two broad stripes of light gray down back; speculum blue, bordered by lines of white; tail feathers chiefly white; *breast deep chestnut*; flanks gray. Bill greenish yellow; feet orange-red. **Ad.** ♀. — General color of upper parts brown, dark line through eye, bordered by a buffy line above; under parts light brown, darkest on breast, feathers with dark centers and light edging, producing *mottled appearance*. Bill orange, mottled with dusky; feet pale orange-red.

Dist. — *Cal.* Fairly common R., much commoner in winter.
Ore. Common R. east, less common west.
Wash. Common S.V. east and west; common in winter on the coast; a few (occasionally many) winter east.

Nest, on or near the ground (sometimes in trees) generally near but sometimes at a long distance from water, lined with reeds or grasses and down. *Eggs*, 8–12 (15) light greenish or grayish buff, or nearly white.

Gadwall. *Chaulelasmus streperus*

In northeastern California and in southeastern Oregon, there are many small ponds with shallow sedgy margins. In the borders of these ponds and even in roadside ditches in spring, pairs of grayish brown ducks are found feeding which show in flight small *white patches in the wings*. The male Gadwall shows a *velvety black area under the tail*. The call note of the female is a loud *quack* similar to that of the female Mallard.

The female when not in company with the male is a difficult bird for the beginner to identify. The head and neck are longer than in the Baldpate, but not so long as in the Pintail; less white shows in the Gadwall's wing in flight than in the Baldpate's, but the presence of any white patch in the wing and the absence of the white border along the after edge distinguishes the Gadwall from the Pintail. The female Gadwall resembles most closely the female Mallard; both have a yellow bill, dusky above, and both have brown breasts with a mottled appearance. The female Gadwall has a *white belly* and a *small white patch* in the extended wing; the female Mallard has a light brownish belly and two white lines enclosing a blue area in the wing.

19–22

Ad. ♂. — Head and neck gray; *white patch in the wing;* under sides of wing silvery white; belly white; *area under tail jet black.* Bill dusky; feet yellow. **Ad.** ♀. — Top of head dark brown; sides of head and throat light gray; *small white patch* in the *wing;* back, breast and flanks brown, the feathers edged with light buff, producing a mottled appearance; belly white or whitish. Bill dusky above, yellow on sides and below; feet dusky yellow.

Dist. — *Cal.* Fairly common R. in the interior, more numerous in winter.
Ore. Common S.V. to the lake region; migrant west.
Wash. Common S.V. (May–Nov.) in the Big Bend region of east Wash.; not common M. and W.V. and casual along the coast.

Nest, in hollows in dry ground generally not close to water, lined with weeds, grasses and down. *Eggs,* 7–13, dull creamy white.

WIDGEON; EUROPEAN WIDGEON. *Mareca penelope*

The European Widgeon occasionally wanders to our coast. The male resembles the Baldpate very closely in size and color except on the head. The forehead is creamy white and the rest of the head *rich reddish brown,* lacking the metallic green and speckled gray on the side of the Baldpate's head.

BALDPATE; AMERICAN WIDGEON. *Mareca americana*

In a mixed company of wintering ducks the male Baldpate has only to swing head on to show the *broad white crown-patch* that gives him his name. Baldpates in winter either spend the day in open bodies of water and come in at dusk to feed, or when unmolested feed close to the shore in tidal inlets and bays. They rise easily from the water; their flight is strong and direct and generally high. The note of the male heard constantly from a feeding flock in late winter and early spring is a sharp, emphatic *whi wheé hoo* or *wheé hoo.*

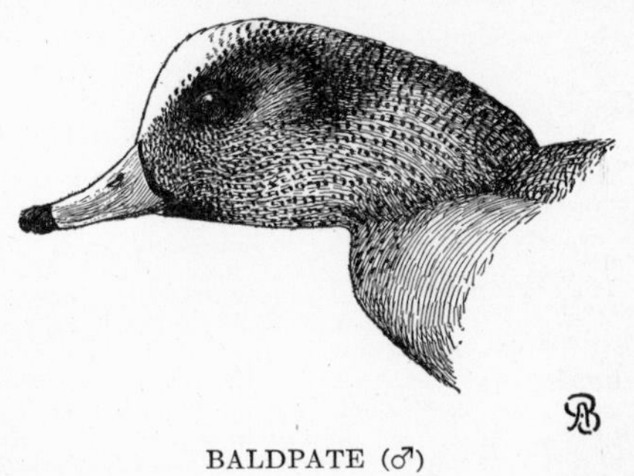

BALDPATE (♂)

The male Baldpate has a *black stern* like the male Gadwall's but its *flanks* are *white,* so that when the male is seen from the side the black and white areas show in marked contrast. In flight both male and female Baldpate show *white* areas in the extended *wing,* more extensive than those of the Gadwall. The stocky figure of the female Baldpate and the wash of unmottled reddish brown on the flanks serve to distinguish her from the other female ducks with which she may be associated. She has a shorter head and neck than the Pintail, Gadwall or Mallard.

18–22

Ad. ♂. — Forehead and *top of head white* or brownish white; sides of head dark (metallic green in strong light); cheeks gray speckled with brown; breast and sides pinkish brown; *white patch on flanks toward the rear*, sharply separated from *black area under the tail;* rest of under parts white; *broad area of white along* bend of outspread *wing*. Bill light bluish gray with black tip; feet gray. **Ad.** ♀. — Head and neck light gray, speckled with brownish; back brown; flanks washed with unmottled reddish brown; *small white area* near *bend* of the outspread *wings*. Breast dull brown; rest of under parts white. Bill dull bluish gray with black tip; feet gray. **Im.** ♂ **in fall.** —Head gray, speckled, no white patch, no dark green.

Dist. — *Cal.* Common W.V. (Oct.–Apr.) throughout, chiefly on fresh water, but occasionally on large shallow bays; has bred in Modoc Co.

Ore. Probably S.V. in southeastern Ore.; common M. and W.V. (Sept.–Mar.) both east and west.

Wash. Common M. and W.V. along the coast; uncommon M. (Sept.–Nov.) east; may breed.

Nest, in hollows in dry ground, generally at some distance from water, lined with weeds, grass and down. *Eggs*, 6–12, creamy white.

Green-winged Teal. *Nettion carolinense*

In the narrow arms of tidal estuaries, along irrigation ditches or at the edges of ponds and lakes pairs of small ducks feed by 'dabbling,' with head submerged and tail in air. When they right themselves, the male Green-winged Teal shows a *cinnamon head* with metallic green sides, a narrow white crescent at the shoulder, gray flanks and a *creamy area on each side of the black area under the tail;* the female is brown, the feathers of the back edged with ashy brown. When startled, they rise with ease almost perpendicularly, and are off with rapid wing-strokes and extremely swift flight. They spend considerable time on muddy banks or shores. When a flock of Green-winged Teal are feeding the males keep up a constant high peeping like small frogs; the female utters a rather faint high-pitched *quack*. The male when seen in good light is unmistakable. The female can readily be distinguished from the female cinnamon Teal in flight by the absence of the blue patch in the wing, and much less easily when at rest by the shorter, narrower bill.

12½–15

Ad. ♂. — *Head chiefly chestnut;* a broad stripe from eye metallic green, ending in a black tuft on hind-neck; upper back and flanks gray, finely barred with black; a white stripe in front of bend of wing; speculum metallic green; upper *breast reddish buff*, with *round black* spots; rest of under parts whitish; *under tail coverts black*, with a *creamy area on each side*. Bill black; feet light brown. **Ad.** ♀. — Top of head and back dusky brownish, feathers of back edged with buff; throat buffy; breast buff, spotted with blackish; rest of under parts whitish. Bill blackish above and on sides, light brown below; feet light gray. **Im.** ♂. — Similar to ♀ but under parts chiefly white.

Dist. — *Cal.* Common W.V. (Aug.–May) throughout; has occasionally bred.

Ore. Common M. and W.V. (Aug.–May); probably breeds sparingly.

Wash. Common M. and W.V. (late July–May) west, more rarely east (Sept.–Feb.); has bred near Seattle.

Nest, in a hollow on the ground, often at a considerable distance from water, lined with soft grasses, weeds and down. *Eggs*, 10–12 (6–18), dull white, cream-color or very pale olive-buff.

Blue-winged Teal. *Querquedula discors*

The Blue-winged Teal is only a rare visitant in California and as a summer visitant in Washington is not common. It is impossible to distinguish a female Blue-winged Teal from a female Cinnamon Teal in the field, but equally impossible to confuse a male Blue-wing with any other duck. There is a conspicuous *white* crescent on the side of the head which no other duck has.

$14\frac{1}{2}$–16

Ad. ♂. — Head deep gray, a *broad white crescent in front of the eye; large area of blue in the wing;* under parts dark gray, everywhere spotted with black. Bill black; feet 'dingy yellow, webs dusky' (Coues). **Ad.** ♀. — Similar to ♀ of next species.

Dist. — *Cal.* Rare M. and W.V.
Ore. Occasional in southeastern Ore.
Wash. Not common S.V. (May–Oct.) on lakes east; casual west.

Nest, of dry grass or other vegetable material with more or less lining of down, in a depression, not far from water. *Eggs*, 6–12 (15), dull white, cream-color or pale olive-buff.

Cinnamon Teal. *Querquedula cyanoptera*

At the borders of a marsh or slough a group of small ducks swim close together, or feed with heads submerged and tail up. Among them are individuals whose *entire bodies*, except for a jet-black area under the tail and a line of black on the back, are *rich cinnamon.* The females with them are brown, rather coarsely spotted on the breast. When startled, Cinnamon Teal rise easily almost straight up from the water, and in flight both male and female show large *pale blue patches in the wing*, and silvery under sides of the wings. The female utters when startled a fairly vigorous *quack.* In the mating season one or more males swim about a female, uttering a faint *quéck-a, quéck-a.*

The male is unmistakable; no other duck is uniform cinnamon-red below. The female can be distinguished from the female of the Green-winged Teal in flight by the large blue patches in the wing; from the very rare female Blue-winged Teal she is practically indistinguishable.

$15\frac{1}{2}$–17

Ad. ♂. — *Head and neck dark cinnamon*, darker on crown; upper back light chestnut, lower back brown; *wings brown with a large patch of blue;* speculum green bordered by white; under surface of wings silvery white; *under parts rich cinnamon*, deepening to black on belly. Bill black; iris red; feet orange. **Ad.** ♀. — Upper parts dark brown, waved with gray; under parts light gray, coarsely spotted on breast with brown; wings as in male but with less blue. Bill dusky above, lighter on sides and below; feet yellow.

Dist. — *Cal.* Abundant S.V. (Mar.–Oct.) on fresh water throughout; a few winter.
Ore. Common S.V. (Mar.–Oct.) east.
Wash. Fairly common S.V. east; casual S.V. and M. west.

Nest, either in a depression in dry ground at some distance from water or in marshy ground in reeds, sometimes fastened to them, lined with grasses and down. *Eggs*, 10–12 (6–14), dull white, cream-color or pale olive-buff.

Shoveller; Spoonbill. *Spatula clypeata*

In a company of ducks, feeding along the surface of shallow water near the shore, the male Shoveller is easily recognized by the contrast of a *large patch of reddish on the sides of the belly,* bounded fore and aft by *large white areas on the breast* and *under the tail.* Companies of Shovellers made up of these bright-colored males and browner females often mill about in shallow water, swimming low, their heads and necks under the surface, straining the water as they swim, or dabble with rear ends up, paddling with orange feet. The male has a green head which looks black, unless in direct sunlight. Both sexes have a *bill* that is *broader at the tip than in the middle.* In flight this heavy bill gives the head the appearance of greater length than in other ducks. The male Shoveller in flight is easily recognized by white longitudinal areas on each side of the black area down the middle of the back. The female utters a *quack,* slightly fainter than the Mallard's, often repeating the note in a descending scale. The male utters a low *took, took, took.* When alarmed Shovellers spring straight upward like Teal and rise to considerable height, before making off with rapid, vigorous flight.

SHOVELLER (♂)

17–21

Ad. ♂. — Head and upper neck apparently black (dark green on the sides in good light); upper parts showing a dark area down the middle bordered by white; wings showing grayish blue near the bend; breast pure white; *belly rich chestnut;* a black area under the tail. *Bill black, much longer than the head,* much *broader at end than at base;* feet orange. **Ad.** ♀. — General color light brown, coarsely mottled; wing as in ♂, but duller. Bill dull greenish brown above, dull orange on sides and below, shape as in ♂; feet orange. **Im.** ♂. — Head dark brown; flanks showing some reddish brown.

Dist. — *Cal.* Abundant W.V. (Sept.–early May), chiefly on fresh water; a few breed.

Ore. S.V. (Apr.–Sept.) in southeastern Ore.; commoner spring and fall M. and W.V.

Wash. Abundant W.V. (Oct.–early Apr.) in the Sound region and along the coast; S.V. (June–Nov.) east, casual in winter.

Nest, in a depression of the ground, sometimes at a distance from water, lined with grass and down. *Eggs,* 10–12 (6–14), from pale olive-buff to pale greenish gray.

AMERICAN PINTAIL; SPRIG. *Dafila acuta tzitzihoa*

In the reedy edges of sloughs or on ponds and estuaries from August to April, the Pintail is generally the commonest duck. After the males have acquired their breeding plumage, the first indication of a flock is often their white breasts showing here and there through the grassy edges as they warily stretch up their long necks. Then as the intruder

PINTAIL (♂)

comes nearer, the scattered flock rise one group after another, with a whirr of wings and low *quacks* from the brown females. Their long slender necks are fully extended in flight, and in the males the long central tail feathers are conspicuous behind. When the birds are resting in the open water and seen from the side, the white neck and breast at one end of the body, and the white area on the rear flanks next to the glossy back under the tail are conspicuous. Pintails feed by dabbling, keeping their rear ends up by vigorous paddling; in this position, the black area under the tail of the males and the long feathers projecting beyond are characteristic marks. In flight both male and female show a *white edge on the after portion of the wings,* close to the body.

Pintails are among the first ducks to reach their winter quarters. Large flocks arrive in southern California in late August and early September, looking in the distant sky like clouds of smoke that form and dissolve again. The males are then in the 'eclipse' plumage; all the characteristic colors and markings are gone; the whole plumage is light brownish gray, and there are no long tail feathers. At this time only the long slender necks and the white inner edging of the extended wings serve to identify the Pintail. From a flock of Pintails from the middle of the winter on, a constant liquid note is repeated like the syllable *kük, kük.* The female when alarmed or in flight utters a low *quack.* The male Pintail is unmistakable; the female is best distinguished by the long neck and the white inner edging of the wing.

26–30

Ad. ♂. — Head, throat and part of fore-neck brown; *hind-neck black, separated from fore-neck by a white stripe;* back gray, with narrow wavy black lines; *middle tail feathers long,* black; lower fore-neck, breast and belly white; *area under tail black.* Bill bluish gray on the sides, black above and at tip; feet grayish blue. **Ad. ♂ in late summer and early fall.** — Similar to ♀. **Ad. ♀.** — Head and neck grayish brown; back brown, mottled with black and buff; under parts whitish or buffy. Bill gray, dusky on top and at tip; feet dull grayish blue.

Dist. — *Cal.* Abundant W.V. (Aug.–May); a few breed.
Ore. S.V. (Apr.–Oct.) east; common W.V. (Sept.–May) along the coast.
Wash. S.V. (Apr.–Oct.) east, a few winter southerly; not common S.V. west, abundant W.V. (Sept.–May) along the coast.

Nest, in a hollow in the ground, often at a distance from water, lined with grass, stubble and down. *Eggs,* 6–12, from pale olive-green to pale olive-buff.

Wood Duck. *Aix sponsa*

A male Wood Duck floating on a woodland pool, showing his glossy *green and violet crest,* the striking pattern of black and white on the cheeks, and the gay color of breast, back and bill, is a sight that few are now fortunate enough to behold. Wood Ducks frequent the quiet waters of sloughs in old river channels where oaks, willows and cottonwoods shade the banks and furnish nesting cavities, or they gather in ponds formed by beaver dams and choked by 'drowned' trees and bushes. In winter they collect in groups, sometimes as many as fifty or sixty (Dixon), but by March they have separated into pairs. At this season pairs fly in and out among the tall trees, the male following the female, and calling with a nasal *kerr-éek.*

WOOD DUCK (♀)

Both frequently alight on the tops of stubs, fifty or sixty feet above the water, or walk along the limbs, or peer into holes, where they cling like Flickers. Both sexes utter the nasal *kerr-éek;* the drake has besides a soft whistled note.

A male Wood Duck is unmistakable; no other duck has a combination of elegant crest and varied and bright color. The female when seen near to may be recognized by the crested appearance of the hind head, by the *white line encircling the eye* and running back toward the nape, and by the pure white chin and whitish under parts. In flight both sexes show the white belly marked off from the dark breast, and an *edging of white on the after side of the wing* next the body. At close range the color of the drake's bill, the black and white markings on his head, and the white eye-ring of the female are evident even in flight.

18–20

Ad. ♂ from Oct. to June. — Top of head metallic green, ending in a *crest of violet,* cut by two narrow lines of white; side of head black; *throat white,* the white running up into side of head and neck; back brown; wings velvety black, purple and white; tail dark, fan-shaped; *upper breast rich reddish chestnut;* flanks buffy brown; rest of under parts white. Bill, sides of upper mandible white along central portion, black at tip and along upper ridge, with a bright red area across the base; feet yellow. **Ad. ♀, and ♂ from June to Sept.** — Top of head blackish; sides of head grayish brown; *ring around eye and patch behind it white;* rest of upper parts brown; throat pure white; breast brown, mottled with buff; *belly white.* Bill dusky; feet yellowish brown.

Dist. — *Cal.* R. in the Sacramento and San Joaquin valleys and westward, commoner in winter; occasional M. southward.

Ore. / *Wash.* } S.V. principally west; a few winter.

Nest, in a hole in a tree, 6–40 feet from the ground, lined with down. ***Eggs,*** usually 10–15, dull white or creamy white.

SEA DUCKS: *Subfamily Fuligulinæ*

Redhead. *Marila americana*

In the lake borders and marshes of interior California and eastern Oregon one of a pair of mated ducks in spring shows a *dark red head and neck* contrasting with the *light gray of the back;* with the drake swims or dives a brown female. Both show in flight an extensive *pale gray area along the after portion of the wing.* In early summer a female Redhead is frequently seen leading a long line of fluffy yellow ducklings, or making frantic efforts to decoy an observer away while her young hide in the reeds. Redheads feed by diving, generally well out in open water, but occasionally by 'tipping' in shallow water. The female utters a hoarse *quack.* In spring the male utters a 'curious drawn-out groaning call, resembling the syllables *whee-ough* given in a high tone.' (Wetmore.)

The male Redhead is readily distinguished from a male Canvas-back by the high forehead and by the darker tone of the back. A female Redhead is distinguished from the female Mallard and Gadwall with which she associates on the breeding ground by her *uniform brown color* without the light edging of the feathers which give the breast and flanks of the other two species a mottled appearance. In winter the female Redhead associates with female Canvas-back, Golden-eye and Scaup. She may be readily distinguished from a Canvas-back by the shape of the head and bill (see colored plate) and from a female Golden-eye by the absence of the white patch in the wing, but less easily from the female Scaup. The Scaup show a marked white area about the base of the bill and a white after edge of the wing in flight, while the area above the base of the bill in the female Redhead is merely light gray, not strictly white, and though there is an extensive light gray area over the after edge of the extended wing, it lacks the pure white edging of the Scaup.

18–21

Ad. ♂. — *Head and upper neck reddish chestnut;* fore part of back black, rest of back light gray; tail black; lower neck and breast blackish; bluish gray area in extended wing; belly whitish. Bill bluish gray, tip black; iris yellow; feet bluish gray. **Ad.** ♀. — Top of head and breast dark sooty brown; cheeks light gray; back and wings grayish brown, slightly waved with light gray (but feathers not with dark centers and buffy edgings); *broad area of light gray along after edge of extended wing;* breast brownish; belly whitish. Bill and feet dusky.

Dist. — *Cal.* Fairly common R. throughout, more numerous in winter (Nov.–Mar.), on both salt and fresh water.
Ore. Common R. in the lake region east, not common M. west.
Wash. Rare M. and S.V. (May–Nov.) east; rare M. west; a few probably winter.

Nest, generally a rather deep structure of dead reeds or tules, lined with down, in a growth of the same, in shallow water. *Eggs*, 10–15, buff to greenish buff.

Canvas-back. *Marila valisineria*

As one approaches a lake where birds are protected, the most conspicuous waterfowl on the lake are the Canvas-backs; the *white backs* of the males are dotted about on the open water, mingled with light brown females. Often the birds are asleep, their *red heads* tucked under their snowy wings, but when they are swimming about, the continuous line made by the *long sloping forehead* and bill readily distinguish them even at a distance from all other ducks. The Scaup, which are often associated with the Canvas-backs, have whitish sides but their backs are speckled with wavy black lines; they are smaller than Canvas-backs, have black heads (purplish or greenish in strong light) with the short bill and high forehead of the usual type. Redheads have gray sides and backs and the usual high forehead of most ducks (see colored plate).

Canvas-backs feed by diving. They sleep much of the day, floating about in the open water at some distance from shore, but where they are fed they become very tame, swimming so close to the shore that the red eye of the male can be seen. The writer has never heard any sound from wintering birds; females have according to other observers a loud quack and the male 'a peeping or growling note.' (Eaton.)

20–23½

Ad. ♂. — *Head and neck reddish brown*, blackish on top of head and about bill; forehead low, sloping down to bill; *back and sides apparently white;*

Above: GREATER SCAUP, MALE (FLYING); LESSER SCAUP, MALE AND FEMALE

Below: RING-NECKED DUCK, MALE; REDHEAD, FEMALE; REDHEAD, MALE; CANVAS-BACK, MALE; CANVAS-BACK, FEMALE

tail and rear of back black; breast black; rest of under parts white. Bill black; iris red; feet bluish gray. **Ad.** ♀. — Head and neck light brown; an indistinct light streak back of eye; back and sides gray, waved with light brown; throat white; breast dark brown; belly whitish, waved with light brown. Bill blackish; feet gray.

Dist. — *Cal.* / *Ore.* } Common W.V. (Oct.–Apr.).
Wash. W.V. (Oct.–Apr.), usually in small numbers along the coast; rare M. and perhaps S.V. east.

Greater Scaup. *Marila marila*

In the many passages and inlets of Puget Sound or on the Straits of San Juan in winter, scattered companies of stocky ducks with apparently black heads and whitish backs float on the water. As one watches them, they dive one after another and after nearly a minute reappear. They often come close to docks or piers and then show in good light *green iridescence* on the *sides of the head.* The Greater Scaup is so like the Lesser in all other particulars and so little larger that it is chiefly by these greenish reflections on the head that it can be identified. Its flight and behavior are the same as those of the Lesser Scaup, and it is equally silent in winter. Farther south it becomes less common.

18–20

Ad. ♂. — *Head, neck, upper back and breast black, the head showing greenish reflections* in strong light; iris yellow; middle of back white, marked with narrow wavy black lines; a *white stripe along after portion of wing* when spread; lower belly and sides pure white; area under tail black. Bill blue or bluish gray, nail black; iris yellow; feet, outer face black, inner lead gray. **Ad.** ♀. — Head, back and breast dark brown; small *area around base of bill white;* wing as in ♂; under parts brownish white. Bill, iris and feet as in ♂. **Im.** ♂. — Head brownish black; sides dull gray.

Dist. — *Cal.* Fairly common W.V. (Dec.–Feb.), chiefly in midwinter, locally and irregularly along the coast; rare inland.
Ore. / *Wash.* } Common M. and W.V. (Oct.–May) along the coast, casual inland.

Lesser Scaup; Bluebill. *Marila affinis*

In every protected body of water, in the open ocean along the beach, and in sloughs and estuaries, a company of medium-sized ducks of compact build includes many drakes whose *black heads and breasts* contrast sharply with a *large area of white on the sides.* Their white sides show almost as conspicuously as the snowy backs of the larger red-headed Canvas-backs with which they are often associated. When seen close to in strong sunlight, the *sides of their heads show purplish reflections.* Among the male Scaup brown-headed females, which lack the white flanks, swim and dive. When the females face the observer a *white crescent-shaped area over the bill* shows against the brown head. Scaup dive with a forward leap. In flight both sexes show a white after edge of the wing, similar to that of the Coot. It is more marked than the similar pattern which the Pintail show; moreover the Scaup's stocky little figure and somewhat zigzag flight could hardly be confused with the steady motion of the long-necked and slender-bodied Pintail. The Lesser Scaup is by far the commonest of the three species of *Marila*, at any rate in California and Oregon, and a beginner should become thoroughly familiar with the unmarked blue bill of the male and the purplish reflections on his head when in direct sunlight, before he attempts to identify the rarer Greater Scaup or the still rarer Ring-necked Duck.

15–16½

Similar to preceding species but *head* of ♂ *with purplish reflections* in strong light.

Dist. — Common M. and W.V. (Sept.–May) in the interior and along the coast, chiefly on fresh water. A few remain through the summer.

Ring-necked Duck. *Marila collaris*

If a trained observer regularly examines with a glass all Scaup wintering on small ponds, he will occasionally note a duck that differs in several details from the common Lesser Scaup. The first point to attract his notice will be a *pale bluish white* band *near the tip of the lead-colored bill*, contrasting with the blackish tip. He will also note that the back is much darker than that of the male Scaup and that the gray flank becomes pure white just aft of the black breast, so that a white line runs up into the black in front of the bend of the folded wing. Any one thoroughly familiar with the Lesser Scaup will also notice a difference in the shape of the head; in the Ring-necked Duck the head is higher, as if an additional thickness of loose feathers had been laid over the top. In very favorable light at close range when the male raises his head and neck, a chestnut collar is visible around the fore part of the lower neck, but the ordinary position of the bird with head somewhat drawn down conceals the collar entirely. The female Ring-neck may be distinguished from the female Scaup by the pale ring near the tip of the bill, by the amount of pale gray on the sides of the head and by the presence of a *white eye-ring*. In flight the Ring-neck shows a bluish gray patch in the wing, lacking the white edging of the Lesser Scaup.

Ring-necked Ducks obtain their food by diving and fly like Scaup swiftly and generally low over the water. They prefer willow-fringed ponds or sloughs formed by old river channels, and are not so often found on large bodies of open water.

15½–18

Ad. ♂. — Head black, with purplish reflections in strong light; back and breast black; sides ashy, separated from breast by *curved white line* extending a short distance upward; area under tail black; rest of under parts white. Bill dark gray with a narrow band of white around the base, and a broader *band of bluish white near the tip*, tip black; iris yellow; feet grayish blue. **Ad.** ♀. — Top of head brown; a small area of white about the base of the bill; *eye-ring white;* back dark brown; *sides of head paling downward*, becoming much lighter than breast; sides light brown; belly whitish. Bill as in ♂ but duller; feet gray.

Dist. — *Cal.* *Ore.* *Wash.* } Rather uncommon M. and W.V. (Sept.–May). Has been reported as breeding at Eagle L., Lassen Co., Calif., and at Klamath L., Ore.

Nest, of grasses sparingly lined with down, in grassy margins. *Eggs*, 6–12, greenish or grayish white to buff.

AMERICAN GOLDEN-EYE; WHISTLER. *Glaucionetta clangula americana*

On the many arms and passages of Puget Sound in winter little groups of fairly large ducks with *snowy under parts* and flanks, and *glossy black heads* are scattered over the water, diving and reappearing, or, when startled, flying swiftly over the water with a *sharp whistling of the wings.* A near view shows a *round white spot between the eye and the bill,* and in strong light the black head shows greenish reflections. With the black-headed male Golden-eyes are females with dusky under parts and brown heads without the white spot. Both sexes have *bushy heads* set off by a white neck, so that the birds have somewhat the appearance of having had their head feathers bobbed. Golden-eyes feed largely on mussels and other shellfish, for which they dive, often coming to submerged flats close to shore. Their flight is strong, either low over the water when not going far, or fairly high when changing from feeding to resting grounds; the sharp whistling of their wings in flight is a characteristic sound of northern bays and inlets in winter.

AMERICAN GOLDEN-EYE (♂)

In late winter and early spring the male Golden-eye elevates his head and neck with the bill pointing straight up, at the same time uttering a nasal note, which suggests the *spee-ick* of the Nighthawk. Then he jerks the head quickly back till it touches the rump, and then brings it forward, often kicking the water back at the same time and showing a flash of his orange feet. The female utters occasionally a harsh *quork.*

On the wing Golden-eyes show a stocky outline which readily distinguishes them from the Mergansers, which have a somewhat similar black and white pattern but long slender necks and bills. The presence of the small spot in front of the eye distinguishes the male Golden-eye from the much smaller male Buffle-head (see p. 50). The uniform brown bushy head and the white in the outspread wing characterize the female Golden-eye. For the distinction between the male American Golden-eye and the Barrow see the following species.

$18\frac{1}{2}$–23

Ad. ♂. — *Head bushy, glossy black* (greenish in strong light); *a round white spot before and below eye;* hind-neck white, contrasting with head and back; middle of back and tail black; *wings showing much white* both when extended and when closed; under parts white. Bill black; iris deep yellow; feet orange. **Ad.** ♀. — *Head and neck* all around *brown;* no white spot; collar whitish, not complete behind; *white patch in extended wing*, showing as a narrow line on bend of closed wing; upper parts grayish brown; breast ashy gray; rest of under parts white. Bill dusky for most of its length, dull orange at tip; feet dull orange. **Im.** ♂. — Like the female but with the white spot more or less developed.

Dist. — *Cal.* Fairly common W.V. (Nov.–Apr.), chiefly in northern half of State.

Ore. / *Wash.* } Common W.V. (Nov.–May) along the coast and inland.

Barrow Golden-eye. *Glaucionetta islandica*

Close scrutiny of male Golden-eyes along the northern coast in winter will occasionally reveal one with a *triangular* instead of a round *spot in front of the eye* (see p. 49). The *head* in strong light shows *purplish* instead of greenish reflections and *the white area on the wing is crossed by a black bar*. Even at a distance, the Barrow Golden-eye can be distinguished, as Major Brooks has pointed out, by the fact that the black of the back 'comes almost, or quite, to the water line in front of the wing.' Females of the two species are practically indistinguishable in the field.

21–23

Ad. ♂. — Similar to preceding species, but *white spot* between eye and bill *triangular or pear-shaped*, head with *purplish reflections*, white area on the closed wing crossed by a black bar. **Ad.** ♀. — Similar to preceding species.

Dist. — Not common W.V. (Oct.–May) along the coast of Wash. and Ore., rare in northern Cal. as far south as San Francisco Bay. Breeds sparingly in the mountains of central Ore.

Nest, in a hollow in a tree, lined with down. *Eggs*, 6–15, various shades of green or bluish green.

Buffle-head; Butter-ball. *Charitonetta albeola*

Here and there among the wintering ducks on inland lakes and ponds or on bays and estuaries along the coast are small ducks that appear at a distance almost snow-white. They ride the water lightly, singly or in small groups. With the male Buffle-heads are slightly smaller females, dark but showing on a closer view an elongated white spot on the side of the head. From time to time they disappear under water; after an interval one after another emerges as if vigorously propelled upwards. If they are approached too closely, they take wing and fly with rapid wing-strokes and a somewhat zigzag flight low over the water, lighting with a splash and a slide that carries them a little distance along the surface.

BUFFLE-HEAD (♂)

The male Buffle-head can readily be distinguished from the much larger Golden-eye (much rarer in southern California) by the *large area of white on the head* and the snow-white flanks. A female Buffle-head when resting on the water can be readily distinguished from a female Golden-eye by the *white spot on the side of the head,* absent in the latter. Both show a white area in the wing in flight, but the Golden-eye is a much larger bird and shows a larger wing-patch. The female Buffle-head may readily be distinguished from female or immature Ruddy Ducks by the much smaller bill and by the shape of the white spot, which is restricted and clearly defined in the Buffle-head but covers the whole lower half of the head in the Ruddy (see p. 56).

$12\frac{1}{4}$–$15\frac{1}{4}$

Ad. ♂. — Head fluffy; top of head and back glossy black (head in strong light with green and purple reflections); a *snow-white patch from back of eye over the back of the neck;* broad ring around neck and under parts white; *large white area in wing.* Bill bluish gray; feet orange. **Ad. ♀.** — Head and upper parts dark gray; an *elongated white spot on side of head;* breast and flanks gray; rest of under parts white; *white patch in extended wing.* Bill and feet dark gray.

Dist. — *Cal.* Common W.V. (Oct.–Apr.) along the coast and less commonly inland. Has bred at Eagle L., Lassen Co.

Ore. } *Wash.* } Common M. and W.V. (Oct.–May) both east and west.

Nest, in holes in trees, lined with down. *Eggs,* 8–12, buff.

Old-Squaw. *Clangula hyemalis*

In severe winters in the many passages of Puget Sound and along the coast, flocks of ducks with a marked contrast of white and brown may be seen diving for food or flying off when disturbed, the brightest colored among the flock showing *central tail feathers much longer than the rest of the tail.* These long tail feathers drop slightly as the bird flies but are cocked up when the bird is swimming. The Old-Squaw even in winter is a noisy duck; a flock often utter musical cries resembling the syllables *honk-a-link, honk-a-link.* Old-Squaws feed in small or large flocks in the surf close to the outer beaches, or in bays or straits, or over shoals at sea. They ride easily over the great rollers or dive into and through them. Little companies are constantly moving here and there, flying after they get under way with great ease and rapidity.

OLD-SQUAW (♀, Winter)

The male, even when the tail feathers do not show, is readily identified by the *white head with a dark spot behind the eye;* females and young show much whitish about the sides of the head and neck, much more than the female Buffle-head or the female Harlequin. The dark lining of the under side of the wing is a good field mark (Brooks).

15–23

Ad. ♂ in winter. — *Patch on side of neck blackish brown* (occasionally nearly absent); *rest of head, neck, upper breast white;* back, wings and tail brown, two white patches extending down back; *two central tail-feathers black, very long and narrow;* outer tail feathers white; breast and upper belly brown, lower belly white. Bill, basal half and tip black, terminal half red; feet gray. **Ad. ♂ in late spring.** — Patch around eye white; rest of head, neck, tail and upper breast black; back light brown, belly white. **Ad. ♀ in winter.** — Head, neck and under parts dusky brown; middle tail feathers not elongated. Bill and feet dusky. **Ad. ♀ in late spring.** — Similar to winter female, but less white on sides of head.

Dist. — *Cal.* Rare and irregular W.V. as far south as San Diego.
Ore. Not common W.V. along the coast.
Wash. Not uncommon W.V. (Nov.–May) along the coast; casual east. A few remain in summer.

WESTERN HARLEQUIN DUCK. *Histrionicus histrionicus pacificus*

Along rocky promontories that project into the ocean or about low-lying reefs and outer islets, from Monterey northward, small trim ducks with *reddish brown flanks* and *grayish blue heads* with *fantastic white markings* dive fearlessly in the swirling surf. When a male Harlequin faces the observer a white crescent shows on each side of the head, separated by a black line through the forehead; a narrow white collar and a white bar in front of the wing set off the grayish blue of the head and breast. In summer a pair of Harlequins are occasionally found in mountain streams or lakes, diving for their food in the rapid current. Both in winter and in summer they frequently climb out of the water and rest on low rocks or logs.

WESTERN HARLEQUIN DUCK (♀)

The male is unmistakable; the female may be distinguished from a female Buffle-head by the *second white patch in front of the eye* (see p. 50) and the absence of white in the wing. The pattern of spots on the side of the female's head is similar to that of the female Surf Scoter (see p. 55), but there should be no possibility of confusing the trim figure of the Harlequin with her short bill with the heavy Scoter with her large bill and sloping forehead.

15–17½

Ad. ♂ in winter and spring. — *Head and neck dark slate blue with conspicuous white, black and reddish brown markings,* a white patch in front of eye; stripe of reddish brown from above the eye to back of head; collar white; white bar bordered with black in front of bend of wing; tail rather long and pointed, blackish; *sides rich reddish brown,* rest of under parts grayish brown. Bill gray, white at tip, darker at base; feet dark brown. **Ad. ♂ in summer.** —

Bright colors absent or much duller. **Ad.** ♀ **and Im.** — General color of upper parts and flanks dark brown, *a white patch* often interrupted by brownish *before the eye*, and a *smaller one behind it;* belly whitish. Bill dusky; feet dull gray. Young males are found in plumage intermediate between that of ♀ and **ad.** ♂.

Dist. — *Cal.* Irregular W.V. on the coast to San Luis Obispo Co.; has bred in the Yosemite.
Ore. Occurs on the coast from Aug. to May; breeds in the Wallowa Mts. and perhaps in the Cascades.
Wash. R., breeding in mountains and occurring from Sept. to May on the coast; a few remain on salt water in summer.

Nest, a hollow in the ground, often close to a stream, lined with grasses and down. *Eggs*, 5–10, light buff or cream-color, with a striking ivory texture.

American Scoter. *Oidemia americana*

From northern California to British Columbia the winter seas break over low reefs or against steep rocky promontories. From the top of some headland one can see on a calm day groups of black ducks scattered over the surface of the ocean, some of which show when they face the observer a *yellow bill against the black head.* In late winter and in spring the American Scoter utters a musical wailing note, *koolee,* which carries a long distance. At the same time the males repeat around the females the courtship display; the head and neck are elevated, the tail is cocked back over the body, and the bird slides a short distance along the surface of the water. The American Scoter as a rule does not come into the bays and estuaries in which the two other species are common, keeping more to the outer shores and the open ocean. It dives for shellfish over banks or near reefs. Its flight is rapid when once under way, generally low over the water, but, according to Brooks, often at a considerable height.

A male American Scoter in adult plumage can readily be distinguished from either of the other Scoters, by the absence of white on the nape or below the eye, and above all by the *butter-yellow bill;* the adult males of both the other Scoters show much red on the bill. The outline of the head and bill of the American Scoter is also distinctive, lacking the long sloping forehead of the other two (pp. 54, 55). Great care must be taken not to mistake a young male Surf Scoter with its uniformly black head for an American Scoter; south of San Francisco the American Scoter is rare. The female American Scoter can be distinguished after careful study from the other two species by the lack of definite whitish spots on the side of the head; the *whole lower half of the head is light gray,* contrasted with the darker upper half. See also under Ruddy Duck, p. 56.

17–21½

Ad. ♂. — *Entirely black,* under surface of wing silvery; bill, terminal half black, protuberance at the base yellow deepening into orange; bill shorter than in the two other Scoters and not making a long sloping forehead; iris black; feet blackish. **Ad.** ♀. — Brown, paler below; *sides of head pale gray or whitish,* the area nearly continuous (not divided as in the females of the two following species). Bill blackish; feet dusky.

Dist. — *Cal.* Rare W.V. on the coast.
Ore. } *Wash.* } W.V. (Sept.–May) along the coast, and off shore.

WHITE-WINGED SCOTER. *Oidemia deglandi dixoni*

Where the surf breaks on a sandy beach, the awkward forms of large black ducks are often seen waddling out from the shallow edge of the incoming water. As soon as they reach the breakers, they dive through the incoming wave or ride easily over it. Farther out scattered individuals or small companies float on the water and when one stands for a moment and flaps its wings, a *white patch in the wing* is disclosed which distinguishes the White-winged Scoter from the Surf Scoter, with which it is usually associated. Even when the wings are closed, the white often shows as a narrow line. When feeding, Scoters dive with a vigorous forward leap and remain under water for nearly a minute. In spring and fall band after band travel north or south along the coast, their white wing-patches offering an easy recognition mark. Although primarily sea ducks, many are found in the large bays and estuaries, and even in small lagoons of brackish water. When disturbed, they rise heavily, often paddling for a short distance on the surface. When riding the water, they often spread their tail feathers and elevate them slightly, suggesting a Ruddy Duck, from which the size, particularly the length of body and bill, should always distinguish them.

WHITE-WINGED SCOTER (♂)

WHITE-WINGED SCOTER (♀)

In late winter and early spring when the young birds are moulting into breeding plumage, there are many different and puzzling plumages in a company of Scoters. The young males have heads and necks of sooty brown, and varying degrees of brown in the back, the females have two spots of whitish, one before and one behind the eye. The adult males have a white spot under the eye; the bill is tipped with reddish and shows more or less orange along the sides and black at the base.

$19\frac{3}{4}$–23

Ad. ♂. — Small white spot below and behind eye; *short broad white patch about the middle of the wing;* rest of plumage black. Bill reddish along sides and at tip, central portion white above, showing against black base when bird is head on; iris white or yellowish; feet, inner face orange or red, outer blackish. **Ad. ♀ and Im.** — Dusky brown with *two dull whitish spots, one below and be-*

hind eye, the other below and before eye; wing-patch as in ♂. Bill dusky; feet, inner face flesh-color, outer black. **Im. ♂ in spring.** — Entire head blackish.

Dist. — *Cal.* *Ore.* *Wash.* } Abundant W.V. (Sept.–May) along entire coast; a few records for eastern Wash.; a few remain in summer.

Surf Scoter. *Oidemia perspicillata*

All along the coast in winter Scoters of two species float here and there on the water. In one group a bird with its back to the observer shows a *square-white patch* on the nape, or, when it faces about, a *snowy forehead.* The rest of the body is black but if the bird approaches, the large bill which makes almost a continuous line with the top of the head shows orange toward the tip, with a black spot like a piece of court-plaster on the white area on the basal portion of the sides. Surf Scoters, at any rate the male, make a whistling sound with their wings when they first rise and fly. Major Brooks has pointed out that the whistling is in a slightly lower pitch than that of the Golden-eye, and that it ceases abruptly very shortly after a flight is begun, but is heard again just before the bird alights. When a male Surf Scoter alights, he often elevates his wings just as his body strikes the water and holds them up for an instant above his back. During courtship, which begins before the birds leave for the north, the males gather about the female, pursue one another a short distance swimming with head down, then take a short flight and, alighting as described above, utter a low grunting note, or a male swims slowly up to the female, and then stands upright with the tail cocked up, calling *quut quut quut.* The female Surf Scoter is very like the female White-winged Scoter, except that no white shows in her wing even when extended. The absence of white is harder to establish than its presence, but by patient waiting the point can often be determined by the sight of some bird flapping its wings. Toward spring as the young males acquire the breeding plumage, there is a great variety of plumage displayed.

SURF SCOTER (♂)

18–22

Ad. ♂. — Patch on *forehead* and another on *hind-neck white;* rest of plumage black (brownish black below). Bill, *sides white at base, enclosing a patch of black,* rest of upper mandible reddish with orange tip, protuberance at base reddish orange; iris white; feet, inner face orange-red, outer blackish. **Ad. ♀ and Im.** — Top of head black; *one dull whitish spot before and below eye, another behind and below* (rarely a grayish nape patch); rest of plumage sooty brown, whitish on belly. Bill, blackish above and toward tip, sides light gray toward base; feet, inner face dull flesh-color, outer black. **Im. ♂ in spring.** — Head blackish.

Dist. — *Cal.* } Abundant W.V. (Oct.–May) along the coast; a few remain
Ore. } in summer.
Wash. Common W.V. (Sept.–May) on the coast; occasional on fresh water near by. A few remain in summer.

SPINY-TAILED DUCKS: *Subfamily Erismaturinæ*

Ruddy Duck. *Erismatura jamaicensis*

Here and there in every assemblage of water fowl on bays and inland lakes, or in the smallest sloughs in marshy country are seen groups of small dumpy brown ducks, with *short broad bills*, and a *short tail* which is generally *carried up at an angle*, revealing a white area beneath. At all seasons most of the birds in a group of Ruddy Ducks show a *light gray cheek*, paler than the top of the head. As spring approaches, this grows brighter in the male, until, in full breeding plumage, it is pure white and his brown body has become a rich reddish brown, almost chestnut. The

RUDDY DUCK (♀)

bright blue bill, the black tail cocked up showing a white area underneath, the white cheek and ruddy body, combine to make a male Ruddy Duck one of the most striking and easily recognized birds. Ruddy Ducks dive for food and when alarmed more often dive than fly; they are as expert as Grebes in escaping under water. When a Ruddy Duck flies, it patters over the surface for some distance and then flies with rapid wing-strokes low over the water.

Ruddy Ducks, though common on brackish bays, are rarely, if ever, found in the open sea. Many remain to breed even in southern California, in small tule-bordered ponds or open marshes. During the courtship display the male puffs out his white cheeks, elevates head and neck and cocks his tail, spreading wide the stiff black feathers. Suddenly he begins to strike his breast vigorously and with increasing speed with his bill, at the same time making a succession of rattling sounds, *beb, beb, beb*, and ending with a gulping *cloop*. The rattling sounds carry only a short distance. The black feathers on the side of the head are slightly elevated at this season, forming a low ridge over the eye. At other times both male and female are silent. The male Ruddy Duck unlike other ducks remains with the female after the young are hatched and assists in their care.

A Ruddy Duck can hardly even by a beginner be confused with any other water fowl. The brown Pied-billed Grebe that is often associated with it has a slender slightly arching neck, while the Ruddy seems to have no neck at all. The tail held stiffly up out of the water is an unfailing mark. Scoters often show their tails above water, but their larger bodies and their long sloping foreheads and bills should readily distinguish them (see p. 54).

13–16

Ad. ♂ in breeding plumage. — Top of head black, *cheeks* and chin *white;* neck, *upper parts and sides rich brown-red;* wings and tail dusky; tail feathers stiff and pointed; white area under the tail; under parts silvery white waved with dusky white. *Bill* broad, *blue,* feet bluish gray. **Ad. ♀ and Im.** — Top of head dark brown, narrow line of brown through the *whitish cheeks;* back grayish brown; under parts dull whitish; white area under the tail. Bill and feet dusky. **Ad. in winter.** — Similar to **ad. ♀** but cheek white.

Dist. — *Cal.* Common R. throughout, chiefly on fresh water.
Ore. Common R. in the lake country east; W.V. (Nov.–Feb.) along the coast.
Wash. S.V. (end of Apr.–Nov.) east, and sparingly in the Sound region; W.V. (Dec.–Feb.) on the coast and in the Sound region.

Nest, a basket-like structure of reeds, etc., 7 or 8 in. above level of water, attached to the reeds, and often concealed by arching reeds. —*Eggs,* usually 6–10 (often more), very large for the size of the parent, dull or creamy white, rough-grained.

MERGANSERS: *Subfamily Merginæ*

American Merganser. *Mergus americanus*

A line of gray ducks with reddish brown heads and slender red *bills* is occasionally seen swimming against the swift current of mountain streams or along the rocky shores of lakes. When they fly, American Mergansers show a broad *white patch in the wings;* the bill, head and neck are conspicuously long and slender. In the breeding season a pair may be seen flying with a hoarse *cruck* over or through tall evergreens or alighting on a dead stub, sometimes fifty feet above the ground. The male riding on a clear mountain lake is a beautiful sight, the *glossy black head* and upper neck contrasting with the *snow-white under parts*. In winter American Mergansers appear along the coast as well as on inland bodies of water, but south of Washington they are not nearly so common as the Red-breasted Merganser.

The male when on the water shows a great amount of white, the white of the flanks being continued well up the sides of the back by the white in the folded wings, leaving only a small wedge-shaped area of black on the back, a small mark in the middle of the wing, and a small area of black between the bend of the wing and the breast. Often there is no crest apparent on the narrow greenish black head of the male but occasionally he shows a short pointed tuft low down on the back of the head. In the female the crest comes to only a single point well back on the hind-neck, but in excitement the tips can be raised and bent forward.

AMERICAN MERGANSER (♂)

The slender head and neck, almost of the same diameter throughout and the bright red bill distinguish the male American Merganser from any other bird but the Red-breasted Merganser; the latter has a much more conspicuous crest and a dark collar across the breast. Females of the two species are indistinguishable at long range but under favorable circumstances the well-defined *white throat* of the female American, entirely surrounded by reddish brown, is a good field mark.

AMERICAN MERGANSER (♀)

21–27

Ad. ♂. — Head and neck apparently black (glossy green in strong light); short crest low on hind-head; upper back black; lower back and tail gray; neck, most of wings and under parts white (the under parts tinged with salmon). *Bill long, slender, red,* hooked tip and ridge along top black; iris red; feet red. **Ad.** ♀ **and Im.** — *Throat white,* rest of head and neck reddish brown; crest of loose feathers on hind-head (with only one prominent point low on hind-neck) reddish brown; back and tail gray; *wings black with a white patch;* sides grayish, rest of under parts white. Bill and feet as in male but duller.

Dist. — *Cal.* Fairly common W.V. on streams and lakes, less common along the coast; breeds about lakes and along streams of the Sierras from Kern Co. north; also in Humboldt Bay district.

Ore. Common R. on lakes and mountain streams both east and west; W.V. along the coast.

Wash. Common R. on lakes and streams both east and west; common W.V. to the Sound and the Straits, and to the larger streams east of the mountains.

Nest, in a hollow tree or on ground, lined with down, weeds, rootlets, etc. *Eggs*, 6–10 (17), white tinged with buff.

RED-BREASTED MERGANSER. *Mergus serrator*

Along the coast and in bays and estuaries, lines of ducks, a few black and white, the rest gray, with long necks and bills fly in winter low over the water, all showing *broad patches of white in the wing.* When swimming the female shows a *bushy head* with a *loose crest of ragged reddish brown feathers* often separated in two tufts, and the male a *glossy black head* with a similar crest, a *white collar* and a *dark band across the breast.* The Red-breasted Merganser dives when feeding or swims along close to shore with outstretched head and neck half under water watching for small fish. The wing-patch shows as a small area of white even when the wings are closed. Mergansers frequently come up on the shore to rest, standing with short red feet wide apart. The Red-breasted Merganser can be distinguished from all other ducks except the American Merganser by the slender head and long bill; in flight the neck, head and bill hardly vary in diameter, instead of presenting as in other ducks a distinct difference in size where the head interrupts the line. The male Red-breasted Merganser is easily distinguished from the male American by the prominent ragged crest and by the reddish brown or blackish collar across the breast. It is very difficult to distinguish the female of the two species at long range, but under favorable circumstances the less clearly defined white throat, which shades gradually into the brown of the neck distinguishes the female Red-breasted. In winter along the coast the Red-breasted Merganser is commoner than the American, particularly south of Puget Sound.

RED-BREASTED MERGANSER (♂)

20–25

Ad. ♂. — *Head and upper neck apparently black* (glossy green in strong light); loose crest with two points on the hind-head, one below the other; a *broad ring of white around neck;* upper back black, lower back gray; wing mostly white; *collar around upper breast buff, streaked with black;* most of under parts white. *Bill long, slender, red;* iris red; feet red. **Ad. ♀ and Im.** — Throat whitish, rest of head and upper neck reddish brown; ragged crest with two points on hind-head; back and tail gray; *white patch on wing;* under parts white. Bill reddish on the sides and below; feet dull red.

Dist. — *Cal.* Common W.V. (Sept.–Apr.) along the coast and on bays and estuaries; less numerous on large bodies of fresh water.
Ore. Common W.V. along the coast.
Wash. Fairly common R. on inland lakes and streams, principally west, probably breeding; common W.V. (Oct.–Mar.) along the coast.

Nest, generally under low branches or roots, lined with down, grasses, etc. *Eggs*, 8–10 (16), buff or olive-buff.

Hooded Merganser. *Lophodytes cucullatus*

In the lower reaches of the streams that run into Puget Sound and the adjacent waters, where stretches of quiet waters are overgrown with trees and bushes, and in small woodland ponds near the Sound, a small duck is occasionally seen in winter or early spring which has a *broad white stripe through the side of a bushy head.* Near by, perhaps preening herself on a log, is a sober-colored female with a loose crest of reddish brown feathers. The Hooded Merganser has the narrow bill that characterizes the family, but shorter than in the other two Mergansers and blackish, not red.

Bowles has commented on the extraordinary ease with which Hooded Mergansers in the mating season pursue one another at a tremendous speed through a dense growth of trees. At this season they may be seen perched or walking about on high limbs. Hooded Mergansers swim with the tail up out of water. They dive for food, keep much in the shelter of brushy edges of streams or ponds, are very wary and fly when startled with surprising rapidity. The ordinary note, heard chiefly in the mating season is 'a rough chatter.' (Bowles.)

When the male in the courtship display elevates the long feathers of the back of the head, the white stripe becomes a large white area spreading fanwise back of the eye. The *rich chestnut along the sides*, the very slender bill and the wholly different proportions of the bird will at once distinguish it from the Buffle-head for any one who knows the latter well, and no student will be likely to see a Hooded Merganser until he has seen a thousand Buffle-heads. The female Hooded Merganser can be recognized as a Merganser by the slender neck and bill, and by the crest of reddish brown elongated feathers on the back of the head. From the other two Mergansers she may be distinguished by the smaller size and by the much grayer color of the head and neck. In flight Hooded Mergansers might be mistaken for Teal, but the distinctly longer tail of the Merganser is a good field distinction.

$17\frac{1}{4}$–$19\frac{1}{4}$

Ad. ♂. — Head and neck black, a crest of loose feathers including a *broad stripe of white from back of the eye almost to the edge of the crest*, which becomes a fan-shaped patch of white when the crest is elevated in the mating season; upper back black; lower back and tail brown; wings with white area barred with black; a black stripe extending over the white of the breast; *flanks rich chestnut;* rest of under parts white. Bill slender, shorter than the head, black; iris yellow; feet brown. **Ad.** ♀. — Upper parts grayish brown; head with a crest of loose grayish brown feathers (pale reddish brown in strong light); wing with a white area; throat whitish; upper breast grayish brown; rest of under parts white. Bill dusky, orange below toward base; feet dusky.

Dist. — *Cal.* Rather rare W.V.
Ore. Not uncommon M. and W.V.
Wash. R., principally west.

Nest, holes in trees or stumps, occasionally at least 75 ft. up (Bowles), lined with down. *Eggs*, usually 10–12, white.

VULTURES, HAWKS AND EAGLES: *Order Falconiformes*

AMERICAN VULTURES: *Family Cathartidæ*

California Condor. *Gymnogyps californianus*

The ambition of every California bird student is to see a Condor. The great size of the bird, its restricted range and the comparative inac-

CALIFORNIA CONDOR

cessibility of its haunts combine to give the student a tremendous thrill when the last canyon wall is climbed and the great black bird is seen soaring over the next jagged peak. In many an earlier hunt a distant Buzzard or a Golden Eagle has been scrutinized in the vain hope that it is a Condor, but when the real Condor appears, the great expanse of black wings, the majestic flight and above all the *clear white along the under side of the wing next to the shoulder* make identification certain. A Golden Eagle often shows white areas in the wings but they are toward the middle of the wing and in this plumage the Eagle also shows a whitish rump. The cut of the wings of the two species is different; the Eagle's wings are comparatively blunt but the Condor's wing-tip extends almost to a point and when the bird is soaring, the tips of the primaries actually point forward. When a Condor's breeding haunt is invaded, the birds are often seen perched on the crags above the breeding cliffs. Occasionally a number are seen in the air at the same time, the old birds showing the white under the wings, the young ones wholly black. At such times the birds seem to wish to examine the intruder and float near enough to show the yellow or orange head and neck. The Condor's flight is like the Buzzard's; when rising from the ground or flying low, it flaps heavily, but soon begins to soar and rise in wide circles or sails off over the mountain-ranges and canyons.

4–4½ ft. Wingspread 8½–9½ ft.

Ad. — Plumage wholly black, *except a white lining under the wings close to the shoulder;* bare neck and head yellowish or orange. Bill yellowish; feet light flesh-colored. **Im.** — Head, neck and bill dusky; no white under the wings.

Dist. — *Cal.* R. in the mountains of southern Cal., chiefly in Santa Barbara and Ventura Cos., locally north to Monterey Co., east to Kern Co. and south to Los Angeles Co.

Nest, egg laid on bare ground in a cave or hole in cliffs. *Egg*, one, white to bluish white.

Turkey Vulture; Buzzard. *Cathartes aura septentrionalis*

Occasionally we pass large *black birds with red heads and necks* perched motionless on a row of fence posts as if grimly waiting for some creature's death, or rising with labored strokes from some carcase. A far commoner sight is that of the Buzzard in flight. One or two are nearly always in sight somewhere in the sky, floating easily along, or circling with wings tilted slightly upward, their forms swaying slightly from side to side. When the bird comes overhead, the under side of the body and the forward portion of the wings show black, while the *after half of the wings are ashy gray*. When rising from the ground or when flying low, the Buzzard keeps its momentum by heavy flapping of its great wings; once in the upper air, it soars and circles for long periods, without a single wing-stroke, nor does it spread and flex its tail at a different plane from its wings as the Red-tailed Hawk does. When soaring, the tips of its primaries are conspicuously separated.

A Buzzard can be told by a trained observer almost as far as it can be seen, but a beginner should look for the black body and the contrast of silvery gray and black on the under sides of the wings. A Red-tailed Hawk shows a light-colored body, and the Golden Eagle shows no silvery gray on the under side of the wings. A hawk can also be distinguished from a Buzzard by the color of the upper parts; if the bird wheels so that a brown back reflects the light, it is a hawk, if black, a Buzzard. A Buzzard is sometimes mistaken by a beginner for a Condor. The white on a Condor is really white and on the forward side of the wing next to the body, not a silvery gray on the after half.

TURKEY VULTURE

$2\frac{1}{4}$–$2\frac{1}{2}$ ft. Wingspread about 6 ft.

Ad. — *Head naked, red,* upper surface of wings and back blackish brown; *under side of wing ashy gray* along much of the forward portion; under parts blackish brown. *Bill white;* feet flesh-color. **Im.** — Head and bill brown.

Dist. — *Cal.* Common S.V. (Mar.–Sept.) throughout (except in the highest mountains); remains through the winter in small numbers as far north as Butte Co., commoner in winter southward.

Ore. Common S.V. (middle of Mar.–Sept.), commoner east.

Wash. S.V. (middle of Mar.–Sept.), much commoner east.

Nest, in crevices or caves in cliffs, hollow stumps or logs. *Eggs,* 1–2 (3), white or creamy, spotted or blotched with brown.

HAWKS, EAGLES, etc.: *Family Accipitridæ*

KITES: *Subfamily Elaninæ*

White-tailed Kite. *Elanus leucurus*

In south-central California the rivers that come from the Coast Range have formed broad valleys with extensive willow thickets. Here one may still see the *white head and breast* of a White-tailed Kite perched in the low willows or on the highest branch of a live oak, or see the bird *hovering with rapid wing-beats* and outspread tail in its search for small game. The softness of its coloring and the confiding and gentle nature of the White-tailed Kite, so different from the wildness of most birds of prey, make a strong appeal to lovers of nature but not alas! to the usual run of gunners.

The bird seems to require such particular conditions for its breeding stations, that even where it is not molested it does not increase or occupy new ground. There are probably not more than fifty pairs left in California, and in spite of protection by law the number is slowly decreasing. The common cry of the White-tailed Kite, heard chiefly in the breeding season, is a high slightly drawled *pee*, with a rising inflection. When the birds are anxious about the nest, they utter a harsh guttural *whew* with a falling inflection like the Western Bluebird's. When much excited they give a series of notes, like a Marsh Hawk's *kek, kek, kek*, often with dangling feet. When the birds light, always on the topmost twig, the tail is several times tilted. The *black patch on the bend of the wing* shows even when the bird is perched.

WHITE-TAILED KITE

$15\frac{1}{4}$–$16\frac{3}{4}$

Ad. ♂. — *Most of head white;* rest of upper parts bluish gray; *tail white; broad black area on bend of wing*, showing also from below; line over eye black; under parts white. Bill black; cere and legs yellow. **Ad.** ♀. — The white of head and breast duller. **Im.** — Head and breast washed with rusty; tail with a bar near tip.

Dist. — *Cal.* R. in river valleys from Santa Clara and Monterey Cos. to Ventura Co.

Nest, in trees of moderate height, usually live oaks, near the top. *Eggs*, 3–5, whitish, blotched with rich reddish and blackish brown.

HAWKS: *Subfamily Accipitrinæ*

Sharp-shinned Hawk. *Accipiter velox*

If a company of birds chirping or singing in a thicket suddenly becomes silent and motionless, a bird student looks up and generally sees a small hawk circling overhead. Too often the hawk with a swift dash from ambush is in the midst of a flock and carries off in its talons a screeching victim. It then flies to a shaded limb and there tears morsels of flesh from its victim. The Sharp-shinned Hawk is silent except in the breeding season; near its nest it utters a high *kee-ki-ki-ki* or a thin whining *whee whee.*

The Sharp-shinned Hawk is an almost exact reproduction on a smaller scale of the Cooper Hawk; a female Sharp-shinned Hawk and a male Cooper Hawk are so close in size that it is often impossible to distinguish them in the field. Both species have *short, rounded wings* and a *long tail;* both are often seen overhead, alternately taking a few rapid strokes and

trasted with the back and tail. The Swainson Hawk, which in eastern Oregon in summer occurs with the Ferruginous Rough-leg, may show whitish on head and under parts and also has a light-colored base of the tail. To be sure of a Ferruginous Rough-leg one must see that a *considerable portion* of the base of the tail is white or whitish and above all note the white areas in the upper surface of the wings.

$22\frac{1}{2}$–$23\frac{1}{2}$ Wingspread $4\frac{1}{2}$ ft. or more

Upper parts brown; top of head often streaked with white; back often showing much reddish brown; *wings with white areas on upper surface* near tips; under surface of wings largely white; *basal half of tail white or whitish;* under parts almost pure white or marked with rusty brown. Bill dusky, cere yellow; feet dusky yellow.

Dist. — *Cal.* Not common W.V. (Oct.–Mar.).
Ore. Not common S.V. in eastern Ore; a few winter.
Wash. Rare S.V. in open country east.

Nest, of sticks, often very large, in trees or on ledges or on the ground. *Eggs*, white, generally blotched with dark brown.

Golden Eagle. *Aquila chrysaëtos*

When a student has become thoroughly familiar with the outline in flight of the Buzzard and the Red-tailed Hawk, he will some day see soaring high over the foothills or mountains a bird whose outspread wings from tip to tip are so much longer than the line from bill to tail, that it is at once noticeable. The Condor alone surpasses in majesty the Golden Eagle. When the Golden Eagle turns in sunlight a suggestion of the golden brown is caught on the back of the head, neck and upper back, but generally the whole body appears black. Eagles often hunt in pairs. They circle and soar with little flapping, and occasionally poise against the wind. The shrill whistling cry is seldom heard except about the nest, on some remote and almost inaccessible cliff. Not infrequently an immature Golden Eagle shows a white area at the base of the tail and small whitish patches in the forward part of the wing. An Eagle in this plumage might be mistaken for a Condor. (See p. 62.)

About 3 ft. Wingspread $6\frac{1}{2}$–$7\frac{1}{2}$ ft.

Ad. — *Entire plumage dark brown;* in strong light top of head and hindneck golden brown; primaries and tail dusky. Bill bluish; legs greenish yellow. **Im.** — A light gray area in the wings and a white area at the base of the tail.

Dist. — Fairly common R. of mountain ranges throughout the Pacific Coast States, except in the humid coast belt.

Nest, a huge structure of sticks, on ledges or in trees. *Eggs*, 2–3, whitish, sometimes almost unmarked or heavily spotted and blotched with rich brown or dark brown.

Southern Bald Eagle. *Haliæetus leucocephalus leucocephalus*

An adult Bald Eagle is unmistakable; when wheeling high over some wide bay or at the mouth of a large river, the *white head* and then, as the bird circles, the *white wide-spread tail* alternately come into view. When perched on a headland along the coast, the white head and upper neck and the bright yellow bill can be seen far off. Its extent of wing is even greater than that of the Golden Eagle, so that the distance from tip to tip as the bird wheels is conspicuously greater than the length from head to tip of tail. The flight is very like that of a Red-tailed Hawk; the bird flaps and sails when getting under way, or when flying about the nest, but soars in great circles when high in air. The cry of the Eagle, heard oftenest near its nest, is a high-pitched very metallic *kweek kuk kuk, kweek-a-kuk-kuk* with the quality of an unoiled castor. An immature bird cannot be distinguished in the field from a Golden Eagle. The Bald Eagle, however, is rarely seen far from the ocean or large lakes; an eagle sailing about over high mountains or along the foothills, obviously hunting, is the Golden Eagle, and a large brown Eagle standing on the beach, devouring a dead fish, even if it lacks the white head, is generally an immature Bald Eagle.

About 3 ft. Wingspread 7–8 ft.

Ad. — *Head, neck and tail white;* rest of plumage dark brown. Bill and feet yellow. **Im.** — Entire plumage dark brown.

Dist. — *Cal.* Not common R. of the Channel Islands and along the coast, chiefly northward, and on some of the larger interior lakes northward; M. elsewhere.

Ore. / *Wash.* Not common R. west; less common east. M. along the coast, on lakes and rivers.

Nest, a bulky structure of sticks in trees or on ledges. *Eggs*, generally 2, white, usually unmarked.

HARRIERS: *Subfamily Circinæ*

Marsh Hawk. *Circus hudsonius*

If one stands in the middle of any large marshy area, or among dry hills covered with low bushes, from somewhere on the horizon a hawk will soon appear, with long narrow tail and long wings, swinging a little from side to side, flapping a few times, then sailing, and sooner or later showing a *pure white rump*, contrasting with the back and tail. This mark is particularly noticeable in the female and young birds which are otherwise dark brown above. The male bird has light gray wings with black tips and white under parts, but the white of the rump is still conspicuous. Marsh Hawks when hunting fly very low, often almost grazing the grasses or bushes below them, ready to drop with outspread talons on their prey. The wings are generally held at a slight upward angle. At times they fly to a considerable height flapping a little and sailing with easy flight. In the breeding season the male performs astonishing tricks in the air, swinging suddenly down in a deep and narrow arc, or making successive loops, rolling partially or completely over at the top of each loop. When one approaches the nest or young on the ground in some low thicket, the birds become violently excited and dart from high in the air close to the intruder's head, uttering excited *keks* or *kiks*.

If the white rump is noted, the young or female Marsh Hawk is unmistakable. The male at a distance might be mistaken for a small gull or for the rarer White-tailed Kite, but both the adult gull and the Kite have an entirely white tail; the Marsh Hawk has only the rump white (see pp. 63, 64).

MARSH HAWK (Adult. ♀)

$17\frac{1}{2}$–24 Wingspread $3\frac{1}{3}$–4 ft.

Ad. ♂. — Upper parts bluish gray; tail crossed by black bars; wings tipped with black; *rump white;* throat and breast gray; belly white, flecked here and there with brown; under surface of the wings (except the black tips) white. Bill blackish; cere and feet yellow. **Ad.** ♀. — Upper parts brown; *rump white;* under parts buffy white; breast thickly streaked with brown. **Im.** — Upper parts similar to ♀; under parts rusty brown, streaked on the breast, unstreaked on the belly.

Dist. — *Cal.* S.V. in marshy country; common M. and W.V. in low or brushy country throughout.
Ore. Common S.V. (Mar.–Oct.) in marshy country east; a few winter.
Wash. S.V. (Mar.–Oct.), common east, casual west.

Nest, on the ground, of dried grasses, sedges, etc. *Eggs*, 4–6, dull greenish or bluish white, often with pale brownish blotches.

OSPREYS: *Subfamily Pandioninæ*

OSPREY; FISH HAWK. *Pandion haliaëtus carolinensis*

Here and there on some of the Channel Is. off the coast of southern California, or on some inland lake or stream, a huge nest of sticks is a conspicuous object on the broken top of a dead tree. From the nest a large hawk with *whitish head and white under parts* flies to the ocean or a near-by lake or estuary, and circles overhead watching for the gleam of a fish near the surface, or hovers with tail spread and feet dangling. From a height often of a hundred feet the Fish Hawk strikes the water with such force that it disappears below the surface, generally emerging with its talons fixed in the back of a fish; then with a labored flight it sets off for the nest. When an intruder approaches the nest, the Fish Hawk begins a shrill *pee, pee, pee,* followed by a low *cak, cak, cak.* At other times its cry is a high-pitched whistled *ki-ik, ki-ik.* When traveling it takes fairly constant wing-strokes, but about the nest it often flaps and sails alternately. The whitish head and white under parts readily distinguish the Fish Hawk.

OSPREY

About 2 ft. Wingspread 5 ft.

Ad. — Sides and top of head marked with dark brown, *rest of head white;* back, wings and tail dark brown above, paler below with dusky bars; much white on under surface of wings; *under parts chiefly white.* Bill blackish; legs long, conspicuous, clothed with white; feet dark gray.

Dist. — *Cal.* M. (Apr.–May; Aug.–Nov.); S.V. on some of the Channel Is., sparingly along the coast on the mainland, and on the lakes northeast; winters occasionally.

Ore. S.V. (Mar.–Oct.) on lakes and streams east, and sparingly along the coast.

Wash. S.V. (Feb.–Nov.) west and (Apr.–Nov.) east; probably winters west.

Nest, huge platform of sticks on dead tree or on the ground. *Eggs*, 2–3 (4), endlessly varied, white, tawny or reddish, sparingly or heavily blotched with brown.

uttering the call even when the tree in which he sits is located. The notes are a succession of about six sounds, which may be transcribed as *broo, broop, broop, burroo broo broo,* increasing at first in volume, then diminishing. The sounds never end in the roll which characterizes the

SIERRA GROUSE (♂)

drumming of the Ruffed Grouse. If the bird comes into plain view, the general color is gray; the male is so dark as to have been given the names Sooty or Blue Grouse. The female is brown above but without the reddish brown hue that characterizes the Ruffed Grouse. In winter the Sierra or Sooty Grouse keeps almost exclusively in the tops of firs, many moving up from lower levels at that season, feeding on the needles, but in summer it is frequently flushed from the ground. When disturbed, Grouse fly rapidly with a whirr and a startled *kuk kuk kuk* to the lower branches of a neighboring tree, where they may walk along the branch, peering at the intruder, or scale off down hill on stiffly set wings. Females with young make anxious efforts to distract attention from their chicks.

$15\frac{1}{2}$–19

Ad. ♂. — *General plumage dark gray;* naked skin above and below eye orange; *tail blackish,* broadly tipped with a light gray band. Bill dusky; feet light olive-green or olive-gray (B.) **Ad.** ♀. — Upper parts brown, mottled with black and buff; tail brownish black, tipped with ashy gray; breast brown, barred with buff; belly white, mixed with gray.

Dist. — Mt. Pinos Grouse. [*D. o. howardi.*]
Cal. From Mt. Pinos to Kern Co.
Sierra Grouse. *D. o. sierræ.*
Cal. Common R. in the high mountains from Kern Co. to Mt. Shasta.
Ore. / *Wash.* } Probably R. along Cascades north to southern Wash.
Sooty Grouse. *D. o. fuliginosus.*
Cal. / *Ore.* / *Wash.* } Common R. from northwestern Cal. north in the humid coast belt.
Richardson Grouse. *D. o. richardsoni.*
Ore. / *Wash.* } Common R. in forests east.

Nest, a depression on dry ground under brush, logs or rocks, sparingly lined with dry grasses, leaves, twigs and usually a few feathers. *Eggs*, 5–10, creamy buff, spotted and dotted with reddish brown.

Franklin Grouse. *Canachites franklini*

A game-bird that is so indifferent to the approach of man as barely to move aside from a trail and to show no fear when made the target of sticks or stones has earned among lumbermen the name 'fool hen.' The Franklin Grouse inhabits the mountains of northern Washington and northeastern Oregon, feeding in winter on the buds of the fir and in summer on berries and insects. The large amount of *black* on the *under parts* of the male and the *black and white banding on the rump* will distinguish the Franklin from the Sooty or Richardson Grouse. The female is blackish on the upper parts rather than brown as in the female Sooty Grouse.

15–16¼

Ad. ♂. — Upper parts dark brown, barred with blackish; a line of orange or yellow skin over the eye; *rump barred with black and white;* tail black; *under parts chiefly black*, barred on flanks with white. Bill black; feet gray (B.). **Ad.** ♀. — Upper parts browner; tail with a narrow tip of buff; under parts white and tawny, barred with blackish.

Dist. — *Ore.* Not common R. in the high mountains of Wallowa Co.
Wash. R. in high mountains north.

Nest, a depression, usually against a stump or log, lined with grasses, leaves and a few feathers. *Eggs*, 5–9, buff, spotted and splashed with chestnut and dark brown.

Ruffed Grouse. *Bonasa umbellus* subsp.

In western Oregon and Washington when the first wild-flowers are pushing up through the mould, the muffled drumming of the Ruffed Grouse reverberates among the willows and poplars in forest clearings. It begins with a few slow, hollow thumping sounds, separated by slight intervals; these soon run rapidly into one another and the performance ends in a reverberating roll. The sound is made by the male standing erect on a fallen log, striking the air with his wings. In May a curious whining or mewing sound is often heard in the undergrowth, and the brown form of the female is seen trailing lamely off or circling about almost at one's feet to distract attention from her chicks; these scatter and 'freeze' till the danger is over, when the mother clucks them together again. A bird flushed in the woods makes off with a loud whirring and a swerving flight which takes it at once behind some sheltering growth; if not alarmed, it often flies into a tree and stands peering down at the intruder.

RUFFED GROUSE (♂)

The general *reddish brown* tone of the Ruffed Grouse, the lighter under parts and the *broad blackish band toward the tip of the tail* distinguish it even in flight from the Dusky Grouse. If a bird is seen on the ground or perched, the elongated black *feathers forming a ruff* on the sides of the neck, very full in the male, shorter in the female, will identify the Ruffed Grouse.

$15\frac{1}{2}$–19

Ad. ♂. — *Upper parts reddish brown; ruff of black feathers* on side of neck; tail with broad band of brownish black near tip, tip gray; throat buffy; rest of under parts *buffy, barred with brown*. Bill dull above, yellow below; feet brownish. **Ad.** ♀. — Breast paler, ruff smaller.

Dist. — Oregon Ruffed Grouse. *B. u. sabini*.

Cal. / *Ore.* / *Wash.* } R. from extreme northern Cal. north through western Ore. and Wash.

Gray Ruffed Grouse. *B. u. umbelloides.*
Ore. R. in brushy country, clearings, etc., east.
Wash. R. in open or brushy tracts in timber in the northern part of the State east of the Cascades.

Nest, a depression under the shelter of a log, rock or tree trunk or in a brush pile, lined with grasses, leaves, needles or feathers. *Eggs*, 6–10, marked with reddish brown or pale drab.

White-tailed Ptarmigan. *Lagopus leucurus leucurus*

On the summits of the Cascades near the snow line a hen-like bird with mottled brown plumage not infrequently walks out from the heather in which it has been feeding. If not startled, a Ptarmigan is as unsuspicious and tame as a domestic fowl, walking about clucking or cackling in a low tone, and allowing the observer a close examination. In flight it whirrs off rapidly or scales with extended wings. In winter it acquires a plumage of snow-white.

12–13

Ad. in summer. — Upper parts mottled with black and buffy brown; breast marked with black, white and buffy brown; belly, wings and *tail white.* Bill black. **Ad. in winter.** — Entire plumage white. Bill and eye black.

Dist. — *Wash.* Not uncommon R. on the summits and higher portions of the Cascades near timber line.

Nest, a depression lined with dry vegetation and a few feathers, ordinarily in the open. *Eggs*, 4–7, buff or light reddish brown, spotted with dark brown or black, or speckled.

Columbian Sharp-tailed Grouse. *Pediœcetes phasianellus columbianus*

In eastern Washington or Oregon a band of pale brown Grouse may rise from a grassy prairie and fly off with a *kuk kuk kuk* of alarm. The smaller size and the absence of a large black area on the belly distinguish the Sharp-tailed Grouse from the Sage Grouse in regions which they both frequent. The paler brown of the upper parts and the *unbanded*, pointed tail distinguish it from the Ruffed and the Sooty Grouse, into whose forest haunts the Sharp-tail, however, does not penetrate. In winter Sharp-tailed Grouse gather in large flocks and feed on the buds of the mountain birch, looking at a distance like huge balls in the branches.

15–19

Upper parts pale buffy brown, mixed with blackish and some white spots; *central tail feathers projecting beyond the others;* throat buff; rest of under parts grayish with arrowy markings of brown; belly almost unmarked. Bill blackish, basal half flesh-color below; feet ash-gray (B.).

Dist. — *Cal.* Formerly common in Modoc Co., now nearly or quite exterminated.
Ore. R. in open country east and north.
Wash. R. on the prairies east.

Nest, a slight depression in open grassy country, sparsely lined with grasses and rootlets. *Eggs*, 10–15, creamy buff or pale olive-brown, unmarked or finely dotted with reddish brown.

Sage-hen. *Centrocercus urophasianus*

As one travels through the endless gray of the sage-brush, one occasionally comes upon a flock of birds almost as large as hen turkeys, dusting themselves in the road, or is startled by the whirr of the birds as they rise from brushy cover. The size, greater than that of any other of the grouse family, and the *black patch on the belly* identify the Sage-hen. In early spring the cocks gather before dawn on open level ground and go through a remarkable mating display. With head erect, wings drooping

SAGE-HEN (♂)

and spike-like tail feathers spread, they strut about with mincing steps or turn in this direction or that; the black head is set off by two white areas on each side of the breast. The strange performance ends with a note resembling the popping sound made when human lips are suddenly separated. When a Sage-hen flies, it flaps a few times and then sets its wings stiffly, rising and falling in a shallow arc. The alarm note given as a bird flies off is like the syllables *kuk kuk kuk*.

♂ 26–30 ♀ $21\frac{1}{2}$–23

Ad. ♂. — Upper parts brown varied with black, gray and buff; *tail very long*, of stiff, narrow, pointed feathers, the central pair longest; under parts whitish, marked with black on throat and breast; *belly black*. Bill black; feet blackish. **Ad.** ♀. — Smaller; tail shorter.

Dist. — *Cal.* *Ore.* *Wash.* } Fairly common R. of sage-brush plains and valleys from northern Inyo Co., Cal., through northeastern Cal., eastern Ore. and eastern Wash.

Nest, a shallow depression under a shrub, sometimes lined with grasses or twigs. *Eggs*, 7–9 (17) grayish or greenish drab, thickly spotted and dotted with reddish brown.

QUAILS: *Family Perdicidæ*

OLD-WORLD PARTRIDGES: *Subfamily Perdicinæ*

Hungarian Partridge. *Perdix perdix*

From stubble fields and weed patches in northeastern Oregon and eastern Washington, a covey of plump brown birds with gray breasts rise with a harsh nasal *gir-éek* and whirr off with vigorous flight, showing a chestnut-red tail. Hungarian Partridges, except in the mating season, occur in small flocks, feeding in the early morning and late afternoon, dusting and sunning themselves in the middle of the day, and enduring snow and severe cold with success. The brown unmarked head and gray breast distinguish the Hungarian Partridge from the Bob-white, the only other game-bird of comparable size.

$12\frac{1}{2}$

Ad. ♂. — Top of head and throat brown; neck and breast ash gray; back and wings brown; tail chestnut-red; flanks gray, with crescent markings of brown; belly white with a dark brown patch. **Ad.** ♀. — Smaller and duller. Bill dark gray; feet ash-gray sometimes tinged with ochre (B.).

Dist. — *Ore.* / *Wash.* } Introduced and R. in northeastern Oregon and Wash.; common in eastern Wash., not common west.

Nest, in depression in fields. *Eggs*, 10–12, grayish green.

QUAILS: *Subfamily Odontophorinæ*

Bob-white. *Colinus virginianus virginianus*

In spring in Oregon and Washington a plump reddish brown bird sends forth a cheery *oh-bob-whoit* from a fence post or limb of a blossoming apple tree. The *pure white throat* of the male Bob-white set off by a black border, or the buffy throat of the female, the absence of any plumes on the head and the *rich reddish brown* of the *back and wings* readily identify the bird. When a covey of Bob-white are startled, they burst from cover with a loud whirr and go off at great speed, finally scaling with wings bent downward in a sharp curve. When a scattered flock are reassembling, they call to each other with a note like the syllables *quoi-ee.*

$9\frac{1}{2}$–$10\frac{3}{4}$

Ad. ♂. — Line over eye white, bordered above and below with black; back and wings chiefly reddish brown; tail gray; *throat white* bordered below by black band; upper breast reddish brown, waved with narrow black lines; sides heavily washed with reddish brown. Bill and feet black. **Ad.** ♀. — Similar but throat and line over eye buff; less black barring on the breast. Bill paler; feet brown.

Dist. — *Ore.* / *Wash.* } R. both east and west.

Nest, depression in the ground, usually sheltered by brushes or weeds, lined with grasses or stubble. *Eggs*, 12–18, dull white.

Mountain Quail; Plumed Quail. *Oreortyx picta* subsp.

From open spaces or brushy cover on the sides of the higher mountains, a single loud call, a resonant, far-reaching *kyork* is repeated at short intervals in spring and early summer. By patient stalking an observer may discover a plump blue-gray bird, standing on some exposed rock with a *rich reddish brown throat and long erect plume.* Later when the young have hatched, one may hear the female Mountain Quail repeating a nasal *kée-err* and hen-like *kut kut kut* which warns her chicks to lie motionless; if the observer comes too near, the mother changes her note to a low *whew whew whew* and the little striped youngsters scurry off into the bushes. During the mating season the brushy hillsides where Quail are breeding resound with a rapidly repeated *küp küp küp,* and in late summer when a covey of Mountain Quail are gathered under cover, there issues a medley of clucking, mewing and whining sounds, mixed with harsh quawks and a *ka-yák, ka-yák* like a guinea fowl's. The *erect plume* and the *reddish brown* throat distinguish the Mountain Quail from either the Valley or the Desert Quail with their drooping plumes and black throats.

$10\frac{1}{2}$–$11\frac{3}{4}$

Ad. — Top of head and upper back bluish gray; *long, slender, erect plume blackish; throat rich chestnut,* bordered on sides of neck with white; breast bluish gray; *sides chestnut, bordered by white and marked by broad black and white bands.* Bill black; feet reddish brown. **Im.** — Plumage chiefly brown; plume short, blackish, throat whitish, sides of throat black.

Dist. — San Pedro Mountain Quail. *O. p. confinis.*
Cal. Common R. in southern Cal. north to San Gabriel Mts.
Mountain Quail. *O. p. plumifera.*
Cal. / *Ore.* } Common R. from Los Angeles Co., Cal., to southern Ore. except as below.
Painted Quail. *O. p. picta.*
Cal. / *Ore.* / *Wash.* } Common R. along the coast from Monterey Co., Cal., northward through western Ore. and Wash.

Nest, depression in the ground, lined with leaves, pine-needles or grass, usually under a bush, log or rock. *Eggs,* 5–15, plain reddish buff.

California Quail; Valley Quail. *Lophortyx californica* subsp.

A whirr of wings and a flight of many plump figures disappearing into the brush, or sailing over a hillside on curved wings held stiffly, is often the first intimation that one has of the presence of a covey of quail. Sometimes the sharp clucking *tek tek* of the birds from the bushes calls our attention to the stocky figures running one after another in the shadow of the bushes, the black curved plume of the male dangling over his forehead. All through the year from the chaparral or from the cover of ornamental shrubs in city parks and estates, the three-syllabled call used to collect a scattered flock is a characteristic sound. The accent varies; if on the first syllable the words '*Come* right here' have been used to describe the call, if on the second 'Where *are* you?' When a flock are scattered there is a constant anxious *whit whit* from some individual or other. In the breeding season, from April to July, the male, perched on a post or bush, repeats at intervals a single, very resonant note, stretching his head and neck at each repetition. When a flock are together, particularly when they are preparing to spend the night, they utter a medley of clucks and calls. They roost in low bushes or trees. During the breeding season pairs are seen, then a pair with young of various sizes, and soon the several families unite in the large coveys seen through the winter.

The short curved plume distinguishes the Valley Quail from the Mountain Quail, which has a long straight plume. The Desert Quail has a plume like the Valley Quail's, but the bird is lighter gray and has streaks of rich chestnut and white on the sides. The male Desert Quail has a conspicuous black spot on the creamy white belly. Both male and female Valley Quail have a pattern of scale-like markings across the lower breast, which the Desert Quail lacks.

$9\frac{1}{2}$–11

Ad. ♂. — Forehead pale gray; *top of head dark brown;* plume short, curved, black; back chiefly brown; tail gray; *throat black*, encircled by white; breast bluish gray; upper belly buffy, feathers edged with black giving them a scale-like appearance; *rich chestnut patch* in *middle of belly;* lower belly buffy; flanks brownish gray sharply streaked with white. Bill black; feet brown.
Ad. ♀. — Chiefly brown; belly scaled and flanks streaked as in ♂.
Dist. — Valley Quail. *L. c. vallicola.*
Cal. Abundant R. in valleys and foothills nearly throughout except on deserts and humid coast.
Ore. In the vicinity of Klamath L.
California Quail. *L. c. californica.*
Cal. *Ore.* *Wash.* } Common R. in the humid coast belt from central Cal. to Ore. and Wash.
Catalina I. Quail. [*L. c. catalinensis*]
R. on Catalina I.

Nest, usually a depression in the ground lined with grasses, and under a log, rock or bushes. *Eggs*, 6–28 (usually 13–17), creamy white, spotted with light golden brown.

Gambel Quail; Desert Quail. *Lophortyx gambeli gambeli*

If a covey of quail run across the road anywhere between Palm Springs, California, and the Colorado River, or among the Joshua trees or desert grease-wood of the Mojave desert, watch closely when a male stops and compare his markings with the familiar Valley Quail. The *hind-head* is *reddish brown*, much brighter than the dark brown of the Valley Quail, and when the bird stands facing the observer, a *black patch* shows *against the buffy belly.* Both male and female Gambel Quail have *streaks of bright chestnut and white along the flanks* where the Valley Quail shows only gray and white. The Gambel Quail lacks the black-edged scale-like feathers across the lower breast which characterize the Valley Quail. The ordinary call of the Gambel Quail is similar to that of the Valley Quail, but more drawn out, less peremptory, and has more often a fourth syllable, *chi-caaa-go* or *chi-quér-ke-ker.* The male with neck and head up utters from a perch in the breeding season a penetrating call like the syllables *whée-err.* When a covey are nervously scuttling through dense cover, they utter a low *whoo-tét* mingled with clucking calls.

GAMBEL QUAIL ♂
GAMBEL QUAIL ♀

MOUNTAIN QUAIL ♂
VALLEY QUAIL ♂
VALLEY QUAIL ♀

9⅓–10½ Bill 1½

Ad. — Upper parts blackish brown; sides of head ash-gray; line from above eye to bill white, bordered below by a blackish line; much of wing dark cinnamon; *breast cinnamon-brown;* lower belly blackish barred with white. *Bill long*, slightly curved toward tip, yellowish brown, darker on top; feet yellowish brown. **Im.** — Upper parts dull black, chin and throat white; rest of under parts mixed black and white. Bill and feet dusky.

Dist. — *Cal.* Common S.V. in marshy areas throughout. Fairly common in winter west of the Sierras, north to central Cal.

Ore. } *Wash.* } S.V. (Apr.–Aug.) throughout, wintering in smaller numbers.

Nest, of dead grasses, sedges or tules, usually well concealed in marsh growth. *Eggs*, 5–12, pale buffy gray, with spots and dots of reddish brown chiefly around larger end, and deeper ones of lavender.

CAROLINA RAIL; SORA. *Porzana carolina*

From any marshy spot bordered by cat-tails or tules there comes in early spring, in the late afternoon or in the early evening, the characteristic cry of the Carolina Rail or Sora, a musical *sō-rée*, the last syllable higher than the first and prolonged. Often this is preceded by a whinnying sound or the whinny alone is given. At any time a stone thrown into the rushes will elicit a sudden sharp *keek* of alarm. If an observer comes cautiously up to the edge of a pool or ditch, he may surprise the small figure of a Sora, about the size of a half-grown chicken, wading over the tangle of decayed reeds, the head and neck up, showing the *short yellowish bill* or if seen from behind, displaying the *white under tail-coverts* below the *short cocked tail.* When alarmed, a Rail slips into the covert of reeds, but if too closely pressed, it rises and flutters a short distance with feet dangling and then drops into the shelter of the reeds. The gray sides of the breast and neck, the short yellow bill and the black about the base of the bill distinguish the Carolina Rail from the long-billed, cinnamon-breasted Virginia Rail.

SORA RAIL

8–9⅓ Bill about ¾

Ad. — Upper parts brown; *area about the base of the bill* and *line down center of breast black;* sides of head, neck and breast ashy gray; belly whitish; *area under tip of tail white. Bill short, yellow;* feet greenish yellow. **Im.** — Lacks the black 'face'; throat whitish; breast brown.

Dist. — *Cal.* Common S.V. in marshy areas throughout, wintering west of the Sierras as far north as Humboldt Co.

Ore. } *Wash.* } Not common S.V. both east and west; casual in winter west.

Nest, of dry grass, weeds, etc. on wet ground or in marsh vegetation, generally well concealed. *Eggs*, 4–15, buffy drab, spotted with reddish brown and dull purplish gray.

Yellow Rail. *Coturnicops noveboracensis*

The Yellow Rail shares with the Black Rail the distinction of being almost impossible to see even where it is known to occur. It hides in grassy fields, lowlands or fresh-water marshes so persistently that one must almost step on it or hunt it with a dog in order to flush it. Its general yellowish color and the *white patch in the outspread wing* will readily distinguish it from other rails.

6–7¾

Upper parts blackish, streaked with yellowish brown; *white patch in extended wing;* under parts yellowish brown on throat and breast, fading to whitish on belly. Bill short, yellow; legs light brown.

Dist. — *Cal.* Rather rare W.V. chiefly to marshes of west-central Cal.; one known breeding locality near Mono Lake (Dawson).

Nest, of grasses on wet ground. *Eggs*, 7–9, pinkish buff, densely but finely spotted at larger end with reddish brown.

California Black Rail; Farallon Rail. *Creciscus coturniculus*

Few people have deliberately set out to see a Black Rail and still fewer have succeeded. There is probably no bird in the United States that eludes observation more successfully than this mouse-like inhabitant of the tangled salicornia. A meeting is usually entirely accidental; there is a brief view of a small black bird with short fluttering wings and dangling legs, that drops hurriedly into the nearest shelter. There is a well-known breeding ground for the bird near San Diego where a few zealous collectors by indefatigable kicking and turning over of masses of salicornia have found a number of nests, but even they have rarely seen the sitting bird, which slips out on the other side and apparently never returns to a nest once uncovered. The notes of the Black Rail are said to be like the syllables *clee-cle, clée-ee* (Huey).

5–6

Head and neck slaty black; a dark chestnut area back of the neck; rest of back blackish brown, thickly barred with white, giving the bird a speckled appearance; under parts varying from dark slate to pale gray. Bill blackish; feet greenish yellow.

Dist. — *Cal.* Fairly common fall and winter visitant to salt marshes about San Francisco Bay and Tomales Bay; in smaller number southward. R. in marshes near San Diego.
Wash. Two birds seen at Tacoma (Bowles).

Nest, on salt marsh, of stems of pickle-weed, usually concealed by arching stems. *Eggs*, 4–8, white, spotted with reddish brown and lavender.

GALLINULES: *Subfamily Gallinulinæ*

Florida Gallinule. *Gallinula chloropus cachinnans*

A patient watch at the border of a marsh is often rewarded by glimpses of its shy inmates. Coot and Pied-billed Grebes swim along the ditches and Rails lift their long toes over the masses of decaying tules. Occasionally among the slate-gray Coot an observer notes a slightly smaller bird with a brown back. When it turns toward the observer, he sees, not the white bill so characteristic of the Coot, but a *bright red bill* and a plate of the same color running well up on the forehead, which flashes at every movement of the head. The Gallinule either swims like a Coot with a forward bob of the head at each stroke, or walks slowly over the fallen reeds, drawing its long toes together each time that it lifts its feet and flirting its tail. Both when it swims and when it walks the white under the tail shows more prominently than in a Coot; it is evident even from the side. Its flight is generally short, with labored wing-beats and dangling feet, and ends with an abrupt drop into cover. The notes of the Gallinule are varied but most of them suggest the common hen. Some are low like the syllable *kuck*, often repeated, others are drawling notes like the slightly discontented notes of a hen talking to herself, others are loud and harsh. When the bird is anxious it utters a short *keck*. The notes are most frequent in the early morning and late afternoon and are rarely heard at night. The *flaming red forehead* and *scarlet bill* readily distinguish the Gallinule from any other bird.

12–14½

Head and neck dark gray, darkest on head; *back brown;* wings and tail dusky; under parts dark gray, except white area under the tail and white streak along the flank just below the folded wing. *Bill and bare plate on forehead bright red,* bill tipped with yellow; iris reddish brown; legs greenish. **Im.** — Bill greenish or brownish; under parts whitish.

Dist. — *Cal.* Fairly common S.V. about marshes and sloughs north to Santa Barbara and the Sacramento Valley; winters sparingly from Los Angeles southward.

Nest, of tules on a platform of the same in marshes. *Eggs*, 6–13, deep pinkish buff, spotted with chocolate and reddish brown, and grayish lavender.

COOTS: *Subfamily Fulicinæ*

Coot; Mud-hen. *Fulica americana*

On nearly every pond or estuary during the winter a company of slate-colored birds with *black heads* against which their *white bills* make a sharp contrast paddle away from the shore at the approach of an intruder, or, if pressed too closely, rise laboriously, splattering the surface for some distance with their feet. In flight the long legs extend out behind and the white after edge of the wings is evident. When a Coot swims, the black head is moved backward and forward. Coots feed either by reaching down for water weeds, by diving, or by 'dabbling' like barn-yard ducks. They often gather in groups on grassy banks and waddle off when disturbed like infirm old men. When seen from behind, a Coot shows an area of white under the short tail, which is divided in the middle by a narrow black bar. The bill seems to curve slightly downward, giving the head when seen from the side a hook-nosed appearance. Coots breed throughout the Coast States in marshes or tule-bordered ponds. They are talkative though not noisy. The commonest note is a single croak like the syllable *kruk* or *kook*, varying in pitch; another note is a harsh *kerk, kerk,* like an ungreased wooden axle. Near the nest they utter a low, dry *kút-up.* In the mating season Coots constantly chase each other along the surface of the water with head and neck down, and then float with wings arched and stern elevated, showing the white under the tail. Very young birds in early summer have red bills and orange on the throat, head and back.

COOT

13–16

Ad. — *Head and neck black;* wings brownish; rest of body slate-gray, except a *white area under the tail. Bill whitish,* with a brownish or blackish spot on each mandible near tip; iris red; feet dull greenish (sometimes tinged with yellow) in front, dusky behind. **Im.** — Under parts more suffused with whitish. Bill lacking the dark spots; iris brown.

Dist. — *Cal.* Abundant R. in marshy areas and on lakes throughout; more numerous in winter in the coastal region southward.
Ore. Common R. in marshy regions and on lakes throughout.
Wash. S.V. (Mar.–Nov.) east; R. on both fresh and salt water west, though less common in winter.

Nest, of tules, sedges, etc., floating on the water or built up in tules, generally not concealed. *Eggs,* 6–15, creamy white, finely speckled or spotted with dark brown or blackish.

SHORE-BIRDS, GULLS, AUKS, etc.: *Order Charadriiformes*

OYSTER-CATCHERS: *Family Hæmatopodidæ*

BLACK OYSTER-CATCHER. *Hæmatopus bachmani*

On rocky ledges along the outer beach, a *large black bird* with a *bright red bill* and short pinkish feet is occasionally seen, prying off shellfish that the outgoing tide has exposed. The bird is larger than the Black Turnstones which often frequent the same rocks, and shows no white. It moves in a sedate fashion with slow, jerky movements, and these with its red bill, bright as if freshly painted, give it somewhat the appearance of the wooden birds set up in gardens. After feeding, Oyster-catchers often squat on the warm rocks. When startled they give a sharp call, *whick, whick,* or when flying a soft *phée-a.* In the mating season pairs are seen in constant flight, one turning or shooting upward, the other pursuing and uttering the *phée-a* note. Young birds are brownish all over and have a dusky bill which is orange at the base.

17–17½ Bill 2½–3

Ad. ♂. — Head, neck and breast black; rest of plumage dark brown (glossed with greenish); iris yellow; eyelids red. *Bill red,* tip paler; feet very pale flesh-color. **Im.** — Browner. Bill blackish toward tip, orange at base.
Dist. — *Cal.*, *Ore.*, *Wash.* } R. on rocky shores, particularly on islands off shore.
Nest, eggs laid in sand, pebbles or shells. *Eggs,* 1–3, buff, heavily spotted with black.

PLOVERS, TURNSTONES, etc.: *Family Charadriidæ*

PLOVERS: *Subfamily Charadriinæ*

BLACK-BELLIED PLOVER. *Squatarola squatarola cynosuræ*

At almost any season, except for a short period in early summer, plump gray birds about the size of half-grown chickens, are seen feeding along the beaches of southern California. They run a few steps, pick up a sand flea with a quick dab that elevates the back and tail, and then stand a moment with head only slightly elevated by the short neck. Their bills are short, compared with those of the Willets and Curlew with which they associate. When the birds feed, they generally scatter and each bird faces in a different direction. In flight their *tails* show *white* except toward the tip, and there are *black areas under the wings* close to the body. In April and May large flocks return from farther south, many of which have already acquired the breeding plumage of deep black on the *under parts, bordered on the forehead* and along the sides *with white.* In midsummer, too, flocks returning from the far North show in many individuals entirely black bellies, in others under parts mottled with black and white. The old birds are very wary; long before one draws near, they are off with a sweet whistled *whoo-ee*. Birds in winter are quite tame and allow a close approach.

BLACK-BELLIED PLOVER (Breeding and winter)

The short bill and the white base of the tail will generally distinguish the Black-bellied Plover from any other shore-bird. The black feathers close to the body under the upraised wing are evident as the birds raise their wings for flight, and often as the birds turn or wheel in flight.

$10\frac{1}{2}$–12 Bill 1.10

Ad. ♂ in breeding season. — *Forehead, broad stripe over eye* and eyelids *white;* top of head and hind-neck grayish white, mottled with blackish on back of head; rest of upper parts mottled with brownish black and white; *tail white at base; under parts black; feathers under the wings close to the body black.* Bill black; feet black. **Ad. ♀ in breeding plumage.** — Similar to ♂, but white and black duller. **Ad. and Im. in late summer and winter.** — Upper parts blackish brown, mottled with white; light gray streak over eye; under parts white, streaked or mottled on breast and sides with grayish brown.

Dist. — *Cal.* Fairly abundant M. (Apr.–May; July–Oct.) along the coast and less commonly in the San Joaquin Valley; winters at least from San Francisco Bay and Los Baños southward.

Ore. / *Wash.* M. (Mar.–May; July–Sept.) along the coast; a few winter. Casual east.

AMERICAN GOLDEN PLOVER. *Pluvialis dominica dominica*

The ardent bird-student looks over every flock of Black-bellied Plover, hoping sometime to find the very rare Golden Plover, which *lacks the white rump* and has *gray brown feathers close to the body* under the outspread wing. The Golden Plover is more apt to be found on the dunes back of a beach than on the flats. Its note is a bright rolling whistle *queep, que-lee-lee,* without the plaintive character and upward inflection of the Black-bellied Plover.

$9\frac{1}{2}$–$10\frac{3}{4}$ Bill .80–1

Ad. in breeding plumage. — Upper parts including rump black, spotted with yellow and white; *tail dark grayish brown,* barred with white; a white line from forehead over eye and down side of neck and upper breast; *feathers under the wing close to the body brownish gray;* under parts black. Bill black; feet bluish gray. **Ad. in fall.** — Upper parts as in spring but duller; dusky area back of eye; under parts white. Bill dark; feet dark gray. **Im.** — Upper parts dusky, mottled with whitish spots, yellowish on rump; under parts ashy.

Dist. — *Cal.* Rare fall M.
Ore. One record.
Wash. Rare spring (May) M. along the coast, somewhat more common in fall (Sept.–Nov.).

KILLDEER. *Oxyechus vociferus*

Along the beaches, on lawns, in city parks, and throughout the flat farming country, the noisy cries of the Killdeer and its conspicuous mark-

KILLDEER

ing both at rest and in flight make it one of the most easily identified birds. As it stands facing the observer, a *white band over the forehead and two across the breast are separated from one another by black bands.* The bird never stands any appreciable time without a sudden upward jerk of the head and body, a movement which of course depresses the rear end. If startled, it flies off with shrill cries, showing a large area of cinnamon at the base of the tail, edged toward the end of the tail with black and then white. The wings are long and pointed, the flight strong and easy. The bill is short and gives the appearance of a slight downward curve.

The ordinary note is a high-pitched *kēē*, *kēē-di-di* which explodes when the bird is excited in a series of nervous shrieks. As the mating period approaches, the male flies about at a considerable height with easy strokes, repeating the note *ki-dée* which has given the bird its name. When a parent bird is concerned for its eggs or young, it trails off before an intruder with one wing down and the tail spread, or squats on the ground with tail up. It often utters at this season a vibrating trill. The Killdeer runs with head up, not crouching like the Snowy Plover. In flight the long, narrow wings show very white underneath. The *two black bands across the breast* and the *cinnamon rump* distinguish the Killdeer from any other shore-bird.

$9\frac{1}{2}$–$10\frac{1}{2}$ Bill $\frac{3}{4}$

Ad. — Forehead and stripe above and back of eye white; top of head and back brown; *ring entirely around neck white*, bordered behind by black; wings black with bar of white spots; *rump and base of tail cinnamon;* tail when spread black toward tip, white at tip; under parts and lining of wings white; *breast crossed* by *two black bands*. Bill slightly decurved, black; eyelids reddish orange; legs grayish brown. **Im.** — Duller; more rusty on upper parts.

Dist. — *Cal.* Abundant S.V. throughout; winters from latitude of San Francisco and Owens Valley southward.
Ore. Abundant S.V. (Feb.–Nov.) both east and west, winters west and perhaps east.
Wash. Abundant S.V. east and west; winters in small numbers on the Sound.

Nest, on ground, usually in bare sandy or pebbly area, sometimes in grass, a shallow depression with or without lining of grasses, weeds, pebbles, etc. *Eggs*, usually 4, light clay or dull cream, boldly marked with dark brown, black or dull lavender.

Semipalmated Plover. *Charadrius semipalmatus*

Among the little sandpipers that feed or doze along the sandy or muddy shores in spring and fall, an observer will notice a few slightly larger birds with a *dark band across the breast*. They are not so active as the sandpipers, nor do they feed or fly in crowded masses. Each keeps more or less by himself, so that when there is a little group on a beach or flat, no two are heading in the same direction. They run a few steps, make a little dart at some creature in the sand, then stand a moment before taking another run. When several are feeding together, they utter a throaty *chii*, and occasionally one will run at another with head down and tail spread, so as to show the white outer edging, repeating the *chii* note several times and ending with a whinny. They fly when approached instead of running on twinkling legs like the smaller Snowy Plover. When they fly, they utter a very characteristic two-syllabled note with a rising inflection, *chi-wée*. The Semipalmated Plover is readily distinguished from the Snowy Plover by its darker coloration and the well-defined band across the breast, and from the much larger Killdeer by the presence of only one band across the breast.

SEMIPALMATED PLOVER

7–8 Bill ½

Ad. — Forehead white; fore-part of head, stripe under eye and over bill black; narrow bar of white in the extended wing; rest of upper parts grayish brown; tail brown; outer feathers black near tips, tips white; throat and narrow ring around neck white; black band across breast; rest of under parts white. Bill orange at base, tip black; feet yellow. **Im.** — Black replaced by brown; upper parts paler.

Dist. — *Cal.* Common M. along the coast (Apr.–May; Aug.–Oct.), casual inland. A few winter in southern Cal.
Ore. Common M. along the coast (May; Aug.–Sept.).
Wash. M. (July–Sept.) along the coast and on the Sound.

Snowy Plover. *Charadrius nivosus*

On the outer beaches, between the lines of kelp left at high tide and the sand dunes, at any season of the year small whitish birds run so rapidly before an intruder that their short feet fairly twinkle on the sand. They run with heads down, and even when they stand still their round heads and short necks are held close to the body. When the soft brown head and white forehead are turned toward an observer, an *incomplete collar of black* shows, beginning at the shoulders but failing to cross the breast. When a Snowy Plover flies, a

SNOWY PLOVER

whitish stripe appears in the long wing. In flight the bird utters a rather faint *tee-teet*, except when anxious about nests or young. Then it wheels about an intruder uttering a tree-frog-like *krrr*, and a clear whistled *koo-whéet*. The female tries to distract one's attention by running low with tail depressed and by squatting in the sand. When standing the Snowy Plover bobs. Snowy Plover keep chiefly to the dry sand of the upper beach, but individuals often feed along the wet sands below the high-tide mark or with the smaller sandpipers and Semipalmated Plover on mud flats. In the latter situation their paler color shows in marked contrast to the dark ground.

The short bill and whitish coloration should distinguish Snowy Plover from the small Sandpipers often found with or near it. It may be distinguished from the Semipalmated Plover by its much paler back, and by the absence of a complete band across the breast.

6–7⅓ Bill ½

Ad. ♂ in breeding plumage. — Top of head clay-color; back pale gray; forehead, stripe over eye, side of head and collar around hind-neck white; a band of black separating white forehead from top of head, spot of black behind eye; *bar of black on sides of breast;* under parts white; white spots down the length of the extended wing; central tail feathers blackish brown toward tips, outer tail feathers white. Bill black; feet gray. **Ad. ♀ in breeding plumage.** — Black markings on head and sides of breast duller, almost brown. **Ad. in winter and Im.** — Markings on head and sides of breast little darker than color of back.

Dist. — *Cal.* Common R. on sandy beaches along the coast, especially southward, and locally in the interior.

Ore. Locally R. on sandy ocean beaches and occasionally inland.

Wash. Not common spring M. (Mar.–May) and very scarce fall M. (Sept.–Nov.) along the coast (casual on the Sound). Perhaps breeds sparingly on the coast.

Nest, on sandy beaches and shores, a slight depression with a few bits of drift or bits of shell. *Eggs*, 2–3, pale buff or cream, speckled with black.

Mountain Plover. *Podasocys montanus*

In broad valleys in California where the tractor has laid bare in winter an expanse of brown earth, a little flock of Mountain Plover are occasionally observed. They lack the conspicuous bands of black and white across the Killdeer's breast, and when they run they lower the head like Snowy Plover, instead of holding it up like Killdeer. When startled they do not fly high and wild like Killdeer, but low over the ground, uttering a low frog-like croak.

8¾–9½ Bill .80–.90

Ad. in winter and Im. — Upper parts brown; sides of head and breast brownish; tail pale at base, crossed toward tip by dusky band; belly whitish. Bill dusky; feet light grayish brown.

Dist. — *Cal.* Not common W.V. (Sept.–Feb.) in the Sacramento and San Joaquin Valleys, and from Los Angeles Co. southward.

SURF-BIRDS: *Subfamily Aphrizinæ*

Surf-bird. *Aphriza virgata*

On rocky promontories where Black Turnstones climb over the ledges exposed by the receding tide, birds of slightly greater size and of similar build, but with head and upper parts dark gray instead of sooty black may in spring and fall be discovered either with Black Turnstones or in a separate flock. Often the birds allow a close approach and then the *base of the lower mandible* is seen to be yellow, not black as in the Turnstone, and the *feet yellow*, not dusky. When a Surf-bird flies, it does not suddenly blossom into the striking pattern of black and white shown by the Black Turnstone in flight; the Surf-bird shows a band of white in the extended wing and a single large area of *white* on the *rump* and the *base of the tail*, but has no white down the middle of the back. Surf-birds feed on barnacles and small mussels uncovered at low tide. They are much less noisy than Black Turnstones, but occasionally utter a shrill *ke-wéek*.

SURF-BIRD (Breeding)

10 Bill 1

Ad. in spring. — Head and neck streaked with black and white, back brownish black, the feathers edged with gray and some reddish brown; a *band of white along the extended wing; rump and base of tail white*, the terminal portion black, narrowly tipped with white; throat almost white, rest of under parts white, heavily marked with dusky arrowy or crescent-shaped spots, darkest on breast. Bill black, *base of under mandible yellow;* feet greenish yellow. **Ad. in late summer, fall and winter and Im.** — Upper parts brownish gray, wings and tail as above; chin light gray; breast heavily washed with gray; belly white. Bill, top and terminal half black, basal half yellow; feet yellow.

Dist. — *Cal.* Not common M. (Mar.–May; Aug.–Oct.) on rocky shores; a few may winter.
Ore. Not common M. (Apr.–May; Aug.–Oct.) on rocky shores, and W.V. (Dec.–Feb.).
Wash. Not common spring M. (May) and fall M. (July–Oct.) on coast; casual in Sound. Has wintered on Destruction I.

TURNSTONES: *Subfamily Arenariinæ*

Ruddy Turnstone. *Arenaria interpres morinella*

On a sandy beach or mud-flat where the kelp is left in long rolls and heaps at the high-tide mark, a medium-sized shore-bird on short stout legs may be seen in spring and fall turning over the decaying kelp and sea-wrack, often butting with its head as well as using its bill. The note of the Turnstone is a rolling call, *chirt-a-chut*, lower and less harsh than the Black Turnstone's. It has much the same pattern of white as it flies; *the middle of the back, rump, tail and wings all show white,* but *contrasted with reddish brown* instead of black. The *legs* too are *orange-red*, while the Black Turnstone's are dark. When facing the observer, the Turnstone shows a broad dark collar on the breast, enclosing a paler area below the *white throat*, which distinguishes it at once from the Black Turnstone, which has a uniformly dark throat and breast.

RUDDY TURNSTONE (Immature)

9–10 Bill .85

Ad. ♂ in spring. — Forehead chiefly white; a black stripe in front of eye and down side of head; back of head white, thickly streaked with black; back black with patches of reddish brown; throat white; *breast black with white running into it from shoulder;* belly white. In flight *middle of back white, white in extended wing*, rump black, *tail white with black tip.* Bill black; *feet reddish orange.* **Ad. ♀.** — Similar but duller. **Ad. in fall and winter and Im.** — Similar to **ad.** in spring, but black somewhat veiled and reddish brown less conspicuous. **Im. in fall.** Head brown, mottled with pale buff; throat white; breast with two light brown areas; back dark brown, mottled with blackish and gray; wing and tail as in **ad.** Bill black; feet orange.

Dist. — *Cal.* Not common M. (Apr.–May; July–Oct.) along the coast; occasional in winter.
Ore. Not common spring, and commoner fall M. along the coast.
Wash. M. (May; July–Sept.) along the coast and on the Sound.

Black Turnstone. *Arenaria melanocephala*

A group of plump black birds of medium size are occasionally seen at any time except in midsummer standing in groups on the top and sides of a rock or ledge against which the surf from the outer ocean is breaking. If the spray dashes over them, they fly a little distance,

BLACK TURNSTONE (Winter)

showing a marked pattern of *black and white* in *wings, tail and back*. At low tide the Black Turnstone probes and pries among the limpets and barnacles. Occasionally a Black Turnstone finds his way into the muddy shores of a bay, but for the most part it is a bird of the outer ledges.

9 Bill .85–1

Ad. in spring. — Head, neck, breast and upper back sooty black, *speckled with white on forehead, sides of neck and breast*. Otherwise as below. **Ad. in late summer, fall and winter.** — Head, neck and upper breast sooty black; in flight showing *white down the middle of the back, on the shoulders and on the rump*, a *white line along the extended wing;* subterminal portion of tail black, narrowly tipped with white; belly white. Bill black; legs dusky.

Dist. — *Cal.* Common M. and W.V. (Aug.–Apr.) along rocky shores. A few remain in summer.
Ore. Common M. (Mar.–May; late Aug.–Sept.) and W.V.
Wash. M. (Mar.–May; July–Sept.) along the coast; W.V. on the coast.

SNIPES, SANDPIPERS, etc.: *Family Scolopacidæ*

SNIPES: *Subfamily Scolopacinæ*

Wilson Snipe; Jack Snipe. *Gallinago delicata*

As one walks in winter through a wet meadow or where water-cress almost dams the current of a little stream, a brown bird with a bill nearly as long as his body rises almost from under one's feet and makes off in rapid zigzags, finally mounting to a considerable height, or drops again at the edge of the brook. When it rises and for a moment or two in flight, it utters a sharp, nasal *scaipe*. If one marks the place where the bird alighted, and tries to see it crouching there before it is off, the chances are ten to one that no bird will be seen, and yet when one takes another step the bird is up and off with another cry. If the observer has quick eyes he notes the *black and white stripes on the head*, the *black and buff on the back* and perhaps the rich chestnut in the short tail.

Where the Snipe breeds, and occasionally over marshes where spring migrants are lingering, there comes from the twilight sky the soft whinnying of the birds going through their mating performance. On springy meadows of northeastern California and eastern Oregon, it is possible to observe this courtship flight of the Snipe, sometimes in broad daylight. The male rises from the grass and mounts to a height of from one to two hundred feet, where he begins to fly about in wide arcs with rapid wing-beats. Presently he makes a sharp downward dip, during which his tail is fully spread. It is only during this downward pitch and while the tail is spread, that the whistling note is heard. When the male finally descends to the meadow again, after many of these downward dips, he utters a series of resonant notes like the syllables *kyuck, kyuck, kyuck,* or *ka-tíck* like a Guinea Hen. This note is also uttered when the breeding ground is invaded, often from a bird perched on a post in the meadow. When taking a short flight on the breeding ground, the bird flies in short pitches with wings upraised.

The plump body and *very long bill* of the Wilson Snipe distinguish it from any of its relatives except perhaps the Long-billed Dowitcher. The

WILSON SNIPE

latter is a bird of the beach or the open mud-flats, hardly ever hiding in vegetation; the Snipe is practically never seen away from cover.

$10\frac{1}{2}$–$11\frac{1}{2}$ Bill $2\frac{1}{2}$

Middle of *crown black, divided by a buffy line,* and separated by two narrow buffy stripes from a brown line running from bill to eye; general color of back and wings brown (at close range black, streaked with buff on the upper back); tail bright reddish brown, barred with black and edged with whitish; throat nearly white; breast light brown, speckled with dusky brown; belly whitish. *Bill long,* greenish gray, dusky toward tip; feet greenish gray.

Dist. — *Cal.* Abundant M. and W.V.; breeds east of Sierras from Lake Tahoe north and west and casually in southern Cal.

Ore. }
Wash. } S.V. (Apr.–Nov.) in marshy country east. R. west but scarcer in winter.

Nest, a depression lined with grass, in moist meadows. *Eggs,* 3–4, grayish olive to greenish brown and yellowish ash, spotted with dark reddish brown.

CURLEWS, TATTLERS, etc.: *Subfamily Numeninæ*

LONG-BILLED CURLEW. *Numenius americanus*

While the female Long-billed Curlew is flattened out on her eggs in an open meadow or on the cattle ranges in the lake country of eastern Oregon or Washington, the brown male stands guard. At the approach of an intruder he launches into the air with a shrill *pi-wi-wi-whee,* and comes

LONG–BILLED CURLEW

sailing up with wings set in a crescent. In winter Long-billed Curlews are found in considerable numbers about several of the large bays and estuaries in southern California. Wintering birds are very noisy, constantly quarreling and squealing with a variety of shrill notes. They gather at high tide in compact groups on exposed bars or flats or above the high-tide mark on the beach, but in feeding scatter about the edges of the flats or in the pools in marshes probing with their enormous bills. Their flight is with steady rapid strokes of the wing with occasional sailing. Before a single bird alights among its fellows, it frequently gyrates on set wings or plunges down and up again.

The light brown top of the head, and the lack of the light and dark lines over and through the eye should be carefully noted in one's first Long-billed Curlew. Then the difference in the general tone of color and particularly the difference in its cries will gradually enable a student to distinguish the species even at long range. When the Long-billed Curlew is startled, it utters a loud, very unmusical *kerr-whéet,* instead of the *whĭ whĭ whĭ* of the Hudsonian Curlew. In migration Long-billed Curlews are more likely to be found on muddy borders of sloughs than along the sandy beach where the Hudsonian Curlews are numerous; they do, however, resort to the outer beach when their feeding grounds on the bay are covered at high tide. A Curlew seen inland in summer is always a Long-billed Curlew.

20–26 Bill 5–7

Top of head pale cinnamon-brown, streaked with blackish brown, a light cinnamon stripe from bill over eye (*no dark stripe through eye*); upper parts light cinnamon-brown irregularly barred and spotted with blackish brown; *under parts*, including under surface of wings, *pale cinnamon-brown*. Bill very long, very decidedly decurved, basal third flesh-color below, rest black; feet light gray.

Dist. — *Cal.* S.V. in northeastern Cal.; M. (Apr.; July–Sept.) along the coast and inland. Winters west of the Sierras from latitude of San Francisco southward, also in Owens Valley.
Ore. Not common S.V. in eastern Ore.
Wash. Rare M. along the coast, on the Sound and in the interior; rare S.V. on the plains of eastern Wash.

Nest, a depression usually in an open meadow or prairie, lined with dried grasses and weeds. *Eggs*, usually 4, light greenish olive, marked with dark brown.

Hudsonian Curlew. *Numenius hudsonicus*

In April and May and from late July to November, the beaches along the coast of southern California are lined with scattered companies of long-legged brown birds about the size of a small hen, with bills far longer than the head that curve distinctly downward. At high tide the birds stand about the upper beach but at low tide walk in an unhurried fashion along the wet sands and probe for shrimps, sand fleas or worms. When alarmed, Hudsonian Curlews utter a succession of shrill notes, *whĭ-whĭ-whĭ-whĭ*, and fly off in a line, the curve of their long bills showing clearly as they pass an observer. They often fly not along the shore but well out over the ocean and then in to the beach farther along. A flock in flight or when about to light utter a rolling *turr, turr.*

HUDSONIAN CURLEW

The downward curve of the bill readily distinguishes the Curlew from the Marbled Godwit with which it often associates. Even when the bill cannot be clearly seen, the gray-brown of the Curlew in flight distinguishes it from the cinnamon-brown of the Godwit. A beginner is often in doubt whether some of the Hudsonian Curlews which he sees with slightly longer bills than others are not Long-billed Curlews. Individual Hudsonian Curlews have bills ranging from two and three-quarters to three and three-quarters inches in length, but the smallest Long-bill has a bill of five inches. To be perfectly sure of the species in the field, where size is so much a matter of comparison, let the observer note carefully the top and sides of the head. The commoner Hudsonian Curlew, which may be found on every beach, has the *top of the head dark brown*, with a *white or buffy line through the middle of the crown; above the eye runs another light line and through the eye a dark one.* The Long-bill has a line of light cinnamon over the eye but as the whole top and sides of the brown head and neck are tinged with cinnamon, there is no such contrast of light and dark lines as in the Hudsonian. Moreover, the whole under sides of the Long-bill are cinnamon-brown, giving the bird a much warmer tint than the white or buffy under parts of the Hudsonian Curlew.

$16\frac{1}{2}$–18 Bill 3–4

General color brown, top of head blackish with a *light line through the crown and over each eye.* Bill long, curved, black, base of lower mandible flesh-color; legs gray.

Dist. — *Cal.* Abundant M. (late Feb.–May; July–Oct.) along the coast and in interior valleys; a few winter in southern Cal.
Ore. Not common M. along the coast (May; Sept.).
Wash. M. (Apr.–June; Aug.–Oct.) along the coast.

Spotted Sandpiper. *Actitis macularia*

In summer along the shores of mountain lakes or streams a medium-sized brown bird with the longish bill of a Sandpiper 'teeters' nervously on some rock or sandbar, or flies low over the water, making an arc over its surface and alighting again farther along the beach. In flight, after a

SPOTTED SANDPIPER (Breeding)

few quick strokes, the Spotted Sandpiper holds its wings stiffly outspread, and vibrates the downward curved tips, not bringing the wings in their strokes above the back. Its notes, given generally when on the wing, are either a single *peet*, repeated in a series or a double *peet weet*, the first higher than the second. When standing, the Spotted Sandpiper not only bobs, but also oscillates the whole hind part of the body, as if the body were swung on the legs with oiled bearings. Just before alighting the head and neck are often held upward for an instant. During the mating season the Spotted Sandpiper goes through a mating performance in which the male (and perhaps the female also) takes a short flight at the end of which it swings upward with head and neck extended, and then comes down to the ground. Males also 'display' before the female with head and neck stretched up and wings and tail spread. Besides the notes described above it utters in the breeding season a peculiar *hrreet* and near its nest or young gives a sharp *pick, pick,* often from a post or rock on which it is 'teetering.' Its notes are frequently heard over the water at night. In winter the Spotted Sandpiper frequents rocky ocean shores, flying ahead from point to point or running up over the rocks.

A beginner might confuse the Spotted Sandpiper in winter with the Wandering Tattler, which also tips up the hind part of the body. The Spotted Sandpiper is smaller and browner, and shows in flight white spots which almost form a stripe along the wing; it does not crouch or hide behind rocks, and its note is not so vigorous and shrill (see p. 112).

$6\frac{3}{4}$–$8\frac{2}{5}$ Bill .80–1

Ad. in breeding plumage. — Upper parts brown; faint white line through and back of eye; a *line of white spots in extended wing;* tail brown, outer feathers barred with white; *under parts* white, *marked with round spots of brownish black. Bill orange-yellow,* dusky at tip and slightly decurved; feet pale flesh-gray. **Ad. in winter and Im.** — Under parts white unspotted, breast washed with gray. Bill dusky above, flesh-color at base below; feet greenish yellow.

Dist. — *Cal.* Abundant M. (Apr.–May; July–Sept.) throughout on the coast, and on borders of lakes and streams; breeds sparingly in northern Ventura Co., regularly from Tulare Co. north. Winters along the coast.

Ore. Common S.V. (May–Sept.) on shores of lakes and streams, and M. along the coast; a few probably winter along the coast.

Wash. Common S.V. (May–Sept.) on lakes and streams throughout from sea level up to nearly 6000 ft.; a few may winter in the Straits and on the Sound.

Nest, a depression, sparsely lined with grasses or weed-stalks or unlined, on gravelly ground or in a wet meadow. *Eggs,* 4, pale cream or buff, spotted with blackish or reddish brown, lavender or pale gray.

Solitary Sandpiper. *Tringa solitaria cinnamomea*

From a sandbar on some brush-bordered stream or from the muddy shore of an inland lake or wet meadow, a medium-sized sandpiper flies off with a swift irregular flight, generally zigzagging wildly at a considerable height before alighting on another feeding ground. On alighting the Solitary Sandpiper often stretches its wings upward to their full extent. When standing, it frequently jerks its head up and then bobs forward, like a Yellow-legs, but it also teeters occasionally like the Spotted Sandpiper (Allen). Its flight differs from that of the latter; it uses a sweeping stroke, mounting rapidly and not flying in an arc low over the water like the Spotted. Its general tone of coloration is darker, contrasted in flight with the *whitish, barred tail;* it lacks the spots on the breast of the Spotted Sandpiper and the white markings in the wing.

SOLITARY SANDPIPER

The presence of dark bars across the whitish tail distinguish it from either Yellow-legs, which have the basal half of the tail whitish and unbarred. The Solitary Sandpiper is never found on the outer ocean beach, frequenting chiefly inland streams and shores, occurring sometimes, however, on lagoons just back of the beach. It is never found in large flocks, but is sometimes seen in the fall in very small companies, though oftener alone or in pairs. Its notes are a sharp whistle of three or four high-pitched notes, *weet, weet, weet,* generally given when it flies off.

$8\frac{1}{2}$–9 Bill $1\frac{1}{4}$

Ad. — Upper parts olive-brown, sparsely speckled with white; head and neck finely streaked; under surface of wings white, barred with dusky (in the Spotted Sandpiper white, unbarred); wing not showing a row of white spots in flight; *outer tail feathers white, barred with black;* throat and breast white, narrowly streaked with dusky; sides barred with dusky; rest of under parts white. Bill *olive-green,* tip black; feet dull greenish. **Im.** — Upper parts brownish gray, speckled with buff; sides of head and neck dusky, unstreaked.

Dist. — *Cal.* Not common M. (Apr.–May; July–Sept.).
Ore. Rare spring M. (May); more common in fall (Aug.–Oct.) both east and west.
Wash. Rare spring M. (May) on the Sound; more common in the fall (Aug.–Sept.) both east and west.

Wandering Tattler. *Heteroscelus incanus*

A bird student examines in the migration season every rocky point and headland along the ocean in the hope of seeing the gray head and *long bill* of a Wandering Tattler cautiously raised above a sheltering rock. If he presses too close, a long-winged bird flies off with a steady flight, uttering a high, clear *whee-wi-wi-wi.* When the bird is walking over the rocks, the tail and rear of the body tip constantly; the Tattler also bobs like a Willet. The general color is dark grayish brown; the belly in spring is barred with black and gray. The Tattler often walks or runs down the face of a steep rock instead of flying. It frequently feeds on the sandy beach, generally close to rocks, probing in the wet sand after the retreating wave. The Tattler often associates with Black Turnstones and Surf-birds but is readily distinguished from them by the longer bill and the *uniform dark gray of the upper parts.* The Yellow-legs and the other Sandpipers and Plovers, with the exception of the Spotted Sandpiper, rarely resort to the rocks which the Tattlers frequent. The dark gray plumage, and the more prominent bill distinguish the Tattler from the Spotted Sandpiper, which has brown upper parts and white under parts. The flight of the latter is also distinctive (see p. 109). A few Tattlers are found along the coast even in summer, but they are commonest in migration in April and August.

WANDERING TATTLER (Breeding)

$10\frac{1}{2}$–$11\frac{1}{4}$ Bill $1\frac{1}{2}$

Ad. in breeding plumage. — *Upper parts dark grayish* or brownish *gray;*

white line over eye; dark line through eye; under parts whitish, heavily speckled or barred with dark gray. Bill long, black, paler below at base; feet yellowish. **Ad. and Im. in fall and winter.** — Under parts unstreaked, breast light grayish brown; belly white.

Dist. — *Cal.* Fairly common M. (Apr.–May; Aug.); a few remain through the summer; winters sparingly on the Channel Islands and the mainland of southern Cal.

Ore. M. (May; late July–Sept.) along the coast, casual inland.

Wash. M. (Apr.–May; July–Sept.) along the coast and westward in the Straits; a few remain through the summer.

WESTERN WILLET. *Catoptrophorus semipalmatus inornatus*

Along the ocean beaches in fall or spring a shore-bird with uniform gray plumage feeds among the larger and browner Godwits and Curlews. When it flies, a *broad area of white* shows conspicuously in the *black wing,* making the Willet the easiest of our shore-birds to identify in flight. Next to the Killdeer, the Willet is the most mobile of the larger shore-birds even when standing; it constantly jerks the head upward and then brings it down again. It is often associated with Marbled Godwits, Curlew and Black-bellied Plover, probing in the wet sand or muddy shore, or like the Sanderling following the receding waves on the outer beach. When a new arrival joins a company already feeding or resting on a bar or flat, just before alighting it often flies crazily about, twisting and gyrating, and when bathing it frequently flops about like a wounded bird. The common call of the Willet when flying has somewhat the form of the Yellow-leg's cry, but is slightly lower and coarser, *whee-wee-wee,* very loud and shrill. When standing it utters a single loud *whee-ee.* In the mating season the Willet flies about in the air calling *píppa-pée-wa-wée-wit,* holding its wings at a downward angle and fluttering the tips as it shoots downward. The straight bill, the uniform gray of the upper parts and its smaller size distinguish the Willet when at rest from the Marbled Godwit or the Hudsonian Curlew; it is larger than a Black-bellied Plover and has a longer bill. The black and white toward the end of the outspread wing enable an observer to pick out at a glance the Willets in a flock made up of different species in flight.

15–16¼ Bill 2¼–2½

Ad. in breeding plumage. — Upper parts blackish gray, spotted with pale gray; *wings black, with a broad bar of white;* rump whitish; under parts whitish; throat almost white; rest of under parts whitish, spotted with dusky. Bill blackish; feet greenish gray. **Ad. in fall and winter.** — Upper parts gray, unspotted; wing as above; throat white; sides of head, neck and breast grayish brown; belly white. **Im.** — Upper parts browner.

Dist. — *Cal.* Rather abundant M., chiefly along the coast (Apr.–May; end of July–Oct.); a few winter. Breeds sparingly in the northeastern portion of the State. A few non-breeders remain on the coast in summer.

Ore. S.V. in marshy regions in Klamath and Harney Cos.

Wash. Rare and irregular fall M. (Sept.) along the coast and on the Sound.

Nest, either a slight depression sparingly lined with grass or well-constructed, on the ground, usually near water and in grass. *Eggs,* 3–4, grayish white, buff or greenish, spotted with brown or purplish gray.

GREATER YELLOW-LEGS. *Totanus melanoleucus*

From the marshy edges of a slough or the muddy shores of bays and ponds a group of long-legged waders rise with a high, sharp call of three or four notes, *wheu, wheu, wheu,* the last note lower than the rest, and as they fly off show a *whitish tail,* behind which extend *orange-yellow legs.* The head and neck are gray, the back and wings are brown. When feeding, Yellow-legs often wade up to the belly in water, stepping forward with quick, precise dabs to the right and left, sometimes running the bill along or sideways under the water. When standing on the shore, they frequently 'bob' with a sharp upward jerk of the head and after alighting frequently stretch their wings upward. Besides the whistled call, Yellow-legs utter a *kip, kip* when startled. There are several other shore-birds whose tails are either wholly or partially white, but none that have the combination of whitish tail and yellow legs, except the Lesser Yellow-legs, a much rarer bird on the Pacific Coast (see next species). The Black-billed Plover has a whitish tail, but has short dark legs, and a much shorter bill. The Dowitcher and the Knot have whitish tails, but both these birds are much smaller than the Yellow-legs and have much shorter legs.

GREATER YELLOW-LEGS

13¼–14½ Bill 2–2¼

Ad. in breeding plumage. — Upper parts blackish and pale gray, speckled with white; whitish stripe from bill to above eye; *basal half of the tail white;* under parts white, fore-neck and breast streaked with black, lower breast and sides with broad irregular bars of brown or brownish black. Bill black; *legs long and slender, yellow.* **Ad. in winter and Im.** — Similar but upper parts ashy brown, the feathers edged with white; under parts white, narrowly streaked with dusky on upper breast.

Dist. — *Cal.* Fairly common M. (Mar.; July–Nov.) throughout; winters sparingly from Monterey Bay southward.

Ore. M. (May; July–Nov.) both east and west; a few may winter.

Wash. M. (Apr.–end of May; July–Oct.) along the coast and on the Sound, casual east; occasionally winters on the Sound.

Yellow-legs; Lesser Yellow-legs. *Totanus flavipes*

The Lesser Yellow-legs is practically a smaller edition of the common Greater Yellow-legs. The difference in size is very evident when the two species are together, but it is unsafe to assume that a Yellow-legs that is by itself and looks small is the Lesser. The presence of some other common shore-bird often affords a criterion of size; a Willet stands higher than a Lesser Yellow-legs and lower than a Greater. The Lesser Yellow-legs has the same habits and flight as the Greater, and is found in the same situations. The notes differ in that the whistled *wheu* is given only once or twice, not three or four times as by the Greater Yellow-legs; the Lesser also utters a sharp *kip*. Most of the records for the Lesser Yellow-legs are for late July, August and September, when the height of the shore-bird migration is reached.

$10\frac{1}{2}$–$10\frac{3}{4}$ Bill $1\frac{1}{3}$–$1\frac{1}{2}$

Practically identical with the Greater Yellow-legs, but about half the bulk of that species.

Dist. — *Cal.* Rare M. (Apr.; Aug.–Sept.).
Ore. Rare fall M.
Wash. Spring M. (Apr.–May) along the coast and on the Sound; fall M. (early July–Sept.) on the Sound and east.

SANDPIPERS: *Subfamily Canutinæ*

Knot. *Calidris canutus*

In August or early September small flocks of stout gray sandpipers, about the size of Dowitchers but with much shorter bills, probe busily

SANDPIPERS IN AUTUMN PLUMAGE
Left to right: Western Sandpiper; Red-backed Sandpiper; Least Sandpiper; Baird Sandpiper; Knot; Pectoral Sandpiper

on the mud-flats of estuaries or sandy shores of lagoons near the ocean. Only small flocks or straggling individuals occur in California; in Washington immense flocks have been recorded.

Knots bunch like Dowitchers and probe either on the muddy shores or in shallow water, sometimes up to their bellies. The note, uttered when a flock is moving, and often when the birds are feeding, is a fairly loud, guttural *quoit.* A Knot in breeding plumage is unmistakable; the lighter shade of its cinnamon breast and its shorter bill distinguish it from the Dowitcher. At all seasons, the absence of white down the back distinguishes the Knot from the Dowitcher; only the rump and tail of the Knot are whitish.

10–11 Bill $1\frac{3}{4}$

Ad. in breeding plumage. — Upper parts blackish, feathers edged with white and some bay; wing with whitish line; *tail white* barred with black; under parts pale cinnamon-brown. Bill and feet greenish black. **Ad. in fall and Im.** — Upper parts light gray; *tail whitish gray*, wing with whitish line; under parts white, breast at close range finely streaked or spotted with blackish. Bill black; feet gray.

Dist. — *Cal.* Rare spring M. (late Apr.–early May) and rather uncommon fall M. (late July–early Oct.) along the coast.
Ore. Rare M. along the coast.
Wash. Spring M. (May) on the coast; fall M. (Aug.–Oct.) on coast, casual on the Sound. Occasionally abundant on the coast in spring.

Aleutian Sandpiper. *Arquatella maritima couesi*

Where rocky promontories project into the stormy winter seas off the coast of Washington, stout dark gray Sandpipers climb up and down the dripping ledges or wheel off when disturbed to another refuge. The Aleutian Sandpiper winters for the most part far north; only a few reach the coast of Washington and northern Oregon. They are generally in company with Black Turnstones and Surf-birds, from which their plainer colors distinguish them; even a Surf-bird shows much more white in flight.

8–9 Bill $1–1\frac{1}{4}$

Upper parts dark bluish gray; rump and tail black, sides showing white in flight; throat whitish; breast and flanks heavily mottled with dark gray. Bill chiefly olive, dull yellow at base, tip black; feet dull yellow tinged with olive.

Dist. — *Ore.* / *Wash.* Irregular W.V. (Oct.–May) in northern Puget Sound and south along the coast as far at least as Netarts Bay, Ore.

Pectoral Sandpiper. *Pisobia maculata*

A persistent student visiting regularly the marshy shores of sloughs may see in July or August a sandpiper smaller than a Killdeer, with the centers of the feathers forming dark brown or blackish lines down the back, separated from one another by chestnut and whitish edgings. The white throat, when it shows, is sharply separated from the *breast,* which is finely streaked and *heavily washed with buff.* The bird is rather phlegmatic as compared with the smaller sandpipers, and often stands with neck erect or half squats. When startled it utters a sharp *kreek, kreek.*

The richer colors of the back distinguish the Pectoral from the Baird Sandpiper, which has a clay-brown back with no chestnut edgings of the feathers. The Pectoral is in general found in or near grassy or sedgy cover, while the Baird is generally a bird of the open flats or beaches.

8–9½ Bill 1.10

Ad. — Top of head brownish black, streaked with chestnut, a not very conspicuous whitish line from bill over eye to back of head, bordered below by a dusky line through eye; hind-neck paler than head or back; *back brownish black, each feather with a large black center edged with chestnut and ashy;* central tail feathers brownish black, outer ones paler; *chin and upper throat white;* sides of neck and *breast buffy,* finely speckled with blackish brown; rest of under parts white. Bill, dusky toward tip, yellowish at base; feet dull yellow. **Im.** — Feathers of back more extensively edged with tawny and white; breast more deeply buffy.

Dist. — *Cal.* Rather rare M. along the coast, chiefly in the fall (middle of Aug.–Oct.); two spring records (Apr.).
Ore. Rare fall M. (Sept.–Oct.) along coast and in lake country of eastern Ore.
Wash. Fall M. (middle of Aug.–end of Oct.) along coast, casual inland; two spring records.

Baird Sandpiper. *Pisobia bairdi*

Some day in August when a student is studying the briskly moving forms of sandpipers on the kelp-lined beach, or on some mud-flat, he will discover a bird feeding near the smaller sandpipers that is *larger than the Western* and yet has a *dark wash across the breast like the Least.* The sides of the head and neck, and the breast of the Baird Sandpiper are brownish gray narrowly streaked with dusky, so that as the bird faces the observer or is seen from the side, these parts look lighter than the back and wings. The feathers of the back are *conspicuously edged with light gray.* The throat is white, but the bird's head and neck must be elevated to show this character. The bill is short in proportion to the size of the bird, about as long as that of the Western Sandpiper. If an observer can pick out the larger bird every time when the flock moves and again alights, and each time note the slightly greater size and the dark breast, he has added to his acquaintance the rare Baird Sandpiper. Some observers find the bird chiefly on the outer beach, but the writer has noted it frequently on muddy shores, but never far from the ocean. There are rarely more than two and often only one, occasionally alone but often with other waders. The note is a rough single *kree.*

7–7½ Bill .87

Ad. — Upper parts pale brown, streaked with blackish brown; pale line over eye, bordered below by a dusky stripe through eye; *chin and throat white,* slightly speckled with brown; *breast pale buffy,* narrowly streaked with brown; rest of under parts white. Bill, shorter than head, black; feet blackish. **Im.** — (Nearly all birds seen in fall on Pacific Coast are immature.) Feathers of upper parts with conspicuous white edgings. Bill and feet dark gray or blackish.

Dist. — *Cal.* Not common fall M. along the coast (end of July–early Sept.); occasional in spring (late Apr.–May).
Ore. Fall M. (Aug.–Sept.).
Wash. Fall M. (end of July–end of Sept.); one spring record.

Least Sandpiper. *Pisobia minutilla*

At any season except in early summer along the beaches or on muddy shores, companies of little sandpipers run along the edge of the water, busily probing in the mud or sand. When startled, the flock rise with a sharp *scree-ee-ee* and fly off, all wheeling and turning together, so that they show now their gray backs, now their white under parts. They often wade up to their bellies in shallow water. When a flock is feeding there is a constant shrill twitter. In April and May many migrant bands come up from farther south. The birds are now in their breeding plumage; the feathers of the *head and back* are almost *reddish brown* with *black centers* that form black lines down the back. When the high tide on the beach drives them from their feeding grounds, they gather in compact groups on the dry sand and sleep in the warm sun, their heads tucked under one wing and one foot drawn up. In such a company there are almost always two species of sandpipers, one a little smaller and darker than the other. The smaller bird is the Least Sandpiper and the larger the Western Sandpiper. Careful study of the group will show that the Least Sandpiper has a dark *wash* on the *upper breast*, and that its bill is *slighter*. If the sun is directly behind the observer and the birds close up, the Least Sandpiper shows dull *greenish yellow legs*, and the Western black legs.

$5\frac{1}{2}$–$6\frac{1}{3}$ Bill .65–.75

Ad. in spring and midsummer. — Upper parts blackish brown, feathers edged with white and some chestnut; narrow white bar down the length of the extended wing; breast washed with brownish, streaked with dusky; central tail feathers dark, outer lighter. Bill black, lighter at base; feet yellowish green. **Ad. and Im. in fall and winter.** — Upper parts grayish brown; breast light ashy gray, narrowly streaked with dusky.

Dist. — *Cal.* Abundant M. throughout; winters in fair numbers as far north as San Francisco.

Ore. Common M. along the coast and in the lake country east of the mountains (Apr.–May; July–Oct.).

Wash. M. (Apr.–end of May; July–Oct.) west of the Cascades; casual east.

Red-backed Sandpiper; Dunlin. *Pelidna alpina sakhalina*

If a student has spent August and early September along the edges of some slough or beach, studying the mixed flocks of little Sandpipers that feed busily along the shore, he should have become thoroughly familiar with their short straight bills. Toward the end of September or early in October he will probably observe a third species with the other two, slightly larger, with a bill that is almost half as long again as even the Western's. Let him study the bill carefully in the brief intervals when it is not sunk in the mud or shallow water, and he will note that it is *slightly downward curved* toward the tip. The general color of the bird is gray, the *throat and upper breast washed with dusky*. This is the Red-backed Sandpiper in winter plumage, always a late arrival from the north. Many of these birds stay in southern California throughout the winter, but in April and May many more arrive from farther south and these are now in breeding plumage. *The top of the head* and the *back* are *reddish brown* contrasting with the gray sides of the head and the gray wings. There is a *black area in the middle of the belly,* squarely cut off from the white breast and white lower belly; this black patch is conspicuous as the birds wheel in flight. The ordinary note of the Red-backed Sandpiper is a harsh *queep* or *kree,* but when a flock is feeding they utter a low chorus of peeping notes. A flock feeds in a compact bunch, moving steadily forward, probing as they go.

In the breeding plumage the Red-backed Sandpiper is easily recognized. In winter plumage the longer bill, with slightly down-curved tip, should be clearly made out in order to distinguish the bird from the smaller straight-billed Western Sandpipers. The Red-backed Sandpiper is darker above than the Western and has a noticeable gray suffusion on throat and breast.

8–9¼ Bill 1.40–1.70

Ad. in spring. — *Top of head and back bright chestnut-brown,* with black streaks on the back; a whitish streak through eye; wings and tail gray; sides of head, throat and breast white streaked with dusky; a *sharply defined black patch on lower belly;* rest of under parts white. Bill much longer than head, slightly decurved at tip, black; feet black or dark gray. **Ad. and Im. in fall and winter.** — Upper parts *ashy gray;* whitish line from bill above and back of eye, bordered below by dusky stripe through eye; sides of neck and *breast washed with gray* and streaked with dusky. Bill and feet as in spring.

Dist. — *Cal.* Common M. and W.V. (middle of Sept.–late Apr. or early May) along the coast, sparingly inland.
Ore. M. and W.V. (Sept.–May) along the coast, occasionally inland.
Wash. M. and W.V. (middle of Aug.–end of May) along coast and on Sound, less common in winter; in spring in flocks of thousands.

Long-billed Dowitcher. *Limnodromus griseus scolopaceus*

A flock of medium-sized shore-birds wheel over a marsh or along the beach and the instant they alight their long bills are sunk into the shallow water or mud and they start the pressing business of feeding. They move forward steadily, keeping close together, probing as they move. If startled, they fly off with a throaty note, *kéekery,* and show from behind a *white line down the lower part of the back,* and *whitish tails.* These markings and their long bills, far longer than the head, identify them as Long-billed Dowitchers. When the birds face an observer, the light line over the eye and the dusky line from eye to bill are readily made out. In winter the throat and breast are dark, the belly white, but in May the entire *under parts* are *bright cinnamon,* speckled and barred on close view with dusky. When the first birds return in late July or August, many still show this breeding plumage; some birds carry more or less of it even into September.

Dowitchers often feed with the smaller Sandpipers — Least, Western and Red-backed — or with the larger Godwits, Willets and Yellow-legs, and even in shallow water with Teal. They are intermediate in size between the three smaller common sandpipers and the larger ones. Their long bills readily distinguish them even in winter plumage from their smaller associates; from other long-billed species they in turn are distinguished by lesser size. To make perfectly sure, however, a flock should be flushed and the characteristic markings of the back should be noted. In the breeding plumage only the bay-breasted Knot can be confused with the Dowitcher. The latter is much commoner in spring than the Knot, so that the beginner may safely call any red-breasted sandpiper with a very long bill and *white lower back* a Dowitcher. In the fall both the Dowitcher and the Knot have as a rule gray under parts, but the Dowitcher still has the *white lower back* and the long bill.

DOWITCHER (Immature)

$10\frac{3}{4}$–12 Bill $2\frac{1}{5}$–3

Ad. in breeding plumage. — Upper parts blackish, feathers edged with reddish brown; light line above eye; a line of white down the length of the extended wing; *lower back, rump and tail white, crossed by many wavy black bars; under parts cinnamon-brown.* Bill, longer than head, black; feet dull greenish yellow. **Ad. in winter.** — Top of head dark gray, with light line over and dark line through eye; upper back dark gray; a line of white across wing; *lower back, rump and tail as above;* under parts gray, white on belly. Bill black; feet dull greenish yellow.

Dist. — *Cal.* Common M. (Apr.–May; July–Nov.) along the coast and in the interior valleys. Winters in small numbers from Morro Bay south along the coast and irregularly in the San Joaquin Valley.
Ore. Spring and fall M. (May; July–Aug.) both east and west.
Wash. Spring M. along coast (Mar.–May), casual on Sound and on east side of Cascades; fall migrant (July–Sept.) on Sound.

Western Sandpiper. *Ereunetes mauri*

The two smaller sandpipers, the Western and the Least, are so constantly together, and their habits are so similar that the account of the latter (p. 118) will serve for both. The *heavier bill*, the *black legs* and in winter the *absence of any dark wash across the breast* distinguish the Western Sandpiper. In April and May when the birds have assumed their breeding plumage (and to a lesser extent in August on their return) Western Sandpipers have lines of dusky speckling on the upper breast and sides but they are even then less heavily marked than the

Least Sandpipers, which are also in breeding plumage. The feathers of the head and back are paler, not so reddish brown as those of the Least at this season.

The ordinary notes of the two birds are hard to distinguish, as the flocks are usually made up of both species, which mingle their calls both on the ground and in flight. If Western Sandpipers are feeding by themselves, their notes will be found to be louder and sharper than the rather musical twitter of the Least Sandpiper. They often give a single *cheet* or *cheep* when rising, whereas the Least separates its *scree-ee-ee*. In spring and midsummer the Western Sandpiper has a low, musical whinny, *whi-hi-hi-hi*, generally uttered when two birds are together.

$5\frac{3}{4}$–7 Bill .85–1.15

Ad. in spring and middle of summer. — Feathers of top of head, hind-neck and back with black centers, edged with whitish and streaked with chestnut; white line from bill above eye to back of head, bordered below by a dusky streak through eye; central tail feathers dark, outer paler; *breast brown*, streaked with dusky; rest of under parts white. Bill stout (slightly decurved at tip but not as noticeably as in the Red-backed Sandpiper), black; *feet black*. **Ad. in fall and winter.** — Upper parts ashy gray; under parts white (only a faint speckling of dusky on breast). Bill and *feet black*. **Im. in fall and winter.** — Similar to **ad.** at same season but with a light buffy wash across breast.

Dist. — *Cal.* Abundant M. throughout (Apr.–June; late July–Oct.); also W.V. from San Francisco southward, commoner southward.

Ore. M. (Apr.–May; July–Oct.) along the coast and at least fall M. in the lake country east.

Wash. Abundant spring M. on coast (Mar.–May); fall M. on coast, Straits and Sound (July–Nov.).

MARBLED GODWIT. *Limosa fedoa*

When the tide in some estuary has covered the mud-flats, a compact mass of large *reddish brown birds* with long *slightly upturned bills* gather on the few bars still exposed, waiting till they can again scatter up and down their favorite feeding grounds. They keep up a continual guttural scolding *ki-kérter* which occasionally rises to a higher pitch, and spar with each other like gamecocks. When Godwits fly, they utter a harsh *kerk, kerk* with something of the quality of a California Woodpecker's note. On alighting a Godwit often

MARBLED GODWIT

stretches its wings upward for an instant. When feeding in shallow water Godwits immerse the long bill and head and probe busily, often keeping close together and moving slowly forward as they feed. At other times they scatter along a beach, but rarely in as loose formation as the Hudsonian Curlew with which they are often associated. When standing or feeding they may be readily distinguished from either Curlew by the *slightly upturned bill;* the tawny color of the plumage, more like that of the Long-billed Curlew's, distinguishes them from the Hudsonian Curlew and from the Willet. When a Godwit flies, the outer portions of the wings are distinctly reddish brown with blackish tips.

$16\frac{1}{2}$–19 Bill $3\frac{3}{4}$–5

Upper parts blackish brown mottled with buff; *wings* when spread *cinnamon-brown* with a patch of blackish just beyond the bend and primaries edged and tipped with black; under parts pale cinnamon. *Bill long, slightly upturned,* flesh-colored at base, blackish for about a third of its length toward tip; legs bluish gray.

Dist. — *Cal.* Common M. (Mar.–end of May; July–Dec.), along the coast and less commonly inland. Winters from Morro Bay south.

Ore. Rare M. along the coast.

Wash. Rare spring M. (Apr.–May) along the coast, and fall M. (July–Nov.) along the coast and on the Sound.

Sanderling. *Crocethia alba*

A line of small white sandpipers fringes the beach in winter, running rapidly out after the receding waves, feeding hurriedly; as the wave rolls

SANDERLING (Winter)

in, they turn and run up the beach with twinkling feet, keeping just ahead of the incoming wave like a fringe of foam. Sanderling in winter are the whitest of all the small sandpipers. Their general white color and their stocky build, and their habit of feeding at the very edge of the ocean distinguish them from the other smaller sandpipers, the Western and the Red-backed. Their bills are shorter and straighter than a Red-backed Sandpiper's, and heavier than a Western's. They fly as well as feed in a compact flock, and utter when startled a single sharp *twit.* In spring and early summer Sanderling show *reddish brown* on the head and neck and are much blacker on the back than in winter. At all seasons there is a line of white in the outspread wing. Although Sanderling keep in general to the outer beach they are not infrequently found on mud-flats or sandy shores of lagoons behind the dunes.

7–8¾ Bill 1

Ad. in breeding plumage. — Head, neck and back pale gray, marked with black and chestnut; bar of white in the outspread wing; outer tail feathers paler than inner; breast white streaked with dusky; belly white. Bill longer than head, black; feet black. **Ad. in winter.** — No chestnut on head and neck; upper parts pale gray; bend of wing dusky, forming a dark spot against the whitish sides; bar of white in outspread wing; under parts white. Bill and feet black.

Dist. — *Cal.* Common M. and W.V. (end of July–early June) along the coast.
Ore. Common M. and W.V. (Aug.–May) along the coast.
Wash. Common M. and W.V. (July–May) along the coast, in Straits and Sound.

AVOCETS AND STILTS: *Family Recurvirostridæ*

Avocet. *Recurvirostra americana*

If one's first introduction to an Avocet is on its breeding ground at the muddy border of a slough or marsh, the meeting is likely to be a startling one. Above the shrill clamor of the fluttering terns and the yelping of Black-necked Stilts, the intruder hears a loud *wheep* and becomes aware of a large black and white bird flying straight at his head, its *long slightly upcurved bill* pointed at his face. One has hardly time to note the *cinnamon-brown of head and neck,* as one involuntarily

AVOCET

dodges and the bird sails past. When not concerned about their eggs or young, Avocets are quite indifferent to an observer and exhibit freely their peculiar method of feeding. They wade or even run in the water almost or quite up to their bellies, submerging the bill and often the head, and sweeping the bill, scythe-fashion, from side to side. Occasionally they swim and dabble like ducks, and in shallow water they often secure their food by single jabs. When an Avocet walks, the tail is often held at an upward angle, higher than the head and neck. When standing, an Avocet bobs from time to time like a Willet or Yellow-legs. When an Avocet joins a flock that are feeding, it often rocks from side to side before alighting, and after alighting stretches its black-tipped wings above its back. In the mating season Avocets indulge in grotesque antics, staggering from side to side with wings extended.

There are no other birds with which an Avocet can be confused. There is never any black on the head or neck, while the Black-necked Stilts, with which the Avocets are frequently associated, show black on the top of the head and down the back of the neck. Young Avocets and the adults in the fall and winter have light gray heads and necks; the birds assume the cinnamon-brown only at the approach of the breeding season.

$16\frac{3}{4}$–19 Bill $3\frac{1}{2}$–4

Ad. in breeding season. — *Head, neck and chest light cinnamon-brown,* except a whitish area around the eye and the base of the bill; *middle of back white,* separating *two longitudinal black areas,* which in turn are bordered by broad white areas; tail grayish white; under parts white. Bill long, slender, upcurved, black; iris red; legs bluish gray. **Ad. in winter and Im.** — Head, neck and chest light gray.

Dist. — *Cal.* Common S.V. (Mar.–Oct.) in the coastal district from Los Angeles southeastward, in the San Joaquin and Sacramento Valleys and in the northeastern corner of Cal.; M. along the coast from San Francisco south. Winters in the southern portion of its range.
Ore. Common S.V. (May–Oct.) on lakes east; casual west.
Wash. Not common S.V.; casual west.

Nest, either a well-made platform of grasses or a rim of grass on the ground near ponds. *Eggs,* 4, dull buff or clay, marked with dark brown or black, lavender and light gray.

Black-necked Stilt. *Himantopus mexicanus*

When an observer first enters a marsh where Black-necked Stilts are breeding, he will think he is in an avian insane asylum. Long-billed birds come yelping through the air over his head; long-legged birds stand yelping in the marsh or hop crazily up and down, or stand with wings dragging, or stagger with one wing up and one down as if in the last stage of collapse. When feeding, the Stilt walks daintily along on its long red legs giving a quick dart here and there; it feeds as a rule in shallower water than the Avocet, rarely standing belly-deep in the water. When a Stilt flies, the legs at first trail downward for a short distance and then are brought nearly in line with the body. Seen from behind in flight there is a narrow line of white down the back and tail, bordered by the solidly black wings, so that the general effect is not nearly so white as in an Avocet. The Stilt's cries vary in pitch apparently with the bird's in-

BLACK-NECKED STILT

tensity of feeling; they begin *yep, yep* and rapidly become *yip, yip, yip*. Another note suggests the syllable *kark*, like the harsh cry of a Forster Tern.

13–17 Bill $2\frac{1}{2}$–$2\frac{3}{4}$

Ad. — Forehead and small area over eye and lower eyelid white; *top of head, back of neck, upper back and wings glossy black* (with greenish tinge in strong light); *lower back, rump and tail white; sides of neck and under parts white.* Bill long, slender, black; legs long, red. **Im.** — Black replaced by brown; legs paler.

Dist. — *Cal.* Common S.V. (late Mar.–Oct.) from Los Angeles southeastward, also in the San Joaquin and Sacramento Valleys and sparingly in Modoc Co.; M. along the coast north to San Francisco.

Ore. Not uncommon S.V. in Klamath, Lake and Harney Cos.

Nest, a platform, or sparse accumulation, of grass or weeds on the ground near ponds. *Eggs*, 3–4, buff or clay, marked with reddish brown, brownish black, gray and lavender.

PHALAROPES: *Family Phalaropodidæ*

Red Phalarope. *Phalaropus fulicarius*

The tide pools on rocky coasts and the beds of kelp beyond the surf occasionally harbor in May hundreds of plump, active birds about the size of a Sanderling, with *deep chestnut-red under parts*. They swim or whirl about and pick off with quick dabs of the bill insects from the kelp or the surface of the pools. Ordinarily the Red Phalarope migrates to its breeding places in the Arctic by a course well out at sea. They rest in large flocks many miles from shore or whirl off when startled like their relatives the Sandpipers. When heavy and contrary winds drive them ashore, they feed with Northern Phalaropes close to the beaches or even on pools and ponds a short distance inland, or in the lines of decaying kelp on the beach itself. In spring the deep chestnut under parts and the *white cheeks* distinguish them at once. When they return in the fall they have already assumed a winter plumage which is very similar to that of the Northern Phalarope at the same season. The chief distinction is the size of the bill which looks stouter and blunter to any one already familiar with the slender, needle-like bill of the Northern Phalarope, and the color of the *back*, which is *bluish gray* with very little streaking. As a rule the Red Phalarope is much less common along the beaches than the Northern, appearing only in exceptional years, but when there are any they are generally abundant. The note given when the bird is startled is a 'low and musical *clink*.' (Nelson.)

$7\frac{1}{2}$–$8\frac{3}{4}$

Ad. ♀ in spring. — Top of head and hind-neck black; *sides of head white;* upper parts buffy brown streaked with black; broad white wing-bar; chin dark gray; rest of *under parts deep chestnut.* Bill yellow, dusky at tip; feet yellowish. **Ad. ♂.** — Similar but top of head and hind-neck brown streaked with black; white area on side of head smaller and duller; chestnut of under parts lighter or mottled with white. Bill and feet duller. **Ad. in Winter.** — Forehead and eyelids white; back of neck and *bar back of eye blackish; back bluish gray almost unstreaked;* wing-bar and under parts white. Bill blackish, yellow at base; feet bluish gray.

Dist. — *Cal.* Abundant M. along the coast (Apr.–June; Aug.–Nov.); some probably winter off the coast southerly. Casual inland.
Ore. Abundant fall and doubtless spring M. along the coast.
Wash. Spring and fall M. (May; Aug.–Nov.) along the coast.

NORTHERN PHALAROPE. *Lobipes lobatus*

In late summer fleets of dainty gray birds are scattered over the surface of small ponds or lagoons along the coast. The birds ride high, their necks and heads held erect, their soft coloring giving them a dove-like aspect. Here and there individuals are whirling like dervishes in order to stir small aquatic creatures from their hiding places; others are daintily picking flies from the floating weeds. In swimming the head is constantly jerked back and forth. When startled Northern Phalaropes rise lightly and fly off with a sharp high *keek*, or a low *kut*, showing a line of white in the outspread wing. Northern Phalaropes are often met well out at sea, particularly where a little floating kelp has attracted the small creatures on which they feed. In the Northern Phalarope, as in the other species of this family, the female is larger and brighter than the male, and leaves to the latter the duties of incubation.

In spring the light gray and white of the autumn plumage is replaced by *bluish gray and deep chestnut,* brighter in the females. In this plumage the Northern should be carefully distinguished from the Wilson

Above: RED PHALAROPE, IM., WINTER; RED PHALAROPE, FEMALE, BREEDING
Below: NORTHERN PHALAROPE, IM., FIRST PLUMAGE; NORTHERN PHALAROPE, FEMALE, BREEDING; WILSON PHALAROPE, FEMALE, BREEDING; WILSON PHALAROPE, IM., WINTER

Phalarope, which is much rarer along the coast but commoner in the interior. The top of the head and nape is dark sooty brown in the Northern but light ashy gray in the Wilson; the Northern shows a white bar in the outspread wing and lacks the conspicuous whitish tail of the Wilson. Northern and Wilson Phalaropes both occur in small inland ponds in fall from Santa Barbara southward. At this season when they are swimming, the contrast of black and white about the head and on the back, distinguishes the Northern; the Wilson is a fairly uniform pale gray. In flight the *white bar along the outspread wing* and the blackish central tail feathers distinguish the Northern. In the fall Red Phalaropes often occur along the beaches but the more slender bill and the black streaking along the back distinguish the Northern Phalarope.

7–8 Bill under 1

Ad. ♀ in spring. — *Top and sides of head and nape dark sooty brown;* eyelids white; back sooty brown, streaked with reddish brown; *white bar in extended wing;* throat white; *sides of neck and upper breast brownish red;* sides streaked with gray; rest of under parts white. Bill slender and sharp, black; feet dark gray. **Ad. ♂.** — Similar but with only a little reddish brown; back with less slaty gray, and more white and black. **Ad. in winter and Im.** — Top of head and bar back of eye dusky; *back streaked with black and white; white bar in outspread wing;* under parts white, streaked on the flanks with dusky. Bill, legs and feet black.

Dist. — *Cal.* M. along the coast (May–June; July–early Nov.), less common in the interior.

Ore., *Wash.* M. (May; July–Sept.) along the coast and in the interior.

Wilson Phalarope. *Steganopus tricolor*

In the marshes and wet meadows of the sage belt along the eastern edge of California, Oregon and Washington, pairs of dainty sandpiper-like birds swim in the shallow pools or feed along their margins. One of each pair is bright-colored, with a broad *bluish gray* band extending from the *top of the head* down the back of the *neck, bordered by deep chestnut;* the other is smaller and dull-colored. An uninformed observer seeing the brighter bird pursuing the dull one, evidently in courtship, is surprised to learn that Phalaropes reverse the usual bird procedure. The female is larger and brighter; she courts the male and when the eggs are laid, leaves to him the task of incubating the eggs and caring for the young. When a meadow is invaded where Wilson Phalaropes are nesting, the pair fly rather timorously about the intruder uttering a low nasal grunt of protest. Two females and a male are often seen indulging in a mating flight over the breeding ground, all grunting in a low tone as they fly. Scattered about the marsh females stand on low tussocks with light gray heads and necks just showing, guarding their breeding territory and uttering at intervals a low *wä'-oo*, more vigorous than the usual grunt.

Occasionally Wilson Phalaropes gather in a compact group in quiet water and whirl about, stirring small aquatic creatures into activity and securing them with their long slender bills. On alighting they often stretch their wings above their backs. The Wilson Phalarope, besides the habit of whirling on the water, employs at times an Avocet-like habit of sweeping for food on the water with a sideward motion of the bill. At other times it walks on muddy shores or in shallow water, and makes sudden dabs for its food. When it walks, its slender neck seems out of proportion to its fat body, giving it when compared with the smaller sandpipers a clumsy look.

In migration the Wilson Phalarope is far outnumbered by the Northern Phalarope, of which there are often thousands in September and October in every pond and slough along the coast, and even far inland. At this time the occasional Wilson Phalaropes that may occur among them can be distinguished when feeding in shallow water or on the shore by their greater length of legs, in flight by the *apparently white tail* and the lack of white in the wing, and when swimming by the uniform pale gray of the head and back.

$8\frac{1}{4}$–10 Bill 1.10–1.40

Ad. ♀ in breeding plumage. — *Top of head* and stripe down back of neck and upper back *ashy gray;* broad black stripe from eye down sides of neck, passing into rich *chestnut on lower neck,* continuing as a stripe down the bluish gray back; white stripe above and white crescent below eye; wings grayish brown; *tail white at base,* tip gray; under parts white. Bill slender, black; feet black. **Ad. ♂ in breeding plumage.** — Similar but duller; top of head, back and wings brown; sides of neck washed with dull reddish brown. **Ad. and Im. in fall.** — *Upper parts ashy gray;* dusky line back of eye; line over eye and under parts white; *tail* as above. Bill black; feet pale yellow.

Dist. — *Cal.* Fairly common S.V. in the northeastern portion of the state, occurs in summer in the San Joaquin Valley; M. (May; late July–Sept.) through the interior and along the coast north to Santa Barbara.

Ore. Fairly common S.V. (May–Sept.) in marshy country and about lakes east.

Wash. Rare S.V. (June–Aug.) about certain lakes east.

Nest, of grass gathered together in marshy ground, or a depression sparsely lined with grass. *Eggs,* 3–4, light buff to very light drab, heavily marked with blackish.

JAEGERS: *Family Stercorariidæ*

A few specimens of a Skua have been taken in summer off the coast of California, Washington and British Columbia. These have been referred by Bent (Bulletin 113, U.S. Nat. Mus., p. 7) to the Chilean Skua (*Catharacta chilensis*).

Pomarine Jaeger. *Stercorarius pomarinus*

The dark figure of a Jaeger in pursuit of a small gull or tern is a frequent sight in the fall a mile or so off shore. It is generally impossible to make out enough details to distinguish one species of Jaeger from the other, but occasionally from a boat one can see the *broad blunt middle tail feathers* which distinguish the larger Pomarine Jaeger. Sometimes, too, this species and the smaller Parasitic Jaeger are seen together and distinguished by the difference in size, or the Jaeger is so much larger and heavier than his victims that it is clearly the Pomarine. The Pomarine has a dark phase in which the plumage is nearly uniform blackish brown, a light phase in which the neck all around and the under parts are white, and intermediate phases of all gradations between the two.

20–23

Ad. in light phase. — Top of head black; nape and sides of head creamy white; rest of upper parts dark brown; *whitish areas showing in the extended wings* and *at base of tail when spread*; *middle tail feathers* projecting, the shafts twisted so that the *broad truncated tips* are at an angle to the plane of the rest of the tail; under parts white, except blackish brown breast. Bill dark, paler at base below; feet black. **Ad. in dark phase.** — General plumage blackish brown; whitish areas in outspread wings and at base of tail. **Ad. in intermediate phase and Im.** — Under parts more or less mottled with black and white.

Dist. — Common fall M. off the coast of Cal. and probably off Ore. and Wash.; occasional in winter.

Parasitic Jaeger. *Stercorarius parasiticus*

When Terns and Bonaparte Gulls are fishing off shore in the spring or fall migration, an observer can often see a dark bird with long wings and

PARASITIC JAEGER (Adult)

rapid hawk-like flight pursuing the light-colored tern or gull till it disgorges the fish it has just captured. The chase is a marvel of speed and agility; the pursuer follows each turn and twist of the smaller bird, doubling with such dexterity that the two are always close together. Sometimes two dark menacing Jaegers chase the same victim. The spectacle can often be viewed from the shore though the birds may be a mile out. In this case it is impossible to determine which species we are watching; we can only make out the general brown of the upper parts with the *light area toward the tip of each* wing and the *light-colored rump*, a pattern shared by all three species. If we are in a boat, the chase often brings the Jaeger close enough for us to note the two long *pointed tail feathers* which distinguish the Parasitic from the larger Pomarine Jaeger. The Long-tailed Jaeger is so rare off our coast that we may assume that the long-tailed birds that we see in any numbers are Parasitic Jaegers. Care must be taken not to assume that a gull-like bird chasing another is a Jaeger; one gull constantly chases another that has secured a morsel, doubling and turning in the manner of a Jaeger.

$15\frac{1}{2}$–21

Ad. in light phase. — Top of head blackish, neck all around white (tinged on the sides with yellow); rest of upper parts blackish brown, with whitish areas in the extended wings and at base of spread tail; under parts white; *middle tail feathers projecting noticeably* and ending in a pointed tip. Bill horn-color, darker at the tip; feet blackish. **Ad. in dark phase.** — Whole plumage dusky. **Ad. in intermediate phase.** — Under parts and sides of neck mottled dusky and white. **Im.** — Middle tail feathers projecting only slightly. Bill and feet bluish.

Dist. — *Cal.* Common fall M. (Aug.–Dec.).
Ore., *Wash.* } M. (May; Aug.–Nov.) along the coast.

The Long-tailed Jaeger (*Stercorarius longicaudus*) is a rare fall migrant along the coast of California and doubtless off Oregon and Washington as well. An adult in full plumage could under favorable circumstances be distinguished from the much commoner Parasitic Jaeger by the length of the central tail feathers, which project from 8 to 10 inches, but in any other plumage it is practically impossible to distinguish the two species in the field.

GULLS AND TERNS: *Family Laridæ*

GULLS: *Subfamily Larinæ*

Pacific Kittiwake. *Rissa tridactyla pollicaris*

Among the larger gulls which gather in winter about fishing boats well off shore, there sometimes appears a smaller gull about the size of a Short-billed Gull, with completely black wing-tips cut off almost squarely from the white under surface of the rest of the wing. The adult Kittiwake can be distinguished from the much smaller Bonaparte in winter by its *yellowish bill* and *black feet* and by the pattern of the wings, which are *tipped squarely across with black,* and lack the white areas inside the black edging of the Bonaparte. Immature Kittiwakes (besides lacking the white areas mentioned) have a blackish crescent across the hind-neck and blackish feet; the immature Bonaparte has pale orange feet. The

Kittiwake is nearly as large as a Ring-bill and is very rare near shore; the Bonaparte is much smaller than a Ring-bill and is common along shore.

16–17$\frac{3}{4}$

Ad. in breeding plumage. — Head, neck, rump and tail pure white; mantle light gray; *black wing-tips cut squarely across* and with very little white tipping. Bill pale yellow, slightly tinged with greenish; feet black. **Ad. in winter.** — Dusky spot back of eye, and nape the color of the back, separated from mantle by white on the upper back. Bill, terminal half pale yellow, basal half dusky. **Im.** — Hind-neck crossed by a black crescent; area of black near the bend of wing; primaries edged with black for a considerable distance; tail crossed at tip by broad band of black. Bill black; feet dusky.

Dist. — *Cal.* *Ore.* *Wash.* Probably irregular M. and W.V. off shore, and in Washington in the Straits and the Sound.

Glaucous Gull. *Larus hyperboreus*

The Glaucous Gull rarely if ever occurs in the Pacific Coast States in adult plumage and in the first-year plumage cannot in the field be distinguished with certainty from the first-year Glaucous-winged Gull. A bird in the second winter is often *almost wholly white.* A gull in this plumage evidently larger than a Glaucous-winged Gull, if seen by a trained observer, may be considered a Glaucous Gull, but the record for scientific purposes will not be valuable unless the specimen is taken.

26–32

Dist. — Rare W.V., probably as far south as Santa Barbara.

Glaucous-winged Gull. *Larus glaucescens*

Even those ordinarily unobservant of bird life notice the gulls that float over the ferry-boats in a city harbor, keeping pace with the boat in some mysterious manner without a single stroke of the wing. They are all gulls to the ordinary observer, but a student notices at once that in winter from San Francisco northward many of the most beautiful adults with white heads and bluish gray wings lack the black wing-tips that are noticeable in other gulls. In Oregon and California the Glaucous-winged Gull is only a winter visitor, frequenting the harbors and beaches or bathing in fresh-water pools inside the beach, and occasionally following the plough like California Gulls, but off the coast of northern Washington the grassy slopes of rocky islets are dotted with the white birds in summer. As one approaches such a breeding ground, the birds standing about in pairs begin a cackling protest. As long as one stays on the island, the cackling, whining cries of gulls are in one's ears, and their shadows pass and repass at one's feet. The cries of the Glaucous-winged Gull are very similar to those of the other larger gulls. When mildly uneasy the birds utter a low *ka-ka-kak,* very like the Western Gull's; when floating about overhead the common call is a hollow *wow.* Their most striking note is a high whinnying cry, *whay-a-kak, a-kak, a-kak,* and when excited over food a high squealing *quee.*

The Glaucous-winged Gull may be recognized in any plumage by the *absence of black on the ends of the primaries;* the gray color of the feathers deepens to dusky gray just before the white tips but it is not black. Immature Glaucous-winged Gulls have entirely deep gray plumage with coarse irregular mottling of grayish white or pale dull buffy on the upper parts; birds in this plumage are commoner than adults along the coast of southern California.

24–27

Ad. in summer. — Head and tail white; mantle light bluish gray, edged behind broadly with white; under surface of wings white; tip of first primary with large white spot, the *next three dusky toward tip* (not black) with white spots. Bill light yellow, with an orange spot near tip of lower mandible; feet flesh-colored. **Ad. in winter.** — Head, neck and breast clouded with dusky gray. **1st Year.** — Entire plumage brownish gray, more or less mottled, especially above, with light gray or pale dull buffy; wings and tail pale brownish gray. Bill black, paler at base; feet dull flesh-color. **2d Year.** — Some bluish gray in the back; wings and tail lighter gray; tail dusky. Bill, terminal half black, basal half flesh-color; feet flesh-color. **3d Year.** — Head and neck mottled with dark gray; mantle nearly as in **ad.**; primaries beginning to show spots at tip; tail nearly white. Bill with some black in the middle; feet deep flesh-color.

Dist. — *Cal.* Common M. and W.V. (Sept.–May) along the coast. A few remain through the summer.
Ore. Common M. and W.V. (Sept.–May) along the coast.
Wash. Abundant along the coast throughout the year; winters commonly from Oct. to May in the Sound region. Breeds on the San Juan Is. in Washington Sound and from Destruction I. northward along the coast.

Nest, of seaweed, etc., on the slopes or rocky sides of islands. *Eggs*, 2 or 3, buff or olive spotted with brown.

Western Gull. *Larus occidentalis* [subsp.]

It would take many pages to describe in full the activities of the Western Gull, its clamorous descent on food thrown into the water, its perfect mastery of flight in strong air currents, its destructive piracy in breeding colonies of cormorants and other waterfowl, whose eggs and young it devours. Its ordinary notes are a high-pitched *whee whee whee*, a high *whee-i* of protest, and a low *kek, kek, kek.* Even on a city wharf in March a pair of adults may sometimes be seen facing each other, elevating the head and neck and bowing, as a preliminary to the mating performance in which they indulge on the rocky islands and promontories where they breed. Unlike several of the other gulls the Western Gull almost never leaves the beach to go farther inland.

The adult Western Gull of southern and central California with its dark gray mantle should be readily distinguished from all other gulls. It is the only gull in which the adult in winter regularly retains a pure white head and neck, unclouded with dusky. From northern California to Washington the Western Gull has a paler mantle but is still distinctly darker than the Herring Gull, and has a stouter and yellower bill. Immature Western Gulls in the first and second years, though considerably larger than California Gulls, might easily be confused with that species, unless seen together. The first-year Western Gull is a distinctly darker bird than the first-year California, with a much heavier bill.

WESTERN GULL
First year; adult; third year

24–27

Ad. — Head and neck all around and tail pure white; mantle dark gray; *tips of primaries black for a long distance especially from below*, the first primary with a large white spot at the tip, the others with tips white; a broad edging of white along after edge of wing. Bill stout, deep yellow, with a red spot on the lower mandible near the tip; iris brown, eye-ring red; feet pale flesh-color. **Im. 1st Year.** — Everywhere dark grayish brown, mottled with light gray, wings and tail darker. Bill black; feet pale flesh-color. **2d Year.** — Head gray, mottled with dusky; back brownish gray; primaries blackish; tail black with white coverts over base; under parts lightly mottled with dusky. Bill, terminal third black, except pale tip, basal third pale; feet flesh-color. **3d Year.** — Nearly as in adult, but with a little black in the tail, less white in tips of primaries and the bill showing more or less black; feet pale flesh-color.

Dist. — Northern Western Gull. [*L. o. occidentalis.*]
(Differs in having a lighter gray mantle.)
Resident from Humboldt Co., Cal., to the northern coast of Wash., where not common.
Wyman's Western Gull. [*L. o. wymani.*]
Common resident along the coast of central and southern Cal. Breeds on many islands off shore.

Nest, of grass, on the slopes of islands, or on niches in cliffs. *Eggs*, 2 or 3, light brown or olive, spotted, blotched or scrawled with dark brown.

Herring Gull. *Larus argentatus*

The eye must be trained to distinguish 'light bluish gray' from 'light neutral gray' in order to pick out the Herring Gulls from a mixed company when the slightly smaller California Gull is also present. If the legs can be seen in good light, the dark flesh-colored legs of the Herring Gull distinguish it from the greenish gray or greenish yellow legs of the California Gull. In southern California the Herring Gull is the rarest of the eight common gulls; it frequents beaches and wharfs but rarely or never comes inland. North of San Francisco Bay it becomes commoner; in Puget Sound it is the commonest winter gull next to the Glaucous-winged.

The adult Herring Gull may be distinguished from the adult Western Gull by the light gray of its mantle and by the *small amount of black showing on the under side of the primaries.* Of the gulls with black-tipped primaries the Herring shows the least black on the under surface of the wing and the Western the most. The bill of the Herring Gull is less stout and not as bright yellow as that of the Western. At close range the *whitish iris* of the Herring Gull is conspicuous.

23–26

Ad. — Head, neck, tail and under parts white; mantle light bluish gray. Primaries *black* tipped with white and white spot inside tip of first, *less black showing underneath than in any other black-tipped species.* Bill yellow with orange spot on lower mandible near tip; iris white or pale yellow, eye-ring yellow; feet pale flesh-color. **Ad. in winter.** — Head, sides and back of neck *streaked* with dusky. **Im. 1st Year.** — General color brown, mottled and streaked with gray; head and neck streaked with white; upper parts mottled and barred with grayish buff and white; wings and tail brownish black. Bill black or lighter at base; feet dull flesh-color. **2d Year.** — Head and fore part of back mottled with dusky; under parts mottled; back showing patches of light bluish gray; wings dusky; tail, terminal half dusky, basal half whitish. Bill, terminal third black, basal two-thirds flesh-color; feet pale flesh-color. **3d Year.** — Tail still showing some black; at least one primary with a white spot, some black in the bill.

Dist. — Common W.V. along the coast, appearing in Wash. in Aug. and in Cal. in Oct. and staying till May. Less common south of San Francisco and Monterey Bays; in Wash., common in the Straits and on the Sound.

The Thayer Gull (*Larus thayeri*) is probably a regular winter visitant along the coast. It is slightly smaller than the Herring Gull and has *slaty* instead of black *wing-tips*, but the differences are not great enough to make a field diagnosis of any value.

California Gull. *Larus californicus*

To one who has only associated gulls with winter seas breaking on rocky shores or thought of them as wary scavengers along the water-front in seaports, it is a surprise to see the white forms of California Gulls, clustered on a lawn in front of a school or hospital, or flying over market gardens far inland. The California Gull is also almost as much a bird of the shore and open ocean as the Western Gull, either watching for refuse about the docks, over the harbors or along the beaches, or scattering over the ocean many miles from shore. If a school of herring appear, California Gulls join the Western and Heermann Gulls that hover over the swarming fish or dip down to scoop up those that come near the surface. They follow fishing boats for the refuse thrown overboard or poise with marvelous ease over a moving ferry-boat. A company may often be seen circling far overhead, apparently for exercise or pleasure. The common notes of the California Gull are a high-pitched squealing *kyarr*, or a longer *ky-ak kee kee kee*. On their inland breeding grounds the birds when anxious utter a low *kak-a-ka-k*.

CALIFORNIA GULL (Adult, winter)

Compared with Western and Ring-billed Gulls, the California Gull is intermediate in size and in the color of its mantle, lighter and smaller than the former, larger and darker than the latter. It generally shows more white in the wing-tips than the Ring-billed Gull. The bill of an adult is by far the surest field mark; the lower mandible shows a *red spot* near the tip, often (especially in winter) with a smaller black spot in front of it. The bill is yellow but the legs in winter are generally grayish green, not yellow as in the Ring-bill. In the breeding season the legs are greenish yellow, lighter than the bill, which at a distance has an orange look due to the red spot; the legs of the Ring-bill in the breeding season are of the same shade of pure yellow as the bill, which in the adult is encircled near the tip by black. California Gulls in the first year can be distinguished from first-year Ring-billed Gulls by the darker upper parts; they lack the larger amount of bluish gray in the back of the Ring-bill and have the base of the tail much more mottled with brown, less white than the Ring-bill; more black, too, shows toward the tip of the tail. First-year California Gulls are lighter and considerably smaller than first-year Western Gulls, with more slender bills.

20–23

Ad. — Head, neck, tail and under parts white; mantle gray; primaries black, tipped with white, the second (and sometimes the first) with a large white spot inside the tip. *Bill light yellow with a red spot near end of lower mandible;* iris dark brown, eye-ring red; feet greenish yellow. **Ad. in winter.** — Head and neck mottled with dusky, often a small black spot in front of red spot and one above it; *feet greenish gray.* **Im. 1st Year.** — Everywhere mottled with grayish brown and grayish white; primaries and tail brownish black. Bill black at tip, basal half light; feet light flesh-color. **Im. 2d Year.** — Considerable of the gray of the adult in the back; primaries black, unspotted; tail whiter at base. Bill chiefly black at tip, basal half light. **Im. 3d Year.** — Almost like **ad.** but some dusky in the tail, primaries incompletely marked with white.

Dist. — *Cal.* Common W.V. along the coast (Sept.–May) and M. on all large inland bodies of water; breeds at Mono and Eagle Lakes, and occurs in summer on many other inland lakes.
Ore. Common M. and W.V. (Sept.–May) on inland lakes and along the coast; S.V. on lakes in Klamath, Lake and Harney Cos.
Wash. Common spring and fall M. (middle of Aug.–end of May) along the coast, Straits and Sound and on inland bodies of water. A few remain through the summer.

Nest, on the ground, generally on islands in lakes, of straw, weeds, etc. *Eggs*, 2 or 3 (4), light brown or olive, spotted, blotched or scrawled with dark brown.

Ring-billed Gull. *Larus delawarensis*

Scattered along the beaches or muddy shores of estuaries or resting in groups on the flats one finds in winter mixed companies of gulls of various sizes. South of San Francisco Bay these flocks generally include gulls of medium size, with *light gray mantles*, *yellow legs* and *yellow bills crossed near the tip by a black band*. These are adult Ring-billed Gulls which have bred on inland lakes and migrated to the coast to winter. They make up part of the flocks that follow the plough or tractor on newly turned fields, and visit freshly irrigated fields or meadows after rains. For the most part they trip daintily along the ocean beach, bathe at the mouths of streams, or sun themselves on the warm sand. The common cry of the Ring-billed Gull, heard chiefly in spring or summer, is a *kyow*, varying in pitch, either shrill or hollow. When alarmed, especially on their breeding grounds, the birds utter either a series of low protesting notes, *kuk*, *kuk*, *kuk*, or high squealing cries.

RING-BILLED GULL (Adult, winter)

One of the most difficult tasks that a bird student encounters is to distinguish the Ring-billed Gull from the California Gull, the next larger, and from the Short-billed, the next smaller. If one can get near enough to an adult bird, the yellow bill encircled near the tip by a black band will always distinguish the Ring-bill. If a bird with the ringed bill is carefully compared with the slightly larger California Gull, which has an orange spot on the lower mandible, the Ring-bill will show a lighter gray in the mantle and less white in the tips of the primaries. The feet, too, differ in color, clear yellow in the adult Ring-bills, greenish gray (occasionally yellowish) in the California. To distinguish young Ring-billed Gulls from young California Gulls by their relative size is only possible when the two are together; the Ring-billed Gull in the first winter has a much grayer back and the base of the tail is whiter.

18–20

Ad. in breeding plumage. — Head, neck, tail and under parts white; mantle light gray; first primary with white spot near tip; sometimes also the second, several tipped with white, but whole effect usually blacker than in California Gull. *Bill yellow, crossed near tip by a dark band,* tip light yellow; iris light yellow, eye-ring red; feet yellow. **Ad. in winter.** — Head and hind neck streaked with dark gray. Bill and feet duller yellow. **Im. 1st Year.** — Head, neck and under parts whitish, mottled on head with brownish and to a less extent on under parts; back with much gray; primaries blackish; bend of wing brown; *basal two-thirds of tail white, mottled with brown,* terminal third blackish, more or less broken by white. Bill, terminal half black, basal half pale flesh-color; feet gray or dull flesh-color. **Im. 2d Year.** — Nearly like winter **ad.** but brown on the shoulders, more or less black toward the tip of tail, and only a small amount of white in the primaries. Feet greenish yellow.

Dist. — *Cal.* Common M. and W.V. (Sept.–May) along the coast south of Tomales Bay, and inland; occurs in summer on many large inland lakes and may breed in Modoc Co.

Ore. Common fall M. along the coast (Aug.–Nov.); S.V. (breeding) in Klamath, Lake and Harney Cos.

Wash. Spring and fall M. along the coast, on the Sound and in eastern Wash., casual in winter, and in summer, but no breeding records.

Nest, on the ground, often on islands in lakes, of dried grasses, weeds, etc. *Eggs*, 2 or 3, light brown, or olive, spotted blotched or scrawled with dark brown.

Short-billed Gull. *Larus brachyrhynchus*

In the harbors about Puget Sound one sees in winter numbers of small gulls with *greenish yellow bills and feet,* and much white at the tips of the black primaries, flying close to the docks or walking daintily at the edges of the exposed flats. They often drop from a height of ten or more feet to secure small fish, striking the water with a splash. Short-billed Gulls often feed with constant fluttering, with wing-strokes suggesting those of the Bonaparte Gull, stooping with dangling legs and head down to pick up floating particles. After rains they gather in companies in wet meadows near the sea, walking about and finding food, perhaps earth-worms, in the grass. In southern California the Short-billed Gull is chiefly a bird of the beaches, where from October to April it walks singly or in scattered companies along the wet sands picking up whatever food the incoming waves may bring. The adult birds stay farther north than the immature, so that most of the Short-billed Gulls seen in southern California are in the brown plumage of the first year. The common note in winter is a high, sharp squeak, occasionally dropping to a lower pitch and becoming a squawk like a distant Night Heron's. The cry is more abrupt than the whining note characteristic of most gulls.

SHORT-BILLED GULL
(Adult, winter)

North of San Francisco Bay the Short-billed Gull is readily distinguished by its small size. Only the Bonaparte Gull, which is rare northward, could be confused with it; the Short-billed Gull in any plumage lacks the broad area of white in the extended wings that distinguishes the Bonaparte. In southern California the Short-billed Gull is often associated with the slightly larger Ring-billed Gull. Immature birds are hard to distinguish; when the two species are seen together the difference in size is noticeable, and also the difference in the bills. The *bill* of the Short-billed Gull is not only shorter but *more slender*, not so deep at the angle, giving the head a more innocent, plover-like appearance. The tail, moreover, is not so light basally as the first-year Ring-bill's; the immature Short-bill in general is a browner bird.

16–18

Ad. in breeding plumage. — Head, neck, tail and under parts white; mantle gray (same shade as in California Gull, darker than in Ring-billed); primaries black, the first with a large white spot near the tip, second also, all but the first tipped with white. *Bill greenish yellow; feet greenish,* webs yellowish. **Ad. in winter.** — Head and neck spotted with light grayish brown. **Im. 1st Year.** — Head, neck and under parts whitish heavily mottled with dark gray; back showing much brown and some gray; primaries dusky; tail, basal half whitish, barred with brown, terminal half dusky. Bill, basal half flesh-color, terminal half black; feet flesh-color. **Im. 2d Year.** — Similar to winter **ad.**, but with brown on the bend of the wing, some black toward the tip of the tail, and only the first primary (occasionally the second also) with a white spot. Bill dull greenish toward base, tip black; feet pale greenish gray.

Dist. — *Cal.* Fairly common W.V. (Oct.–Apr.) along the coast.
Ore. Probably common M. and W.V. (Oct.–Apr.) along the coast.
Wash. Common spring and fall M. and W.V. (Oct.–early May) on or near salt water.

Heermann Gull. *Larus heermanni*

The study of the gulls along the Pacific Coast is so difficult for an observer who depends on a field-glass that he is thankful to find at least one species that is unmistakable in any plumage. A gull whose *whitish head and neck* offers a marked contrast to the dark gray body and *black tail* is already differentiated from the other species; now add a *deep red bill* and you have an adult Heermann Gull. Immature birds lack the whitish head, but their blackish under parts and the bill, red toward the base, distinguish them from all other gulls.

Heermann Gulls frequent the beaches and wharves along the coast in summer and fall as far north as Puget Sound, scavenging much as other gulls, with which they are often associated. They are also found well off shore and make up part of the mixed company of gulls, pelicans, cormorants and shearwaters that gather over schools of herring. They have a habit of robbing Brown Pelicans when the latter are fishing. One or two gulls attach themselves to a single Pelican, following its manœuvres, and the instant the Pelican dives, lighting on the water close to the point where it has plunged. When the Pelican's head and bill appear above water, the gull often seizes the fish which the Pelican has in its bill and pulls some or all of it away. The Heermann Gull reverses the usual direction of migration. It breeds along the coast of Lower California, over the Mexican border, and after the breeding season comes north to pass the summer and fall on our coasts. The Heermann Gull is for the most part silent during its stay with us but occasionally, when a flock are roosting, they utter a whining or cackling note to greet a new arrival, and when hungrily flying about a fishing boat, they utter a high-pitched short *whee-ee*.

18–21

Ad. in breeding plumage. — *Head and upper neck white*, changing to *deep slate on the back;* primaries black, often slightly tipped with white; tail black tipped with white; base of tail and under parts light gray. *Bill red*, tipped with black; eye-ring red; feet black. **Ad. in winter.** — Top and sides of head mottled with grayish brown. **Im. 1st Year.** — Entire plumage sooty brown, darkest on head; primaries and tail blackish. Bill, basal half dull reddish brown, terminal half black; feet brown. **Im. 2d Year.** — Similar to first year but head and back of neck blackish; mantle slaty gray. Bill dull reddish at base, tip black. **Im. 3d Year.** — Similar to winter **ad.** but head darker.

Note. Individuals occasionally occur with conspicuous white patches in the wings.

Dist. — Fairly common summer and fall visitant (June–Nov.) along the whole coast as far north as Puget Sound, and W.V. in Cal. until the middle of Mar. A few remain through the spring.

BONAPARTE GULL. *Larus philadelphia*

In *spring* flocks of small gulls with *black heads* appear along the coast showing much white in the outspread wings and bright red legs. In the *fall* Bonaparte Gulls have lost the black head and show only *two dusky spots on the side of the head*, one before the eye and a larger one behind it. They float very lightly on the water, much of the body being above the water line, with wings and tail projecting at a slightly upward angle. When they fly, the wings show at all seasons a *conspicuous white area just inside the edge* extending along the terminal half of the wing. This silvery white area is evident at a considerable distance, when the birds wheel in their graceful flight. Their movements on the wing are quicker and lighter, more tern-like, than those of the larger gulls. They occasionally spend consider-

BONAPARTE GULL (Adult, winter)

able time in the air, catching insects on the wing. When fishing, Bonaparte Gulls often drop from a few feet in the air to the water but not with the plunge that carries a tern under. The common note, not uttered freely in winter, is a rough *cherr.*

12–14

Ad. in breeding plumage. — *Head* with a *black* (very dark gray) *hood;* a narrow white crescent just over and another below eye; neck white all around; mantle light gray; *primaries white,* ending in black tips (the outer narrowly edged with black); tail white; under parts white (tinged with rose at close range). Bill black; feet orange-red. **Ad. in winter.** — Top of head grayish white, sides white with a *dusky spot before eye and a larger one back of eye;* back, wings and tail as in summer. Bill black; feet paler orange or flesh-color. **Im.** — Similar to winter **ad.** but with brownish areas on bend of wing; more black on after edge of extended wing, but much white also showing as in adult; *tail with a subterminal bar of black or dusky.*

Dist. — Common M. along the coast and frequently in the interior; W.V. (Aug.–May) as far north as Puget Sound, rarer northward.

Sabine Gull. *Xema sabini*

In May and again in August flocks of graceful gulls pass well off shore, about the same size as Bonaparte Gulls and showing in spring similar black heads. The Sabine Gull, however, has the *terminal portion of the outer primaries chiefly black* (where the Bonaparte Gull shows much white) and a *large area of white* at about the *middle of the after edge of the wing.* Its tail is forked, not deeply but enough to show clearly at short range when the tail is spread. The flight of the Sabine Gull is light and tern-like.

13–14

Ad. in spring. — Head slate-gray; neck, tail and under parts white; mantle gray; *terminal portion of extended wing black* up to the bend; a *large white patch* at the *middle of the after edge of the wing;* tail forked, but not deeply. Bill, basal half black, terminal half yellow; feet black. **Ad. in winter.** — Head white, usually grayish on hind-neck (sometimes the black hood retained till Sept.). Bill black. **Im.** — Upper parts grayish brown; wing with large white patch; tail broadly tipped with black.

Dist. — Spring and fall M. well off shore (Apr.–May; Aug.–Sept.). Many records for California; fewer for Ore. and Wash.

TERNS: *Subfamily Sterninæ*

Caspian Tern. *Sterna caspia imperator*

In the lake country of northeastern California and southeastern Oregon, a long-winged bird, about the size of a California Gull, is seen in summer flying slowly along the shore of a lake or patrolling the course of a sluggish stream. At a distance it seems entirely white, but as it approaches, an observer sees a black cap, and a bright red bill which is pointed downward when the bird is fishing. When a fish is spied near the surface, the Caspian Tern hovers a moment, then setting its wings plunges into the water with a splash. The notes of the Caspian Tern are a very harsh *wear-ów* or *ka-ka-káow*, and an angry *carr*. On the breeding ground they often soar at a considerable height.

The black cap and *red bill* readily distinguish the Caspian Tern from any gull. It is the only large tern found on inland waters, but along the coast of southern California it is difficult to distinguish a migrant Caspian Tern in spring or fall from the slightly smaller Royal Tern. The Caspian Tern is a heavier, stockier bird, with a stouter bill and a much less deeply forked tail, but the best field mark is the *large amount of* blackish *shown on the tips of the under surface of the wings.*

CASPIAN TERN (Adult)

19–22½

Ad. in breeding plumage. — Top of head black, feathers not noticeably lengthened behind; back and upper surface of wings pale gray; tail white, not deeply forked; sides of head, neck and upper parts white, *tips of wings for some distance when seen from below apparently blackish.* Bill heavy, *deep coral-red,* the tip orange or yellowish; feet black. **Ad. in winter.** — Forehead white, crown black mixed with white. Bill more orange-red. **Im.** — Forehead grayish white; upper parts spotted with brownish black. Bill dull orange-red, dusky toward the tip.

Dist. — *Cal.* Not uncommon spring and fall M. (Apr.–June; Aug.–Dec.) in the interior and along the coast south of San Francisco Bay. Occurs in summer on large bodies of water inland from Buena Vista L. north and northeast. May breed.

Ore. S.V. (May–Aug.) in small colonies on lakes in Klamath, Lake and Harney Cos.

Wash. Rare or casual spring and fall M. along the coast.

Nest, eggs laid on the ground in hollows lined with straw and rubbish, generally on islands in lakes. *Eggs*, 2–3 (4), buff marked or blotched with dark brown.

Royal Tern. *Sterna maxima*

Among a company of gulls resting on the beach from San Francisco Bay south to San Diego at any time from August to April, close scrutiny will often reveal a few smaller birds whose short legs scarcely raise their bodies from the sand. Their heads are either entirely black, or black with a white area on the forehead. The feathers of the head are long and extend loosely a short distance behind. The necks are short so that the head, body and bill are all in line, unlike the gulls whose heads and necks are held up from the body; the long folded wings extend backward at a slightly upward angle. The entire *bill is red.* The Royal Tern, like the rest of its family, flies with vigorous strokes of its long pointed wings up and down the ocean parallel to the shore, the bill pointed downward when the bird is fishing. When the bird sees a fish, it hovers for a moment, then plunges down, striking the water with a splash. The ordinary notes are a shrill *tsirr*, not so hoarse as the *carr* of the Caspian Tern, a high sharp *kree*, and a succession of *kaks*.

Even at a distance when the color of the bill cannot be discerned, the long, pointed wings with no black tips, and the rapid, direct flight distinguish the Royal Tern from the gulls that may also be winging along the shore. The heavier Caspian Tern occurs as a spring and fall migrant on or near the coast of southern California and might easily be confused with the Royal Tern (see preceding species); the slightly smaller Elegant Tern occasionally occurs with the Royal Tern and can be distinguished only by comparative size (see next species).

18–21

Ad. in breeding plumage. — Top of head black, feathers on back of head loosely elongated backward; upper parts of back and wings pale gray; under sides of tips of wings not blackish; tail white, deeply forked; under parts white. *Bill orange or reddish orange;* feet black. **Ad. in Winter.** — Forehead white, *top of head black mixed with white,* elongated feathers black. Bill paler orange; feet black. **Im. in Aug.** — No elongated feathers on nape; upper parts mostly white marked with small brown spots; tail chiefly dusky, white-tipped.

Dist. — Fairly common at any season off the coast of southern Cal. as far north as Tomales Bay, less common in early summer.

Elegant Tern. *Sterna elegans*

If in a company of Royal Terns a distinctly smaller tern is occasionally discovered with an orange or reddish orange bill, it may be set down as the much rarer Elegant Tern. It has been observed along the coast of California as far north as San Francisco in late summer, fall and winter. It is so like the Royal Tern in appearance and habits that great care and exactly the right conditions are necessary for a certain identification in the field. An observer must be thoroughly familiar with the smaller Forster Tern and be able by actual comparison to determine the size of the Elegant Tern as between that of the Royal and the Forster.

16–17

Ad. in breeding plumage. — Similar to the Royal Tern, but smaller with under parts tinged with rose. Bill more slender. **Ad. in winter.** — Forehead white; under parts pure white. Bill orange. **Im.** — Probably similar to **Im.** of Royal Tern.

Dist. — Rare and irregular along the coast of southern Cal. chiefly in Sept. and Oct.

Forster Tern. *Sterna forsteri*

A company of silvery white, long-winged birds with black crowns and long deeply forked tails fly easily up and down the ocean shore with bills pointed downward, hover for a moment outside the breaking surf and then plunge straight down, striking the water with a splash. When they have satisfied their hunger, they rest in companies on the beach, their short legs hardly raising them above the sand. If we follow their migration route to the marshes of the interior, in the San Joaquin or Sacramento Valleys, or to the lakes of eastern Oregon, we find their white forms flying back and forth over the cloud of Black Terns that beat up and

FORSTER TERN

down the marshes. On the breeding ground a Forster Tern keeps up a constant *kit, kit, kit,* like the cluck of a driver to a horse, or a hoarse high *kee-dee-dee-dee,* but if we approach too near the nest the Tern breaks into a low hoarse *kyarr* or *kerr.* In the mating season two birds fly with long sweeping strokes till they have reached a considerable height and then scale down side by side with wings stiffly set, or one, with head and tail depressed and wings arched, weaves back and forth over the other. Forster Terns often hawk over the marshes after insects like their smaller cousins the Black Terns. Young birds when calling for food keep up an incessant squealing *cree-cree-cree.*

All the medium-sized terns with pearl-gray upper parts seen in summer over inland breeding grounds are Forster Terns, but along the coast in spring and fall, the rarer Common Tern also occurs. Unless the latter utters the long, angry *tée-arrr,* more prolonged than the *kyarr* of the Forster, it is practically impossible to distinguish the two species with certainty in the field.

14–15

Ad. in breeding plumage. — Top of head black; upper parts pale gray; primaries more silvery than back; rump white; under parts white; tail deeply forked, *outer tail feathers from $2\frac{1}{2}$ to 5 inches longer than the central feathers.* Bill, over half the basal portion dull orange, rest blackish; feet orange or orange-red. **Ad. in winter.** — Top of head white, back of head gray; a broad black stripe from bill through eye; tail feathers shorter. Bill duller orange; feet paler. **Im. in fall.** — Upper parts and sides of head washed with brown; outer tail feathers not noticeably prolonged.

Dist. — *Cal.* S.V. (Apr.–Sept.) from Buena Vista L. northward to northeastern Cal.; common M. in southern Cal., and along the coast as far north as Monterey. Winters sparingly as far north as Morro Bay.

Ore. Common S.V. (May–Aug.) on lakes and marshes in Klamath, Lake and Harney Cos., and probably elsewhere in eastern Ore.

Wash. S.V. (May–Aug.) in a few localities in eastern Wash.

Nest, of dead tule stalks, etc., in marshes or lake borders. *Eggs*, 2–5, tawny olive or buff, spotted or blotched with dark brown.

Common Tern. *Sterna hirundo*

The Common Tern is not a common tern along the Pacific Coast, at any rate south of Washington. Moreover, it resembles the very common Forster Tern so closely that it is almost impossible to distinguish the two species by their appearance, but a trained ear will be able to identify the Common Tern if it gives the characteristic prolonged *tée-arrr tée-arrr*, which fairly tears the air with its piercing harshness. The Forster Tern has a corresponding cry, a hoarse *kyarr*, but it is lower and not so prolonged. The Common Tern in migration associates with the Forster Tern, and has the same habits; it frequents the sea beaches and estuaries, plunging into the surf or the tidal lagoons, basking in companies on the sand or screaming overhead when disturbed.

13–16

Ad. in breeding plumage. — Top of head black; upper parts pale gray; rump white, outer tail feathers elongated, forked for about $3\frac{1}{2}$ in., outer web of outer tail feather dusky or gray, inner web white; under parts light gray, rather than white. Bill red for nearly $\frac{2}{3}$ its length from the base, the tip black; feet orange-red. **Ad. in winter.** — Forehead white; under parts whiter than in summer. Bill and feet duller. **Im. in late summer.** — Upper parts marked with brownish; forehead grayish white. Bill dusky brownish, reddish toward base; feet flesh-color.

Dist. — Regular, perhaps common M. along the whole coast (late Apr. and May; Aug.–Oct.) and in Wash. on the Sound.

Arctic Tern. *Sterna paradisæa*

An Arctic Tern, in passing from its breeding ground in the Arctic to its winter home in the Antarctic and back, may make a round trip of twenty-two thousand miles each year, the longest migration of any known bird. In its passage in spring and fall, the Arctic Tern occasionally appears on the beaches and in the estuaries of southern California and possibly in the many arms and passages of Puget Sound. It may be distinguished from the Common and Forster Terns under favorable circumstances by the color of the *bill*, which is *red quite or almost to the tip.* Its cry is harsh, not prolonged and suggests pigs quarreling in a trough.

14–17

Similar to the Common Tern but grayer below, outer tail feathers longer and *bill* in adult *deep red* for *the entire length*.

Dist. — Spring and fall M. probably along the entire coast (early May; Aug.–Oct.).

Least Tern. *Sterna antillarum*

For miles the Pacific Ocean in southern California breaks against steep clay cliffs, but at intervals, where a stream has formed a delta plain, there are white dunes behind a gravelly beach, and behind the dunes a quiet lagoon. As we pass through the dunes to the beach, we may be greeted by a company of small terns, which hover over our head with sharp cries, *kit, kit* or a harsh *kreet*, or pursue one another calling *kit-tíc, kit-tíc.* Several have small fish in their bills; others are plunging into the breaking surf. If we hide and wait, we may see a Least Tern settle on the beach and feed a downy young one that has escaped our notice on the sand. The Least Tern plunges for small fish either in quiet lagoons or in the ocean off shore; it occasionally stoops without plunging, like a Black Tern, and picks insects off the surface of weed-filled lagoons.

LEAST TERN

The Least Tern is the only tern that breeds along the seacoast of southern California, but in May and again in August and September migrant terns of several other species may be feeding along the same beaches. A Least Tern in adult spring plumage may be distinguished from the adult of any other species by the pattern of black and white on the forehead. The *black* from the top of the head extends *through the eye to the base of the bill, enclosing the white forehead.* Immature terns of other species and adults in winter plumage have white foreheads which merge gradually with the black on the top and back of the head, but in the adult Least Tern the white forehead is sharply defined from the black cap, which extends below the white on each side in a narrow black line. The bill of the Least Tern is *yellow* tipped with black, and the feet are *yellow.* The other terns have red or reddish orange feet and red bills tipped with black. The Black Tern is only a little larger than the Least Tern, but even in winter plumage the Black Tern always has sooty gray upper parts, where the Least Tern is light gray.

$8\frac{1}{2}$–$9\frac{3}{4}$

Ad. in breeding plumage. — Top of head black *enclosing a white V-shaped area on the forehead;* upper parts gray; a narrow line of black along bend of wing, under parts white. *Bill yellow,* tipped with black; feet orange-yellow.
Im. in Aug. — Top and back of head varied with white and brownish black; upper parts marked with brownish; under parts white. Bill brownish black.
Dist. — S.V. (May–Sept.) along the coast of southern Cal., north as far as Moss Bay, Monterey Co.

Nest, eggs laid in a hollow in the sand on beaches above high tide, often on bits of rock or shells. *Eggs,* generally 2, buff or olive-buff, sprinkled with small spots of dark brown.

BLACK TERN. *Chlidonias nigra surinamensis*

Over the dark rushes that border the lakes and sloughs in eastern Washington and Oregon and northeastern California, a cloud of Black Terns hover from May to August like giant mosquitoes. Their sharp cries, *keek, keek,* occasionally rising to a shriller *kick, kick,* fill the air.

BLACK TERN (Immature)

They wheel and catch an insect in the air or hover with wings uplifted and stoop to pick something from the tops of the reeds or from the surface of the water; they occasionally plunge like other terns into the water after fish. During the mating season a pair fly with rapid strokes to a considerable height and then scale sharply downward side by side with wings extended, rising at the end of the downward glide or swinging off still side by side. In migration Black Terns appear sometimes in large numbers over small ponds, sloughs and marshes in the interior or along the coast of southern California and occasionally over the beds of kelp a little distance off shore. The adult in breeding plumage is unmistakable; no other tern has a *black head and body.* In the fall the old birds lose the black and have whitish under parts, but their upper parts are always dusky and distinguish them from the slightly smaller Least Terns. Even in summer on the breeding grounds a few adults are found in mottled plumage or with the whitish under parts of the winter plumage.

9–10¼

Ad. in breeding plumage. — *Head, neck and under parts black;* back, wings and tail dark gray; bend of wing white; *area under base of tail pure white.* Bill black; feet dusky. **Ad. in winter.** — Forehead, back of neck and under parts white; top of head mottled gray and white; *area back of eye black;* wings lighter gray. **Im. in Aug. and Sept.** — Upper parts brownish; forehead dirty white; top of head mainly black; area back of eye black. **Im. in first spring.** — Among breeding colonies a few birds are often found in the winter plumage.

Dist. — *Cal.* Common M. (late Apr.–early May; Aug.–Sept.) inland and less commonly along the coast as far north as Monterey. Breeds from Buena Vista L. northward through the San Joaquin and Sacramento Valleys, and in northeastern Cal. from L. Tahoe northward.
Ore. Common S.V. (May–Aug.) on lakes and marshes east.
Wash. S.V. (May–Aug.) on lakes and sloughs east; casual on the Sound in the fall.

Nest, of a floating mass of rubbish, in marshes or borders of lakes. *Eggs*, 3, olive or buff, usually heavily marked with dark brown.

AUKS, MURRES and PUFFINS: *Family Alcidæ*

AUKS and MURRES: *Subfamily Alcinæ*

California Murre. *Uria troille californica*

One's first sight of an assemblage of Murres standing close together in a breeding colony can never be forgotten. Birds fly in from the sea, dropping with the greatest carelessness into the midst of their fellows, balancing for a moment with wings fluttering, or pushing their way through the crowd to their own particular bit of ledge. At a sudden noise the whole company fly off and alight on the water. Their dark heads and long slender bills at one end and the feet extending beyond the tail at the other, give the bird in flight the appearance of being conical fore and aft. The white under parts are conspicuous in flight and show above the water line when the bird is resting on the ocean. When a Murre rides the water, the head is drawn back so that little of it is visible; the bill is pointed slightly

CALIFORNIA MURRE (Winter)

upward and the body ends abruptly, no tail being visible. A Murre often stands and flaps, showing the white under parts. When a boat approaches, Murres either fly, rising rather easily up wind but flapping heavily with the wind or in a calm, or dive, opening the wings just as they go under. Murres fly in lines close to the surface with rapid wing-strokes; in winter or in migration Murres not infrequently join a line of Red-breasted Mergansers or Pacific Loons. The ordinary note is a hoarse *arrh-a.* In the breeding season a California Murre may be recognized by the marked contrast of the dark neck with the white lower parts. In winter the markings are similar to those of the Marbled Murrelet, but the Murre is a distinctly larger bird, with a longer bill, and lacks the white stripe on the back above the folded wing.

17

Ad. — *Head and neck all around apparently black* (dark brown at close range); upper parts dark gray; *under parts white,* sharply demarcated from the dark throat. Bill fairly long, pointed, black; feet, outer face black, inner dark brown. **Ad. in fall and early winter.** — Throat, sides of head and neck white, a narrow blackish line back from eye, separating white throat from white back of neck; rest of upper parts and under parts as in summer. This plumage is seen in adults often only till December, when full spring plumage is again assumed. **Im.** — Similar to fall **ad.**, but plumage worn till spring.

Dist. — *Cal.* Breeds on San Miguel I. and on the Farallones and at one or two points on the mainland. Common M. and W.V. chiefly off shore north of Los Angeles Co.

Ore. Breeds on Arch Rocks. Common M. and W.V. chiefly off shore.

Wash. Breeds on certain islands off the coast. Common M. and W.V. off shore and in the Sound region.

Nest, egg laid on bare rock. *Egg,* one, showing almost endless variation in ground color and markings.

Pigeon Guillemot; Sea Pigeon. *Cepphus columba*

When one rows into the high-vaulted sea caves on any of the islands off the coast, stout *black-bodied birds* with *large white wing-patches* and *bright red feet* fly from recesses in the rock over the boat and out to sea. In coasting along a rocky shore Pigeon Guillemots are frequently seen, singly or in pairs, riding the water buoyantly or diving at too near an approach. Pigeon Guillemots swim with head and neck up, not drawn back as in the other Alcids, and with the black bill pointing forward. They spatter along the surface for a short distance when they rise, unless in a strong wind; but once up, their flight is rapid, close to the water, veering a little from side to side. In the mating season Pigeon Guillemots fly about in twos or threes, ending the flight by dropping into the water and diving; often a number engage in playful submarine activities. Paired birds rest on the water close beside each other 'billing,' or on a rocky ledge waddle about with wings extended or face each other and bow, making a sound like the hiss of escaping steam. The broad area of white in the wing is conspicuous even on the folded wings when the bird is swimming, or standing on the rocks, much more evident than in the

White-winged Scoter, where only a line of white shows on the folded wings. In flight the Pigeon Guillemot shows the white only on the upper surface of the wing and near the center of the wing; in the Scoter the white shows from below as well as above and extends across the lower half of the wing to the inner margin.

PIGEON GUILLEMOT (Winter and summer)

Pigeon Guillemots are the most widely distributed of the family to which the Auklets, Murrelets and Murres belong; they breed on many rocky undisturbed bits of shore along the whole length of the coast, and in burrows in clay banks in the Sound region in Washington. Their wide distribution and their striking pattern of black and white make them generally the first of the Alcidæ with which a beginner becomes acquainted. In winter the black is largely replaced by white. Adults are then almost wholly white below and the black feathers of the back are edged with white, but the white wing-patches are prominent even in this plumage.

13–14

Ad. in breeding season. — Plumage wholly black except for broad *white wing-patches.* Bill black; *feet red.* **Ad. in winter.** — Head and back mottled black and white; under parts mainly white; wings and tail as in breeding season. Bill black; feet dull red. **Im.** — Similar to **ad.** in winter, but throat and breast mottled with dusky, and white wing-patches mottled with black.

Dist. — Breeds from Santa Barbara Co., Cal., northward on islands and rocky coasts and in clay banks. Winter distribution about the same, but mostly off shore.

Nest, in burrows or crevices. *Eggs,* 1 or 2, pale green, greenish or bluish white, or pure white, blotched with pale gray or lavender and dark brown.

Xantus Murrelet. *Brachyramphus hypoleucus*

If one spends a night on the Coronados Islands off San Diego amid the fluttering forms and clamor of petrels, small dark birds come whistling past and light in the crevices of rocks. By day the Xantus Murrelet incubates its two eggs far back under the heaped-up fragments of rock, but after the breeding season old and young are met at sea some distance from their breeding grounds. The note of the Xantus Murrelet, generally heard after dark, is a 'shrill whistle' (Howell). The Xantus Murrelet

(Left to right: Marbled Murrelet, winter; Marbled Murrelet, summer; Xantus Murrelet; Ancient Murrelet, winter; Cassin Auklet)

has been found breeding only as far north as Anacapa I. The only other bird with which it can be confused in summer is the Cassin Auklet, from which its pure white throat distinguishes it. In winter the Xantus Murrelet is confined to the coast south of Monterey Bay, but the Ancient Murrelet and the Marbled Murrelet also winter along the same part of the coast. The uniform color of the upper parts distinguishes the Xantus Murrelet from the Marbled Murrelet, which shows a white stripe above the wing, and from the Ancient Murrelet, which has a blackish head contrasting with the gray back. Moreover, the Xantus Murrelet has a white throat whereas the Ancient Murrelet even in winter generally has a blackish throat.

$9\frac{1}{2}$–$10\frac{1}{2}$

Upper parts apparently black (dark ashy in strong light); under parts white. Bill black; feet pale bluish.

Dist. — *Cal.* Breeds on Anacapa and Santa Barbara Is., and on the Coronados Is. Winters as far north as Monterey Bay, chiefly off shore.

Nest, generally a cranny in the rocks with no nesting material. *Eggs*, 1 or 2, chocolate, blue, green or drab, either nearly plain or clouded, spotted or blotched with brown or lavender.

The Craveri Murrelet, *Brachyramphus craverii*, indistinguishable in the field from the Xantus Murrelet, has been taken off Monterey Bay from August to early October, and probably from November to February.

Marbled Murrelet. *Brachyramphus marmoratus*

An especial interest always attaches to a bird which can hide its nest and eggs from man's indefatigable search. The Black Swift gave up its secret in 1901; the Wandering Tattler and the Surf-bird have been run down in the mountains of Alaska; of all the birds occurring commonly on our coast only the Marbled Murrelet still keeps its breeding haunts a mystery. We know that it remains off our coast in summer even as far south as northern California. The rocky islands and steep cliffs where its relatives breed have been searched again and again but in vain. There is a strong suspicion that unlike the other Murrelets it breeds inland, perhaps far up on the sides of mountains. Some one has a tremendous thrill before him when he first takes a Marbled Murrelet off her eggs.

In winter the Marbled Murrelet is found off shore from British Columbia to southern California; it is especially common in Puget Sound and the adjacent waters, often coming close to the docks to fish. When the bird is resting on the water, a nearly complete *collar of white* runs up *between the sides of the head and the back,* and a *narrow white line* shows *along the back* above the folded wing. It flies swiftly with rapid wing-beats but with a slightly wavering flight, close to the water, often dropping into the water from swift flight with a splash. It is the only Alcid that is talkative in winter, uttering frequently both in flight and from the water a sharp high *keer, keer* or a lower *kee.* Its ordinary attitude on the water is with the head drawn back and no neck apparent, the tail slightly cocked and showing the white beneath; when excited it raises its head and shows a short neck. Like the other Alcids it travels under water by using its wings, and dives with a flirt of its wings, so that after the rest of its body is under water the tip of its tail shows for an instant between the tips of its wings.

The Marbled Murrelet in winter shows more contrast of black and white than any of the other small Alcids, both when resting on the water and in flight. The white collar, the white stripes on the back above the wings, the white flanks contrasting with the rest of the upper parts give it a pied appearance. The California Murre in winter often shows a similar pattern of dark gray and white, but the Marbled Murrelet is a much smaller bird and has a stripe of white above the wing which the Murre lacks.

9½–10

Ad. in breeding plumage. — Upper parts dark brown, at close range barred (except on the wings) with chestnut-brown; *under parts white waved with brownish black.* Bill black. **Ad. in winter.** — Upper parts dark gray; eyelids white, line from eye to bill white; a line of *white on sides of neck* making almost a collar; *two white areas along the back,* under parts white.

Dist. — Occurs along the coast in summer from Monterey northward, in winter from Santa Barbara northward; abundant in winter in Puget Sound and neighboring waters.

Ancient Murrelet. *Synthliboramphus antiquus*

Along the shore of Monterey Bay from the Marine Laboratory toward the Lighthouse are rocky coves into which sea birds come in winter and dive for their food. Here among the cormorants and grebes, one may occasionally see an Ancient Murrelet, a compact little bird, far smaller than any gull or duck, resting on the water or diving with the quick flirt of opened wings characteristic of its family. Its head rests almost against the back, and the tail is hardly evident. In good light the *top of the head* and usually the *throat are black*, contrasting with the *dark gray of the back*. In the breeding season the black head is streaked with delicate white feathers, as if old age were turning it gray; this plumage has suggested the name. With a boat one may often approach an Ancient Murrelet close enough to see the *whitish bill* conspicuous against the black head, but at long range the blackish throat (when present) and always the contrast of the blackish head and gray back distinguish the Ancient Murrelet from the Cassin Auklet and the Xantus Murrelet, which have the upper parts of a uniform color. The absence of white markings on the back distinguish the Ancient Murrelet from the Marbled Murrelet.

$9\frac{1}{2}$–$10\frac{3}{4}$

Ad. in breeding season. — As in winter except for delicate white feathers forming a crescent on the back of the neck and streaks along side of neck; *throat black*. **Ad. in winter and Im.** — *Top and sides of head* and *back of neck black*, rest of *upper parts dark gray;* throat either black or speckled with white, or occasionally pure white; rest of under parts white, the white reaching up the side of the neck. Bill black on upper mandible, sides bluish gray tinged with light flesh-color, contrasting with the black of head.

Nest, either of dry grass in a burrow 2–3 ft. long, or eggs deposited on the bare ground in crevices or under rocks. *Eggs*, 2, creamy white or buff, often heavily speckled with small markings of light gray or lavender and brown.

Paroquet Auklet. *Phaleris psittacula*

The Paroquet Auklet is perhaps not uncommon well off shore in winter. A number have been taken at San Francisco and off Monterey, and one has been found dead on the beach at Netarts Bay, Ore.

Cassin Auklet. *Ptychoramphus aleuticus*

Only the most ardent bird students will ever hear the love notes of the Cassin Auklet. To hear them one must pass the night on a desolate islet well out at sea and face the possibility of an enforced stay if rough weather prevents a landing through the surf. If the slopes of the island are formed of loam mixed with crumbling rock, one will find in such banks the mouths of burrows extending several feet into the earth. In a flourishing colony of Auklets there may be hundreds of such burrows, and among them or near them hundreds of shorter burrows occupied by petrels. All this submerged population constitutes the noisy and active night-life of the island. While the petrels' cries might be called musical, the note of the Cassin Auklet suggests the cry of a child in an agony of pain, *eeee-ti-ti-ti*, or are harsh and rasping 'as if made by a squeaky buck-saw passing through a knot' (Littlejohn). At dawn the night sounds cease, and the cries of gulls, the clamor of a Duck Hawk or the shrill whistling of Oyster-catchers take their place.

One can, however, see Cassin Auklets without making the effort to visit their summer homes. They winter in great numbers all along the coast well out at sea. Look from a steamer in fall or winter for chunky little birds with apparently no necks that ride the waves often in pairs, and as the vessel approaches, disappear with a flirt of the opened wings or, rising, skim off just over the waves with rapid flight in an irregular course. Taylor writes that 'they often emerge from the water and take wing with a single jump, in marked contrast to the Marbled Murrelet, which skips along the water over several waves before taking flight.'

There are three other small sea birds, very similar to the Cassin Auklet in shape, size and color, which occur off the coast in winter, the Xantus Murrelet (as far north as Tomales Bay, California), the Marbled Murrelet and the Ancient Murrelet. The dark throat of the adult Cassin Auklet should distinguish it at close range from either the Xantus Murrelet or the Marbled Murrelet; the Cassin Auklet, moreover, lacks the white on the sides of the neck and along the wing which the Marbled Murrelet shows in winter. The uniform color of the upper parts and the dusky sides of the neck distinguish the Cassin Auklet from the Ancient Murrelet. In the writer's experience Cassin Auklets are seen near shore much less often than Marbled and Ancient Murrelets, but are very frequently found dead on the beach.

8–9½

Ad. — Upper parts blackish; small white spot over eye; *throat and upper breast dark gray;* rest of under parts white; wings long and narrow. Bill short, black. **Im.** — Throat whiter.

Dist. — Common R. on the ocean off the entire coast. Breeds (Apr.–June) on many of the islets off the coast of Wash. and Ore., in Cal. on the Farallones, San Miguel, Santa Cruz and Santa Barbara Is., and formerly at least on the Coronados.

Nest, of a few grass blades or dried stalks at the end of a burrow from 2 to 6 ft. long in steep banks or in crevices in rocks. *Egg*, white, often stained.

Rhinoceros Auklet. *Cerorhinca monocerata*

In winter when herring come into the bays of California or smelt are running up the streams of Oregon and Washington, fish-eating birds of many species gorge themselves on the abundant food. Here and there among the gulls and grebes, *dark chunky birds* smaller than the California Murre are seen resting on the water, singly or in small groups, with the bill pointing forward and the head so close to the body that they seem to have no neck. When they dive, they plunge the head down, at the same time opening their wings, so that we see for an instant the tip of the tail pointing upward between the tips of the wings, and the white lower belly. Rhinoceros Auklets fly with rapid wing-strokes close to the surface. Toward the end of the winter birds are seen in full breeding plumage with two sets of delicate white feathers on each side of the head. The horny projection at the base of the bill which gives the bird its name can hardly be distinguished in the field.

RHINOCEROS AUKLET (Immature, winter)

To study the Rhinoceros Auklet at home, one should visit Destruction Island, off the coast of Washington. Here on a flat-topped island covered with a dense growth of sal-lal bushes, the birds have made numerous deep burrows either at the edge of the bushes or among their roots. They keep in the burrows or out at sea by day, but at dusk their dark bodies pass an observer at full speed, the birds hurling themselves into the brush and scrambling into their burrows. The place resounds at night with their growling and shrieking cries.

Many of the birds that sojourn in our winter seas keep so far off shore that they must be studied from a boat. The Rhinoceros Auklet, however, when following fish at times comes into bays and rocky coves so near that it can be identified from shore. It may be recognized in winter by its size, intermediate between the California Murre and the Marbled Murrelet, its *uniform dark coloration* and its chunky figure. Under favorable conditions the dull yellow sides and base of the bill are evident. All the other Alcids with the exception of the Tufted Puffin show in winter white under parts even when resting on the water; the Rhinoceros Auklet shows its white belly only in flight and for an instant when diving. An immature Puffin in winter could be mistaken for a Rhinoceros Auklet but the Puffin in winter rarely comes inshore.

14–15½

Ad. in breeding plumage. — *Upper parts blackish;* two sets of white feathers along side of head above and below eye; sides of head, *throat and upper breast brownish gray;* rest of under parts white, mottled with dusky. Bill dusky above, dull orange on sides and below, a short projection from base of upper mandible; iris yellow. **Ad. in winter.** — White plumes shorter. Bill dusky above, brownish yellow on sides and below. **Im.** — White plumes lacking. Bill smaller and darker, without 'horn.'

Dist. — *Cal.* Common M. and W.V. (Sept.–May) off shore.
Ore. Probably common M. and W.V. off shore.
Wash. S.V. (Apr.–Sept.) on certain rocky islands off the coast from Destruction I. northward; common fall M. along the coast and in the Sound.

Nest, at the end of a burrow from 5 to 15 feet in the steep sides of islands, made of a little grass, leaves or feathers. *Egg*, one, dull white, often with spots of pale lavender, gray or light brown.

PUFFINS: *Subfamily Fraterculinæ*

TUFTED PUFFIN. *Lunda cirrhata*

The grassy slopes of some of the rocky islets off the coast of Washington are dotted in May and June with heads of Puffins standing at the mouths of their burrows. Only a little of their *black bodies* shows above the grass, but their *white cheeks* and *bright red bills* give them a ridiculously solemn appearance. From behind the eye two crests of silky yellowish feathers extend backward on the head and droop over each side of the back of the neck. After a time they throw themselves over the edge of the cliff and go hurtling down to the sea, their bright red legs wide apart at first and then brought together under the tail. In flight the outline is that of a stocky bird with the heavy head extending only a short distance in front and the square tail a short distance behind, easily distinguished from the Murres, whose outline is conical at each end. The flight is strong with rapid strokes. Seen from the side either in flight or on the water, the white cheeks are conspicuous. Puffins dive for food, but when disturbed on the water generally fly, getting under way with ease against the wind but with difficulty in a calm. They feed somewhat by day but are particularly busy at twilight and in the early morning, their bullet-shaped bodies continually rising up to the cliffs or falling from them, singly or in pairs. In winter Puffins lose the silken streamers and their cheeks are dusky, but the red of the bill together with its shape, much deeper than long, serve to distinguish them from the other wintering sea birds, most of which are slender-billed. Puffins apparently winter chiefly well off shore, and are rarely seen in the bays, harbors and rocky coves frequented in winter by many of their relatives.

TUFTED PUFFIN (Breeding)

$14\frac{1}{2}$–$15\frac{1}{2}$

Ad. in breeding plumage. — *Sides of head white* connected by narrow lines of white over forehead and across chin; long streamers of silky yellowish feathers extending back from above eye; *top of head and back black;* iris white or whitish, eye-ring red; under parts dark brown, paling on belly. *Bill* very deep at base, *vermilion* on terminal two-thirds, horn-color at base; feet vermilion. **Ad. in winter.** — Cheeks dusky, streamers absent; under parts paler. Bill smaller and darker at base; feet paler. **Im. in first winter.** — Cheeks not paler than rest of head; bill smaller than in **ad.** In this plumage closely resembles Rhinoceros Auklet.

Dist. — *Cal.* S.V. (Apr.–Sept.) on certain rocky islands from Santa Barbara I. northward, abundant on the Farallones; winters off shore in the same range.

Ore. Breeds (Apr.–Sept.) on rocky islands off the coast (common on Three Arch Rocks); winters off shore.

Wash. Breeds (May–Sept.) commonly on rocky islands off the coast and more sparingly in Washington Sd. northerly; probably winters off shore.

Nest, at the end of a burrow. *Egg*, one, dull white, often irregularly blotched with light brown.

Note. — The Horned Puffin (*Fratercula corniculata*) has been occasionally found dead or dying in winter on ocean beaches in all the Coast States, and is, presumably, in some winters at any rate, a visitant well off shore. A specimen may be distinguished from the slightly larger Tufted Puffin, which it resembles in the great depth of its bill, by the *white under parts*, encircled at the throat by a black collar.

PIGEONS, DOVES, etc.: *Order Columbiformes*

PIGEONS AND DOVES: *Family Columbidæ*

BAND-TAILED PIGEON. *Columba fasciata fasciata*

In the foothill valleys in winter a flock of pigeons rise suddenly from a grove of oaks with a whirr of wings and are off in rapid flight. They alight perhaps in some tall sycamore, fifty or more in one tree, sitting upright in rows and little groups on the naked upper branches. When not alarmed, their necks and heads are drawn in against the breast, but as one approaches, the small head is stretched warily up. A bird often moves its head forward once or twice after alighting. The band across the tail is not very conspicuous, but when birds alight, sailing down to their perch and checking their flight with many short wing-strokes, the *tail* is fully spread and shows a *wide border of light gray across the end.* Seen from above in flight the *bluish gray back and wings* are contrasted with the *blackish tips of the wings.* Band-tailed Pigeons fly in more or less compact groups, but there are often straggling companies behind or to one side. Besides acorns, which they gather either from the trees or from the ground, Band-

BAND-TAILED PIGEON

tailed Pigeons eat berries of various sorts or grain in open fields. In the breeding season the call of the male *whoo hú whoo*, or often only two notes *hú whoo, hú whoo*, is heard in the higher mountains of California or the red fir forests of western Oregon and Washington; when courting the male bows and nods like a domestic pigeon.

In size, figure and flight the Band-tailed Pigeon resembles the domestic pigeon more nearly than the Mourning Dove; it may at once be distinguished from the Dove by its short square tail. If a large flock of pigeons are seen in wooded hills far from any ranch, or if the flock light in trees they are Band-tailed Pigeons; domestic pigeons almost never light in trees. The rump of the Band-tailed Pigeon is dark gray, not contrasting with the back and tail as the light gray rump of the domestic pigeon does.

$13\frac{3}{4}$–$15\frac{3}{4}$

Back of neck blackish; ends of wings blackish; rest of upper parts dark gray, except a *dusky band across middle of tail;* tail rounded; under parts ruddy brown, lighter on belly. Bill yellowish orange, tipped with black; iris dark red; feet yellow.

Dist. — *Cal.* S.V. in small numbers in the mountains; W.V. in the foothills, varying in abundance.
Ore. S.V. (Apr.–Nov.) west, especially along the coast.
Wash. Common S.V. (Apr.–Oct.) west; casual east.

Nest, a loose bulky platform of sticks, on a horizontal branch of a tree (generally an oak) from 8–40 ft. up. *Egg*, 1, white.

Mourning Dove. *Zenaidura macroura* subsp.

When one drives in late summer or fall through stubble fields or among the brown cattle ranges, a sharp whistling of wings is heard from the roadside and the long slender forms of Mourning Doves fly off low over the fields. As the birds near the spot where they intend again to alight, the tail is spread to check their momentum, showing in all but the *long central tail feathers* a deep white border edged on the inner side with black. On the ground Doves walk with a dainty tripping motion, their pink feet raising the body only slightly off the ground. Except for an occasional Sparrow Hawk, Doves

WESTERN MOURNING DOVE

are the largest bird that perch commonly on telephone wires; when perching in trees they generally alight on a bare branch or limb.

Early in the year the cooing of the male, *coo-ah-coō, cuk coō*, becomes a characteristic sound. In the mating season the male flies up forty or fifty feet with a slow wing-stroke and then, setting his wings, glides downward at a gentle angle, curving to one side and then to the other. When surprised on the nest, the female tries to decoy the intruder away by fluttering off as if crippled. During the breeding season, Doves feed and fly in pairs, but after the young are fledged, they gather in loose companies often up to twenty or thirty.

If one sees a Mourning Dove perched or feeding on the ground, the gentle look of the head characteristic of the family is unmistakable. In flight the rapid cleaving of the air by the long trim form marks the bird as far as one can see. Mourning Doves and Band-tailed Pigeons are occasionally found in the same region in winter when the pigeons come down the open wooded valleys in which a few Doves are wintering (see preceding species).

$11\frac{1}{4}$–$12\frac{3}{4}$

Ad. ♂. — General plumage brownish; top of head bluish gray; *central tail feathers very long, outer feathers* gradually shorter, *broadly tipped with white*, edged on the inner side with black; breast tinged with pink. Bill bluish gray; feet pink. **Ad.** ♀. — Similar but with brown head, and very little iridescence. **Im.** — Duller colored than female.

Dist. — Western Mourning Dove. *Z. m. marginella.*

Cal. Common S.V. in open country. Winters sparingly as far north as the Sacramento Valley, and commonly south of Los Angeles Co.

Ore. / *Wash.* Common S.V. (Apr.–Oct.) east; a few winter.

Northwest Mourning Dove. *Z. m. caurina.*

Ore. S.V. west of the Cascades, exact range not known; a few winter.

Wash. Uncommon S.V. (Apr.–Oct.) in clearings and cultivated sections west.

Nest, a carelessly built platform of twigs, rootlets, etc., on the limb of a tree, in a bush, or on the ground. *Eggs*, 2, white.

White-winged Dove. *Melopelia asiatica trudeaui*

Early in May a note is heard from the broad green bands of willow along the Colorado River that is unmistakably from a dove, but distinct from the four-syllabled call of the Mourning Dove and from the repeated single *coos* of the little Ground Dove. The notes may be written *cuck-cuck, cuck-óo*, like a very hoarse rooster; these are often followed by four more notes with a different accent, *coo-cóo, cóo-ee*, and these again by three more *cóo-ee, coō*. The White-winged Dove has a stouter figure than the Mourning Dove's with a much *shorter tail, rounded* like a pigeon's. The *wings* are marked with a *conspicuous white crescent* and the tail when fully spread shows large white spots at the tips of all but the central tail feathers, forming a bar across the end of the tail. The bird's flight is not such a rapid cleaving of the air as the Mourning Dove's and is generally at a greater height from the ground. In the breeding season the male flies up from a perch and with set wings and tail spread, scales to one side and the other, much like the Mourning Dove. In the late summer large flocks gather in the stubble fields, flying with marked regularity from their feeding grounds to their roosts near water.

$11\frac{1}{4}$–$12\frac{1}{2}$

Upper parts chiefly brown, purplish on head, bluish on lower back; *wings* dusky *with a broad white crescent; tail rounded;* all but central feathers broadly tipped with white; throat and breast pale brown; rest of under parts light bluish gray. Bill black; feet dull red.

Dist. — *Cal.* Common S.V. along the Colorado R. from Yuma to Needles, not rare in the Imperial Valley, casual further north.
Wash. One record.

Nest, in a mesquite, or other tree; a carelessly built platform of twigs. *Eggs*, 2, white.

MEXICAN GROUND DOVE. *Chæmepelia passerina pallescens*

In the willows that line the ditches that carry water from the Colorado River near Yuma the soft cooing of the Ground Dove often mingles with that of the Mourning Dove. The notes are single *coos*, repeated from seven to twenty times in succession; then there is an interval and another series is uttered. If one is close to the bird, the notes seem to be almost double, *coo-oók* closely run together. At each repetition the bird makes a slight forward movement of the head. The bird feeds on the ground, is quite tame and is readily told by the *reddish brown area in the wing,* and the *short blackish tail* which has no long middle feathers. When one is close to the little dove, the feathers on the back of the head and the neck have a scale-like appearance.

$6\frac{1}{2}$–$6\frac{3}{4}$

General color grayish brown; *wings showing reddish brown when spread;* tail blackish, outer feathers with small white tips; under parts pinkish brown, passing into white on belly; feathers of throat and upper breast with dark edgings, giving a scale-like effect. Bill yellow with dark tip; feet yellow.

Dist. Fairly common R. along the Colorado R. from Yuma northward, less common in the Imperial Valley; accidental as far north as San Francisco.

Nest, in bushes or trees, from $2\frac{1}{2}$ to 25 ft. above the ground, of rootlets and grasses, often with a decided depression in the center. *Eggs*, 2, white.

CUCKOOS, etc.: *Order Cuculiformes*

CUCKOOS, etc.: *Family Cuculidæ*

CUCKOOS: *Subfamily Cuculinæ*

CALIFORNIA YELLOW-BILLED CUCKOO. *Coccyzus americanus occidentalis*

From the willow thickets along stream beds from May to July the long, guttural call of the Cuckoo is frequently but nowhere commonly heard. It resembles the syllables *kuk-kuk-kuk-kuk-kyow-kyow-kyow.* Besides this long explosive call, the Cuckoo often repeats a series of soft low notes, *co͞o*, *co͞o*, *co͞o*, suggesting a Mourning Dove, but without the marked accent of the Dove's call. In the rare cases when the bird is seen, it flies quickly into cover, but the long wings and tail and the glimpse of *cinnamon* in the *outspread wing* will identify it. If the tail is fully spread the white spots at the tips of the feathers are conspicuous. When the bird lights, it has a habit of slowly raising the tail.

$12\frac{1}{2}$–$13\frac{1}{2}$

Ad. — Upper parts brown, under parts white; tail long, graduated, the three outer blackish tail feathers ending in large white spots; a broad *area of cinnamon* in *the outspread* wing. Bill dusky above, lower mandible yellow; feet dark gray.

Dist. — *Cal.* Fairly common S.V. (May–Sept.) in the willows along streams.
Ore. Not common S.V. in western Ore., rare S.V. east.
Wash. Rare S.V. in western Wash., casual east.

Nest, a frail platform of sticks, rootlets, etc., in bushes or low trees. *Eggs*, 3–4, pale greenish blue.

ROAD-RUNNERS: *Subfamily Neomorphinæ*

Road-runner: *Geococcyx californianus*

The days are nearly over when a large gray bird with a long tail held straight out behind runs ahead of horse or wagon on long stretches of brush-bordered trail. The Road-runner has apparently gauged the speed of a motor car, and nowadays crosses the road and makes off into

ROAD-RUNNER

the brush. When at a safe distance, it stands for a moment elevating its black crest feathers and bringing the long narrow tail slowly upward or, when not excited, letting it droop. If pressed for time or when clearing an obstacle, it flies or glides a short distance, showing a crescent of white in the extended wing, and large white spots on the ends of the tail feathers.

A Road-runner's mating call in early spring is by no means a passionate outburst of melody. The bird perches in a bush or low tree, and at intervals of about fifteen seconds, lowering the bill slightly and with an effort that distends the whole breast, utters a succession of low notes, each a little lower in pitch and more prolonged than the preceding, *cŏo, cōō cōo cōō-ōō cōō-ōo*. The pitch is very nearly the same as that of the Mourning Dove, but any one familiar with the regular four-syllabled song of the Dove will not confuse the two. When excited the Road-runner utters a rattling *brrr* apparently by clicking the mandibles rapidly together.

The Road-runner is one of the most picturesque elements in Western country. It is characteristic of the dry cactus-covered ranges of the early cattle country, where it even has its own particular myth as a shrewd antagonist of the rattlesnake. In such country it is common, but it also inhabits brushy mesas throughout the drier parts of southern California, and may be seen even in plantations on large estates, but like the cowpuncher, the horned-toad and the rattlesnake it will not persist unless there is some land left too broken for cultivation, where cactus or chaparral still flourishes.

20–24 Bill $1\frac{3}{4}$–2

Ad. — Top of head black (often elevated as a loose crest), speckled and mixed with tawny in front; naked patch of bluish gray back of eye, bordered above with white and ending in a red spot; sometimes concealed if the head feathers are not erected; back, wings and tail dusky (with greenish reflection in strong light); wings and tail streaked with white; wings when spread showing white crescent; outer tail feathers tipped with white; breast tawny streaked with black; belly white. Bill stout with decurved tip; feet light gray (yellowish in front). **Im.** — No metallic reflections; streaked with more white and less tawny.

Dist. — *Cal.* Common R. (rarer northward) in valleys and brush-covered foothills north to Owens Valley and Shasta Co.

Nest, a platform of sticks and grasses in bushes, cactus or low trees. *Eggs*, 4–6, white.

OWLS: *Order Strigiformes*

BARN OWLS: *Family Tytonidæ*

BARN OWL. *Tyto alba pratincola*

If any of our birds could be classified 'as but a wandering voice,' it would be the Barn Owl, whose high-pitched hissing snore sounds suddenly out of the night with startling emphasis. Only the shadowy form is occasionally seen in the gathering dusk, flying with noiseless strokes to the hunting ground. In the daytime Barn Owls may be observed on the rafters of favorite barns, blinking their yellow eyes, or they may be detected hiding in some thick tree or in the crevices of a barranca in the hills. When seen in daylight, the *whitish* or *tawny under parts*, gray and tawny upper parts, the long legs and the characteristic 'monkey face' with white or whitish areas encircling the eyes, easily distinguish them from other owls.

BARN OWL

15–18 Wingspread $3\frac{3}{4}$ ft.

Upper parts tawny, dotted with blackish; *under parts white or tawny*, area around the eye generally white, narrowly bordered with dark brown and including a dark brown center. Bill light colored.

Dist. — *Cal.* Common R. in valleys and foothills, absent from heavily wooded regions.
Ore. R. east and west.
Wash. Casual along southern border and along coast.

Nest, in hollows in trees, in crevices in cliffs, or in lofts of buildings. *Eggs*, usually 5–7, white.

HORNED OWLS, etc.: *Family Strigidæ*

Long-eared Owl. *Asio wilsonianus*

Two tufts of feathers projecting above an old crow's nest are sometimes the reward of a long hunt through endless willow thickets. A close inspection reveals the gray head of an owl blinking at the intruder with half-closed eyes surrounded by a dark tawny disc, and two tufts of feathers rising from near the center of the forehead. If a Long-eared Owl flies, a brown patch shows conspicuously on the buff lining of the wings. Both the Screech Owl and the Horned Owl also have 'ear' tufts. The greater size of the Long-eared Owl (larger than a pigeon) and the tawny facial disc distinguishes it from the Screech Owl; the Long-eared Owl is much more slender than the Horned Owl and lacks the white collar of the latter. The gray tone of the plumage, the situation (generally in thick trees) and the long 'ear' tufts distinguish it from the Short-eared Owl. The ordinary hoot of the Long-eared Owl is low, mellow and long drawn out, and bears a resemblance to the note of the Band-tailed Pigeon. (Grinnell and Storer.) When alarmed about the nest, the adult birds utter cat-like calls.

LONG-EARED OWL

14–16 Wingspread $3\frac{1}{4}$ ft.

Two narrow tufts of feathers from near middle of forehead; area about eye chestnut (bordered with black); under parts tawny, streaked with dark brown and mottled with gray. Bill black.

Dist. — *Cal.* Fairly common R. of extensive willow thickets or groves of aspen, west and north of the deserts.

Ore. S.V. east (Mar.–Dec.), a few probably winter; not common S.V. west; not common M.

Wash. S.V. (Mar.–Dec.) east, a few probably winter; casual M., perhaps occasional R., west.

Nest, usually in a deserted nest of some other bird — crow, magpie, etc. *Eggs*, 3–6, white.

Short-eared Owl. *Asio flammeus*

When one walks in winter over a marsh or low fields where the dried yellow grasses still make coverts for shelter, a large brown bird occasionally springs up from the ground, and flies off on noiseless wings. It flies fairly low with easy strokes of its broad wings, and finally lights again either in the brown grass or on some post or low mound. In the late afternoon the Short-eared Owl is often seen hunting backward and forward watching closely for mice. The ordinary note on the breeding ground is a short sharp *weck*. When hunting, the Short-eared Owl takes slow easy strokes during which the wings describe a wide arc, each stroke carrying the tips of the wings well below the body. At other times a Short-eared Owl soars easily at a considerable height.

SHORT–EARED OWL

The Short-eared Owl may readily be distinguished from a female Marsh Hawk, by its short tail and by the tawny spots toward the outer edges of its wings. The 'ears,' that is the tufts of feathers on the sides of the head, are so short that they cannot be as a rule distinguished unless the bird's head is silhouetted against the sky. There is no other owl that hunts regularly in the daytime by beating low over the ground. The Burrowing Owl stands about all day on points of vantage or takes a short flight when startled, but may readily be distinguished from a Short-eared Owl by its conspicuous legs, which are not concealed by the feathers of the thighs.

14–17 Wingspread 3½ ft.

Upper parts yellowish brown, streaked with black; *wings with buffy patches on the upper surface*, under surface buffy with a black 'wrist' mark; under parts buffy, streaked with dark brown, particularly on the breast; disc light gray, blackish around the eyes; 'ear' tufts very short. Bill dusky. **Im.** — Upper parts dark brown; 'face' blackish; under parts pale buffy, almost unstreaked.

Dist. — *Cal.* Common M. and W.V. to marshy or open country in the lowlands. Common S.V. northeast, occasional elsewhere.
Ore. Common R. east, less common west.
Wash. Common R. both east and west.

Nest, on the ground, of a little dried grass and feathers. *Eggs*, 4–8, dull white.

SPOTTED OWL. *Strix occidentalis* subsp.

A series of deep notes like the barking of a dog issuing from the wildest mountain canyon or from deep forests occasionally reveal the presence of the rare Spotted Owl. No one has given a better account of one chapter in the life of the Spotted Owl than Mr. Donald Dickey. (Condor, Vol. XVI, pp. 193–202.) He found the adult bird, presumably a female, feeding the young in a pot-hole in a steep cliff. The bird was astonishingly tame and gentle, allowing an approach within six feet. The call note was very similar to that of the Eastern Barred Owl, two long notes followed by two shorter ones, *whoo whoo hoo hoo* with 'much of the full-throated explosive effect of a baying hound.' The bird also uttered a 'low musical, indrawn whistled *whee-ee*.' The rounded head without 'ear' tufts, the lack of a yellow iris and the heavy barring across the sides of the breast readily distinguish the Spotted Owl from the Horned Owl.

18–19 Wingspread about 3¾ ft.

Upper parts *brown with numerous white spots;* facial disc yellowish brown, faintly ringed with dark brown; under parts yellowish brown, breast spotted with white, *flanks* with *broad white spots*, giving the effect of barring. Bill dusky, yellow at tip; iris lead-color.

Dist. — Southern Spotted Owl. *Strix o. occidentalis.*
Rather rare R. of remote mountains and dense forest canyons north to Mount Pinos, Ventura Co., and along the edge of the Sierras.
Northern Spotted Owl. *S. o. caurina.*
Rare R. from the coast regions of northern Cal. northward.

Nest, in a crevice of a cliff, or in hollow trees. *Eggs*, 2–3, white.

GREAT GRAY OWL. *Scotiaptex nebulosa nebulosa*

The largest North American Owl, a bird with a wing-expanse of nearly five feet, was known in the Coast States only as a rare winter visitant from Canada, until it was found in 1915 presumably breeding in the Yosemite region. The excited call notes of small birds are often an indication of the presence in the daytime of this or other large owls in thick trees. The size of the Great Gray Owl, its rounded head which lacks 'ear' tufts, and the 'slow flapping of its broad rounded wings' are given by Grinnell and Storer as easy recognition marks. The note is 'a deep reverberating *whoo* uttered at irregular intervals' (Grinnell and Storer).

25–30 Wingspread 4½–5 ft.

Upper parts dark brown, mottled with grayish white; under parts light gray, breast streaked with dark brown, rest of under parts barred with brown; facial disc light gray with faint concentric rings of brown. Bill yellow; iris yellow.

Dist. — Uncommon R. in the Sierras and probably in the mountains of Ore. and Wash.; irregular W.V. in wooded regions from northern Cal. northward.

Nest, in trees, of sticks and moss. *Eggs*, 2–4, white.

Saw-whet Owl. *Cryptoglaux acadica acadica*

If a student should surprise a Saw-whet Owl in the daytime the absence of ear-tufts and the white spots on the wing would distinguish it from the Screech Owl, which is of about the same size. The Saw-whet can be distinguished from the smaller Pygmy Owl, which also has a round head unadorned with ear-tufts, by the lack of a conspicuous tail, which the Pygmy Owl generally holds at an angle with the body. The notes of the Saw-whet are thus described by Dr. Ralph: 'The call is a frequently repeated whistle, sometimes uttered in a high, again in a low key, given in either a slow or a rapid cadence. Generally it is commenced slowly and gradually becomes faster and faster till it ends quite rapidly. This call sounds not unlike the noise made during the operation of filing a saw, and it is easily imitated.'

SAW-WHET OWL

7.50–8 Wingspread $1\frac{1}{2}$ ft.

Ad. — Upper parts *brown, more or less spotted with white;* no 'ear' tufts; facial disc whitish with a blackish area around and in front of the eye, border of the disc dark brown spotted with white; *wing, when spread, crossed by several rows of white spots;* under parts white, striped with brown. Bill black.
Im. — Upper parts unspotted; under parts unstreaked.
Dist. — *Cal.* Irregular R. and W.V. in forested areas.
Ore. R. west of the Cascades, probably also east.
Wash. Fairly common R. in timbered regions.
Nest, in holes in trees. *Eggs,* 3–6, white.

Screech Owl. *Otus asio* subsp.

From live oaks standing black in the moonlight or, farther north, from groves in any open country, one hears at night a succession of tremulous mellow sounds, like the sound of a ball bounding more and more rapidly over a frozen surface, often preceded by a *whorroo.* At other times the Screech Owl utters a short cry like the syllable *kyeek.* During the day the Screech Owl hides in holes in trees or draws out his gray form into an imitation of a dead limb in a dense mass of foliage. The general gray color and the 'ear' tufts distinguish the Screech Owl when seen from any other small owl. Young birds in summer are gray but lack the 'ear' tufts.

SCREECH OWL

8–$9\frac{3}{4}$ Wingspread $1\frac{3}{4}$ ft.

Ad. — *General color light gray,* everywhere finely streaked with black; *two tufts of feathers* about an inch long *on the sides of the head;* wings dusky, barred with buffy spots. Bill dusky on sides, whitish at tip; iris yellow. **Im. in summer.** — Lacks the 'ear' tufts.

Dist. — Sahuaro Screech Owl. *O. a. gilmani.*
Cal. Along the lower Colorado R. and probably in the Imperial Valley.
Southern California Screech Owl. *O. a. quercinus.*
Cal. R. west of the desert and south of Monterey Co.
California Coast Screech Owl. *O. a. bendirei.*
Cal. R. along the humid coast belt of Cal.
Brewster's Screech Owl. *O. a. brewsteri.*
Ore. R. in western Ore.
Kennicott's Screech Owl. *O. a. kennicotti.*
Wash. Fairly common R. west.
Macfarlane's Screech Owl. *O. a. macfarlanei.*
Ore. } R. east.
Wash. }

Flammulated Screech Owl. *O. flammeolus*

The beginner might as well strike the Flammulated Screech Owl from his list of possible acquaintances; the great majority of field ornithologists have never met the bird. It is smaller even than a Pygmy Owl. Its 'ears' are not conspicuous. Notes heard by Grinnell and attributed by him to this species 'consisted of a single mellow "whoot" repeated at regular intervals.'

$6\frac{1}{2}$–7

Upper parts brown; under parts whitish, heavily marked with blackish; 'ear' tufts very short; iris brown. Bill dark.

Dist. — R. in the mountains of southern Cal. and the Sierras. Two records for eastern Wash.

Nest, in holes in trees. *Eggs*, 2–3, white.

Horned Owl. *Bubo virginianus* subsp.

As dusk settles over the valleys, the deep measured hooting of a Horned Owl sounds from a grove of live oaks or from the barrancas in the cliffs, *whōō, hŭ-hōṓ, whōō, whōō,* all the notes on the same pitch. Often there are only four notes instead of five. Occasionally we come upon a bird that has taken refuge for the day in some thick tree, or are guided to his retreat by the excited cries of jays. The size of the Horned Owl, the tufts of feathers rising obliquely from the sides of the head, and the conspicuous white collar readily identify him. In flight the 'ear' tufts are flattened back but the white collar is conspicuous. The Horned Owl may be distinguished from the Long-eared Owl, which also has 'ear' tufts, by its greater bulk; the Long-eared Owl, especially when it is endeavoring to escape observation, is a long slender figure.

About 2 ft. Wingspread 4–5 ft.

Upper parts blackish or dusky, spotted or mottled with white and tawny, the general effect varying in the forms given below; *two tufts of feathers projecting upward and outward from above the eyes;* facial discs gray, encircled with black; under parts light brown, barred on lower breast and belly with dark brown; a *white collar across upper breast.* Bill dusky, lighter toward tip; iris yellow.

HORNED OWL

Dist. — Western Horned Owl. *B. v. pallescens.*
Cal. Common R. of the deserts.
Pacific Horned Owl. *B. v. pacificus.*
Cal. Common R. west of the deserts as far north as Santa Barbara Co.
Coast Horned Owl. *B. v. icelus.*
Cal. Coast region from San Luis Obispo to San Francisco Bay.
Dusky Horned Owl. *B. v. saturatus.*
Cal. *Ore.* *Wash.* } Common R. along the humid coast belt northward.
Pale Horned Owl. *B. v. occidentalis.*
Cal. *Ore.* } R. from northeastern Cal. probably through eastern Ore.
Northwestern Horned Owl. *B. v. lagophonus.*
Wash. Common R. east and probably in the Cascades; M. and W.V. (Aug.–Feb.) west.
Arctic Horned Owl. *B. v. subarcticus.*
Ore. *Wash.* } Casual in winter.

Nest, in hollow trees or cliffs, or in open nests in trees. *Eggs*, 2–4, white.

Snowy Owl. *Nyctea nyctea*

When the hares, lemmings and ptarmigan of the Arctic tundras fail as a food supply, a 'wave' of Snowy Owls moves southward, occasionally reaching northern California. The bird hunts chiefly by day and its snowy plumage, which serves so admirably to hide the bird on snowy wastes, makes it a conspicuous object on bare ground. It is a bird of the open treeless country, following the coast lines, or seeking its prey along lake borders or on the open prairie.

About 2 ft. Wingspread $4\frac{1}{2}$–5 ft.

Ad. — In winter *upper parts white*, more or less waved or flecked with black; *under parts pure white*. Bill black; iris yellow.

Dist. — *Cal.* Rare and irregular W.V. as far south as San Francisco Bay.
Ore., *Wash.* Irregular W.V.

HAWK OWL. *Surnia ulula caparoch*

The Hawk Owl, like the Snowy Owl, is a resident of the Far North but occasionally moves southward in winter across the Canadian border, sometimes in great numbers. 'On the wing [the Hawk Owl] might easily be mistaken for one of the Buteos, as the flight consists of a series of slow wing-beats and a vast deal of circling on motionless wings' (Bowles). It often takes up a position on some stub or post in broad daylight. The *long tail*, long slender figure and hawk-like flight distinguish this owl from any other species.

15 Wingspread $2\frac{3}{4}$ ft.

Upper parts blackish, spotted with white; *tail long*, barred with white or pale gray; facial disc whitish, bordered on sides of head with blackish; dark band across breast; *lower breast and belly* whitish, *closely barred with brown.* Bill yellow at tip.

Dist. — Probably casual M. and irregular W.V. in Wash. both east and west.

BURROWING OWL. *Speotyto cunicularia hypogœa*

As one drives through country where cultivation ends and barren ground or cattle ranges begin, the round head and staring eyes of a small owl are often seen in the entrance to a large burrow in the ground. If the observer stops, the head is withdrawn a little so that only the top is visible. In the breeding season the heads of both male and female often appear side by side and are withdrawn together. Farther out in the plain Burrowing Owls are seen standing on the mounds that surround the mouth of the burrow or on fence posts. Their legs are not hidden by the body feathers but are conspicuous for much of their length. When one approaches, the little owls bob and give a chuckling call. If alarmed, they draw their bodies in and down with the motion that causes a bird standing in his burrow apparently to withdraw into the hole, or they fly a short distance, mounting in the air in a short curve before they descend and making one or two leaps in the air just before they alight. If one camps in 'Billy Owl' country, at dusk and again before dawn and all night when the moon is bright, their mournful calls come from far and near. When near the call is like the syllables *cook-a-róo*, but further off suggests a frightened child calling *pa-pá* in a high anxious voice. Burrowing Owls are occasionally seen in the twilight hovering about twenty feet above the ground, evidently hunting; they are often startled from the roadside in the evening and fly off, visible for a moment in the light of the automobile lamps. The ordinary call consists of two or three notes like the syllables *quēē*, *quick-quick-quick* with a throaty, chuckling quality.

BURROWING OWL

The only other owl that is often seen in the daytime is the Short-eared Owl, whose easy wing-strokes and tawny coloring will distinguish it readily in flight. The Burrowing Owl's feet are prominent; the Short-eared Owl's legs are hidden in feathers.

9–11 Wingspread 2 ft.

Ad. — Upper parts brown, heavily speckled or dotted with white; *white line over eye;* tail short, brown, spotted with white; under parts white, heavily spotted or barred with brown; a white collar (concealed unless bird straightens up). Bill dull yellow; iris greenish yellow; *legs long, conspicuous.* **Im.** — Under parts buff without brown barring.

Dist. — *Cal.* Common R. of barren country or the edges of cultivated fields both east and west.
Ore. Common R. locally, east; not common R. west.
Wash. Common R. on plains east, and more rarely in north Puget Sound region.

Nest, at the end of a burrow, 5–10 ft. long. *Eggs*, 6–11, white.

Pygmy Owl. *Glaucidium gnoma* subsp.

If a band of small birds are protesting about some thick conifer in the mountains, a little Owl no larger than a thrush may at last fly out and light in full view. The *tail* of a Pygmy Owl is a characteristic mark; it is *longer* in proportion to the bird than in any of the other small owls, and when the bird is perched projects backward at an angle with the body (see frontispiece). The flight of a Pygmy Owl is like a Shrike's, 'the little owl closing its wings to pitch downward with a certain amount of whirring and then by rapid strokes regaining its former level' (Dawson). The note of the Pygmy Owl is a soft whistle, repeated either singly or in a rapid succession of staccato notes, suggesting the syllables *kewk, kew, kew, kew;* the note is frequently heard during the day. The absence of ear-tufts distinguishes the Pygmy Owl from the Screech Owl; the blackish streaks on the under parts distinguish it from the Saw-whet.

7–7½ Wingspread 1¼ ft.

Upper parts grayish brown, very lightly spotted with light buff (spots thickest on head); a not conspicuous collar of blackish around back of neck; no 'ear' tufts; *tail conspicuous*, dark brown, barred with white; throat white, collar of dark brown across upper breast; rest of under parts white, streaked with blackish. Bill greenish yellow, tip yellow; iris yellow.

Dist. — California Pygmy Owl. *G. g. californicum.*
Cal. / *Ore.* / *Wash.* } Fairly common R. of the mountains along the coast north to Santa Barbara, along the Sierras and Cascades and in eastern Ore. and Wash.
Coast Pygmy Owl. *G. g. grinnelli.*
Fairly common R. of the humid coast from San Luis Obispo, Cal., northward through Ore. and Wash.
Rocky Mt. Pygmy Owl. *G. g. pinicola.*
A specimen taken on the Panamint Mts.

Nest, in holes in trees. *Eggs*, 3–5, white.

Elf Owl. *Micropallas whitneyi whitneyi*

If one visits a group of giant cactus at nightfall, one begins to hear at dusk the whistled call of the Elf Owl, first from one part of the grove and then, as the birds emerge from their hiding places, from every side, even from the low mesquites and palo verdes between the columns of cactus. The commonest call is a musical *whee, whee, whee, whee*, generally repeated four or five times, but occasionally in a series of ten or twelve notes. At intervals one is startled by a sharp *keer*, at first low, then becoming higher and more emphatic till it suggests a puppy that has been tied up and finally loses all patience. Sometimes a single guttural *wow* is heard, and frequently there is a succession of guttural chattering whines and squeals, apparently when two birds are together. It is possible even at night by lying on the ground to get the figure of the little owl on the low branch of a mesquite silhouetted against the sky, or to see him fly down to the ground. The flight is rapid for an owl. Toward dawn an Elf Owl may be discovered sitting at the opening of its hole, its white eyebrows conspicuous as it turns its head quickly to watch the observer.

5¾–6¼ Wingspread 1¼ ft.

Upper parts brown flecked with buff; *line over eye white; tail barred with white spots;* narrow throat-band white; rest of under parts reddish brown, flecked with white.

Dist. — *Cal.* S.V. in a small stand of giant cactus above Potholes, Imperial Co.

Nest, in deserted woodpecker holes in giant cactus. *Eggs*, usually 3, white.

GOATSUCKERS, etc.: *Order Caprimulgiformes*

NIGHTHAWKS, POORWILLS, etc.: *Family Caprimulgidæ*

POORWILLS: *Subfamily Caprimulginæ*

POORWILL. *Phalænoptilus nuttalli* subsp.

When a traveler in summer has made camp, and is lying on his blankets watching some favorite star, the first faint *poor-wíll* floats across from the opposite hillside. The bird seems like a disembodied spirit, and it is with surprise that we come upon one in the dusk, sitting in the trail or making short leaps into the air in the pursuit of insects. When the bird is near, the cry sounds more like *pol-dúc*, and when very near a third slight note is heard. When startled, the Poorwill utters a sharp *pweek*. Occasionally a Poorwill flutters off from a steep hillside in the daytime, or, flying from the road at night, is caught for an instant in the light from the motor lamps; at such times one catches a glimpse of the white tips of the tail feathers. Poorwills never hawk about in the air and never show the white bars across the wings characteristic of the two Nighthawks.

7–8

General tone of plumage grayish brown with black markings; throat banded with white bordered below by black; under parts blackish brown; outer tail feathers tipped with white.

Dist. — Nuttall Poorwill. *P. n. nuttalli.*
Cal. Fairly common S.V. in eastern Cal.; W.V. to the deserts.
Ore. / *Wash.* } S.V. (May–Aug.) east.
Dusky Poorwill. *P. n. californicus.*
Cal. Common S.V. west of the Sierras except in the humid coast belt; R. south.

Nest, eggs laid on the bare ground. *Eggs*, 2, white.

NIGHTHAWKS: *Subfamily Chordeilinæ*

NIGHTHAWK. *Chordeiles virginianus* subsp.

A long-winged bird with a *white bar across each wing* flies in summer over some bare mountain ridge uttering a high nasal note, *spee-ick, spee-ick*. Suddenly it shoots steeply downward sometimes from a height of two hundred feet and when it has almost reached the ground sweeps upward in a narrow arc, producing just before the upward sweep a loud, booming or rushing sound like the syllable *porrk*. The bird then sails about far overhead for a few moments and then repeats the dive and rushing sound over the same spot, near which a careful search would reveal the female brooding her two eggs on some bare stony spot. Alden Miller has shown that the Nighthawk produces the sound by bending the wings sharply downward at the end of the dive. When hunting, the Nighthawk flies high in the air with easy, graceful flight, often making a quick upward sally during which it 'changes gear' to a more rapid wing-stroke. During migration and after the breeding season, Nighthawks gather in large numbers, hunting in loose companies high over mountain valleys. Most of the Nighthawk's hunting is done in the late afternoon, early evening and just after dawn, but occasionally, particularly on a cloudy day, it hawks about in broad daylight. During the middle of the day, Nighthawks rest on the limbs of trees, logs or fence rails, sitting along, not across the perch. The eggs are laid on bare ledges or even on gravel-covered roofs in large cities.

PACIFIC NIGHTHAWK

A Nighthawk can be distinguished from any other long-winged bird of the air by the white wing-bars. The Pacific and Texas Nighthawks both show the wing-bars and both have an easy buoyant flight with quick turns and sudden sallies. As a rule the two species do not overlap; the Texas Nighthawk is a bird of the lowlands and deserts from the Sacramento Valley southward; the Pacific Nighthawk is found in southern California only in the mountains but reaches the coast in extreme northwestern California (where the Texas Nighthawk is absent) and in Oregon and Washington. As a rule the Pacific Nighthawk flies much higher when feeding; the *spee-ick* note is never made by the Texas Nighthawk. The position of the wing-bar is a good field mark for the practiced eye; in the Pacific Nighthawk it is about halfway from the tip to the bend, in the Texas it is nearer the tip.

9

Ad. ♂. — Entire upper parts black, mottled with gray and marked with buffy brown; outer tail feathers crossed near the tip by a white band; a broad band of white across throat; breast black, speckled with gray; *wings long and narrow crossed by a broad white bar;* tail forked. Bill very small, black; feet flesh-color. **Ad.** ♀. — Throat-band buff, no white bar on tail.

Dist. — Eastern Nighthawk. *C. v. virginianus.*

Wash. The Eastern Nighthawk has been taken about Puget Sound and may be the common form in western Wash.

Pacific Nighthawk. *C. v. hesperis.*

Cal. Common S.V. in high mountains.

Ore. Common S.V. throughout (May–Sept.).

Wash. Common S.V. (May–Sept.) east and perhaps west (see above).

Nest, eggs laid on bare ground, rocks or flat city roof. *Eggs,* 2, grayish white, everywhere spotted with olive, lavender and dark gray.

Texas Nighthawk. *Chordeiles acutipennis texensis*

In the lowlands of California, particularly where there are extensive fields and deserts, at the approach of dusk, the air is gradually occupied by long-winged birds with easy, graceful flight, which show as they pass overhead a conspicuous *white or buffy bar across the under surface of each wing* a short distance from the tip. Where the ground is bare, they glide close to the surface or take short upward flights with more rapid wing-beats; where there are trees, they fly as high as fifty feet from the ground, but never one or two hundred feet up like Pacific Nighthawks. In flight they take three or four quick strokes of their long wings, then sail for an instant with wings held upward at a sharp angle, constantly changing their direction with sudden turns and twists, as they pursue the insects and engulf them in their cavernous mouths. Where the birds breed, an insistent purring sound fills the air, as the twilight deepens, sometimes with such vigor that it sounds like the rhythmic beat of a distant motor-boat. Breeding birds pursue each other with a nasal, mewing note, *wa wa woo woo woo woo-oo-oo,* which is followed by the purring sound; at the same time the wings are set at a downward angle for a few seconds.

It is difficult for a beginner to distinguish the Texas from the Pacific Nighthawk, even though he knows that the white bar is nearer the tip in the former and at about the middle of the wing in the latter. For the most part it is quite safe to assume that any Nighthawk seen in summer in the lowlands of California, especially on the deserts or in the hot interior valleys, is the Texas; if the bird utters the purring sound it is surely this species. A bird in the mountains or any bird that utters the *spee-ick* note high in air or rushes earthward with a boom is the Pacific.

8–9

Ad. ♂. — Entire upper parts brownish gray, finely streaked and speckled with black; outer tail feathers dusky, crossed by buffy bands and near the tip by a broader band of white; *wings long and narrow crossed by a white bar;* a white band across the throat; rest of under parts brownish gray. Bill very small, black. **Ad.** ♀. — *Wing-bars buffy,* white bars across tail lacking.

Dist. — *Cal.* Common S.V. (Apr.–Sept.) in the lowlands north to Owens Valley and Glenn Co.

Nest, eggs laid on the bare ground. *Eggs,* 2, usually white, finely dotted with dark olive and gray.

SWIFTS AND HUMMINGBIRDS: *Order Micropodiiformes*

SWIFTS: *Family Micropodidæ*

Subfamily Chæturinæ

BLACK SWIFT. *Cypseloides niger borealis*

The flight of the Black Swift is amazingly swift; it includes sudden sharp turns, steep downward plunges and hurried upward flights. The long, narrow wings at times 'twinkle' rapidly, or when the bird is sailing, are either held uplifted over the back or curved downward with the tips well below the body. The tail is very slightly forked but in flight it is constantly spread and appears fan-shaped when the bird makes a sudden turn. The Black Swift is apparently even more silent than the Vaux Swift; its only note seems to be a 'high-pitched twitter' (Grinnell and Storer). It nests in such remote regions and in places so difficult of access that it was not until 1901 that the first egg of the species was taken on the sea-cliffs near Santa Cruz. There is no difficulty in distinguishing the Black Swift with its uniform dark under parts from the White-Throated Swift, which has a marked pattern of black and white on the under parts. The beginner may take the much commoner Purple Martin for a Black Swift; the deeply notched tail, never spread like a fan, the habit of perching on stubs, the loud, musical notes and the difference in the sexes should readily identify the Martin. The smaller Vaux Swift might be mistaken for a Black Swift, if there were no other birds to compare in size. The Vaux Swift is smaller than the Violet-green Swallow (apparently about the same size in flight), distinctly smaller than the White-throated Swift; the Black Swift is larger than the latter.

$7–7\frac{1}{2}$

General appearance black, forehead and under sides of wings showing silvery at certain angles (Grinnell and Storer); wings long and narrow, tail broad, slightly forked. Bill black.

Dist. — *Cal.* Rare and local S.V. (May–Sept.) on sea cliffs near Santa Cruz, Cal., and in high mountain cliffs at scattered points; M. chiefly along the coast.
Ore. Only one record, though undoubtedly a regular M.
Wash. S.V. (May–Sept.) principally west.

Nest, in crannies in sea cliffs and in crevices of rocks. *Eggs*, one, white.

VAUX SWIFT. *Chætura vauxi*

In summer over dense forests from northern California to Washington, especially where dead stubs stand high in clearings, small black swallow-like birds circle overhead, or cleave the air with rapid zigzag twists. A close observation of the tail shows that it never displays a forked tip; it either ends in a point like a cigar or is spread like a fan when the bird makes a sudden turn. The throat and breast are light gray, but the rest of the under parts are sooty, never pure white as in all the small forest-haunting swallows. In migration the Vaux Swift generally flies low, straight and swiftly along the valleys, often in cloudy weather, for the most part silently. On the breeding ground pairs of Vaux Swifts pursue each other with a faint *chip-chip-chip*. When one has become well acquainted with the Vaux Swift and has learned to distinguish it by its dark under parts and unforked tail from the Swallows, one notes a marked difference in flight; the Swift takes a number of very rapid strokes, its wings fairly twinkling through the air, and then sails with the long narrow wings curved backward and slightly downward. The absence of the marked black and white pattern on the under parts and the short stubby tail readily distinguish the Vaux from the White-throated Swift; the lesser size alone distinguishes it at a distance from the rare Black Swift.

VAUX SWIFT

$4\frac{1}{2}$

General plumage blackish brown, paler on rump and tail, ashy on throat and breast; wings long and narrow, tail short, not forked, fan-shaped when spread, lighter brown. Bill and feet black.

Dist. — *Cal.* Common M. (Apr.–early May; Sept.). S.V. locally along the coast from Santa Cruz northward.

Ore. / *Wash.* Common M. and S.V. (May–Sept.) in wooded districts both east and west.

Nest, of small twigs, glued to inside of hollow tree, occasionally in chimneys. *Eggs*, 3–5, white.

Subfamily Micropodinæ

White-throated Swift. *Aëronautes melanoleucus*

Out of a clear sky a scattered company of long-winged birds suddenly appear, wheeling and turning with utmost swiftness over a deep canyon, along a cliff or over the marshes of the lowland. As one of them passes for an instant directly overhead, the outline of the long narrow wings, slightly curved, mark it for a Swift, and a glimpse of a *white pattern on the throat and breast* determines the species. White-throated Swifts turn and twist with such rapidity that it is difficult to make out exactly where the white is, but even from above there is white visible on the sides of the rump. In spring and during the breeding season while pursuing each other about the cliffs in which they nest they utter a shrill twitter, suggesting the syllables *tee-dee, dee, dee, dee.*

Violet-green Swallows are often associated with White-throated Swifts in the same rock-walls and might be confused with them. The outline formed by the long narrow wings of the Swift distinguishes them from the Violet-green Swallows, whose wings are rarely set to make the cross-shaped figure characteristic of a Swift when sailing. Moreover, the Swift gives from below a mottled appearance of black and white while the Swallow's under parts are pure white. The Swift's wing-strokes when it is not sailing are more rapid than the Swallow's. The Swift's evolutions in the air, too, are much more varied, as they dash through the air at tremendous speed, now plunging almost directly down from a height, then checking their course and sailing upward, or sailing with wings curved slightly downward.

WHITE-THROATED SWIFT

6½–7

Top of head brownish black, palest on forehead, rest of upper parts apparently black; patch in flanks white, showing even from above; *throat and breast white, line down belly white;* rest of under parts black; tail long, slightly forked. Bill black.

Dist. — *Cal.* Common S.V. locally except on the northwest coast, less common northward; occurs irregularly in winter as far north as Santa Barbara and San Benito Cos.
Ore. No records.
Wash. Rare M. and S.V. (May–July).

Nest, in crevices in cliffs (rarely in buildings), a saucer-like structure of feathers glued to the rock. *Eggs*, 4–5, white.

HUMMINGBIRDS: *Family Trochilidæ*

Black-chinned Hummingbird. *Archilochus alexandri*

Long after the Anna Hummers have startled us with their explosive screech as they dive over a hidden female, we may hear in the gardens of southern California a whirring sound, repeated again and again, and become aware of an atom, dashing back and forth in a wide and relatively shallow arc. Tiring at last, the tiny creature perches on a twig and shows a *black throat* set off sharply from the white under parts. If the light is right, a *shimmering violet band* becomes evident across the lower part of the seeming black area. Often the little suitor begins his performances by buzzing back and forth in short dashes over the female hidden among the leaves, and then in the height of his ardor indulges in the wide sweeps described above.

The male Black-chinned Hummer is readily distinguished from the other Hummers by the small area which shows brilliant color. In the other Hummers the whole throat and often the top of the head blaze out when the light strikes at the right angle. The female can be distinguished from the female Anna, which is generally present wherever the Black-chinned occurs, only by her slightly greater size. A female Black-chinned can hardly be told from a female Costa; the latter, it is true, prefers drier situations, deserts and dry stony wastes, but the two overlap in many parts of their range.

$3\frac{1}{3}$–4

Ad. ♂. — Upper parts bronzy green; *chin black*, a *violet band across the throat below the black chin;* white collar across breast below the violet; belly whitish or dusky, with a dull greenish wash. Bill and feet black. **Ad.** ♀. — Upper parts bronzy or yellowish green; under parts chiefly white; throat obscurely speckled with dusky; outer tail feathers black toward tip, tips white. **Im.** ♂. — Like ♀, but showing traces of black or violet on throat.

Dist. — *Cal.* Common S.V. (Mch.–late July) at lower levels north to San Francisco Bay, to Shasta Co. and Owens L. Casual in winter in the Colorado Desert.
Ore. Probably S.V. east.
Wash. S.V. (May–July) east.

Nest, a cup made of plant down, generally at no great height from the ground and usually near water. *Eggs*, 2, white.

Costa Hummingbird. *Calypte costæ*

In the foothills of southern California the dark green belt of orange orchards is here and there interrupted by wide tongues of stones and gravel poured out by the canyon streams. These stony plains are overgrown by cactus, sumach and occasional junipers, but in May and June are gay with scarlet larkspur, tall white yuccas and other humbler bloom. If one stands for a moment in the midst of this bee paradise, the tiny figure of a Hummingbird shoots past or stops to probe the tall spikes of the white ball-sage. After feeding, the little creature perches perhaps on a dead twig, and, protruding its long needle-like tongue, wipes off the last bit of honey against its slender bill. If it is a male Costa, the *throat* from one angle looks black but in the next moment turns to an exquisite *violet*. Two long narrow sets of feathers of the same color extend back and downward from each side of the throat. In April and May when the birds are mating, the male shoots in a U-shaped arc over the female hidden in some low bush, and flashes this bright-hued gorget back and forth directly over her; during the descent a noise like the hiss of escaping steam is produced.

The Costa Hummer, though characteristic of semi-desert regions, is found as far north as Santa Barbara. In much of its range it shares territory with the Anna and the Black-chinned Hummers. From the male Anna, which also has the divergent feathers extending from the

CALLIOPE HUMMINGBIRD ♂

RUFOUS HUMMINGBIRD ♀ BLACK-CHINNED HUMMINGBIRD ♀

RUFOUS HUMMINGBIRD ♂ BLACK-CHINNED HUMMINGBIRD ♂

ANNA HUMMINGBIRD ♂

ALLEN HUMMINGBIRD ♂ COSTA HUMMINGBIRD ♂

sides of the throat, the male Costa can be distinguished by the violet or amethyst color of the 'ruff,' and its greater extent; the Anna's ruff is red and shorter. The Black-chinned Hummer shows violet below the black, but it is a narrow band only and there is no suggestion of the long side feathers. A female Costa can be told after sufficient practice from a female Anna by the smaller size, but it is impossible to distinguish the female Costa and the female Black-chinned in the field.

$2\frac{3}{4}$–$3\frac{3}{4}$

Ad. ♂. — *Top of head, throat and long narrow 'ruff,' violet purple, or amethyst;* back, rump and central tail feathers bronzy green; wings and outer tail feathers dusky brown; rest of under parts dusky, washed with bronze or yellowish green. Bill and feet black. **Ad.** ♀. — Upper parts bronzy or yellowish green; outer tail feathers black toward tips, tipped with white; throat obscurely speckled with dusky; under parts chiefly white. **Im.** ♂. — Like ♀ but traces of color of ♂ appearing in the throat.

Dist. — Common S.V. (Apr.–July) in southern Cal., north to Santa Barbara and to Owens Valley; casual in winter on the Colorado Desert.

Nest, a cup composed of plant down, or fibers, on the stem of a plant, branch of a bush or low in trees. *Eggs*, 2, white.

Anna Hummingbird. *Calypte anna*

On the Pacific Coast in every garden, no matter how small, a Hummingbird is a familiar sight, probing with a blur of wings and vibrating tail into one flower after another on a stalk, or flying to a dead twig to preen its breast. The male Anna Hummer has a green back but the top of the head and the throat show black one instant, the next flash into crimson. A close view reveals two sets of crimson feathers, from below the eye down and back on the sides of the throat. When Anna Hummingbirds feed, they keep up a little *chick, chick,* which becomes a wild outburst of excited notes when another Hummingbird appears and has to be driven off. After feeding, a bird often perches on an exposed twig or even in the middle of a low tree, turning its head constantly to one side or the other. After the rains, often in January, the male Anna mounts high over the female, who is perched near the ground, and darts down in a narrow arc directly over her. At the bottom of the arc he makes a shrill explosive sound that startles one with its intensity. At other times from a perch he utters a meditative squeaking song, his tiny throat swelling as the sound emerges.

A female very early in the year gathers cobwebs from leaves and twigs, and builds the tiny cup in which her two eggs are laid. The young are fed by the female only, the male as in all hummingbirds taking no interest in the family after the eggs are laid. The process of feeding is at first sight startling; the female sticks her long bill down the young one's open mouth and pumps in the partially digested food.

A trained observer can usually distinguish either a male or a female Anna by its greater size; the male can be readily distinguished by the color of the throat and by its 'ruff.' (See preceding species.)

3.40–4.15

Ad. ♂. — *Top of head, throat and short extension down sides of neck deep rose* (but at certain angles apparently black); back, rump and central tail feathers green; wings and outer tail feathers dusky; under parts dusky, washed with green. Bill and feet black. **Ad. ♀.** — Upper parts and middle tail feathers bronzy green; throat often flecked with rose; rest of under parts dusky gray, washed on the sides with green. **Im. ♂.** — Shows flecks of rose on throat and crown.

Dist. — *Cal.* Common R. at lower levels west of the Sierras, north to San Francisco Bay region and to head of Sacramento Valley; in autumn north to Humboldt Co.

Nest, a cup of plant down decorated with mosses and lichens, in trees or bushes. *Eggs,* 2, white.

The Broad-tailed Hummingbird (*Selasphorus platycercus*) has been found in the mountains of eastern California along the Nevada line, and may occur in extreme eastern Oregon and Washington. The male has a *rose-purple* or *deep rose-pink throat;* the female could hardly be told in the field from a female Rufous Hummer except by the shrill rattling sound characteristic of both sexes in flight.

Rufous Hummingbird. *Selasphorus rufus*

An equable state of mind is evidently not necessary to good digestion among Hummingbirds. A blossoming lemon or orange grove in southern California in early spring is not only a banquet hall for migrating Hummingbirds but a battle ground as well. Hardly has a bird poised before a spray of blossoms before another feathered atom dashes toward the first, and the two are off in a tempest of angry squeaks. The Rufous Hummer, with reddish brown upper parts and coppery red throat, is in the thick of every quarrel; even before we catch sight of his bright colors we hear his high-pitched *bzee.* The male is unmistakable, easily distinguished by the uniform reddish brown of the back; the Allen Hummer, which has a reddish brown tail and under parts, is distinguished by the greenish back; the female is undistinguishable in the field from the female Allen.

The Rufous Hummer is only a migrant in California; in western Washington and Oregon it is the common breeding Hummer, guarding its chosen nesting site by driving at any feathered intruder with a fearless disregard of size. The male in the breeding season dashes from a height of fifty or sixty feet downward and then up again, emitting a shrill note as he reaches the bottom of the arc.

3.25–3.90

Ad. ♂. — *Upper parts bright reddish brown,* with a greenish tinge on the top of the head and often some greenish feathers in the back; *throat bright coppery red;* band below throat white; rest of under parts reddish brown. Bill and feet black. **Ad. ♀ and Im.** — Upper parts reddish brown, with bronzy green back; tail with outer feathers black and white toward the tip, rufous at the base; throat dusky, occasionally with a bit of red; belly whitish; flanks tinged with reddish brown.

Dist. — *Cal.* Common M. west of the deserts, in the spring in the valleys and foothills west of the Sierras (late Feb.–early May), returning chiefly along the mountains (late June–Aug.).

Ore. Common M., in spring west and in summer east, and common S.V. west (Mar.–Oct.).
Wash. Abundant S.V. west (Mar.–Oct.); less common on east slopes of the Cascades and still scarcer east.

Nest, a cup of plant down, decorated with lichens, moss, etc., in low plants, bushes or trees up to 40 ft. *Eggs*, 2, white.

Allen Hummingbird. *Selasphorus alleni*

A garden in central California in midsummer is a continual battleground of Allen Hummers. From dawn to dusk their excited squeaks and angry little buzzings sound from their favorite flowering shrubs or vines, as the hot-tempered little creatures pursue each other in rapid flight with reddish tails wide-spread. Both the male and female Allen Hummer are easily identified by the *reddish brown tail*, except in the early spring when the closely allied Rufous Hummer is also present. The female of the two species cannot be distinguished in the field, but the male Allen shows a *distinctly greenish back*. Both species utter in flight a sharp *bzee*, distinct from the notes of other Hummers.

3.25–3.40

Ad. ♂. — Top of head and *back metallic green;* throat bright red; *tail reddish brown;* rest of under parts, except whitish breast, reddish brown. Bill and feet black. **Ad.** ♀. — Upper parts metallic green; tail chiefly rufous tipped with black and white; throat spotted with dusky; belly whitish; sides reddish brown.

Dist. — *Cal.* Common S.V. (Feb.–Sept.) along the coast from northern Ventura Co. northward; M. farther inland. Winters on some of the Channel Is.

Nest, a cup of plant down, decorated with moss or lichens, usually low. *Eggs*, 2, white.

Calliope Hummingbird. *Stellula calliope*

The flowering shrubs and vines about dwellings attract nearly all the different hummingbirds of the coast. One species, however, still keeps to the natural gardens on mountain slopes, where Indian paint-brush, mountain heather and columbine splotch the springy slopes with red, or wild currant forms extensive thickets. Here the little Calliope Hummer, the smallest and most delicately adorned of them all, flashes the lavender streaks on its gorget as it chases off some rival or pursues a female. The individual feathers of its throat are long and lance-like, contrasting with a whitish background; when the bird is excited, they stand out like colored rays. During courtship the male Calliope mounts a short distance upward and then dives down in a very narrow U-shaped arc, making so slight a sound at the bottom of the arc that it can be heard only a short distance off.

The color and shape of the separate feathers of the gorget distinguish the male Calliope from any other Hummingbird. The female Calliope is very like the female Rufous, which also occurs in the high mountains in July and August, and can only be distinguished in the field by her small size, and by the smaller amount of reddish brown on the tail.

$2\frac{3}{4}$–$3\frac{1}{2}$

Ad. ♂. — Top of head and back golden green; throat whitish, thickly speckled with lilac, *lance-shaped feathers at sides of throat with lilac tips;* under parts white; flanks marked with dusky green. Bill black above, flesh-colored below. **Ad.** ♀ **and Im.** — Head and back bronzy green; throat white, thickly speckled with dusky; under parts tinged, especially on the flanks, with pale reddish brown; tail greenish, reddish brown at base, crossed with black and tipped with white.

Dist. — *Cal.*, *Ore.*, *Wash.* Common S.V. (May–Aug.) in the higher mountains throughout; M. along the slopes and occasionally to the coast.

Nest, of plant down, decorated with lichens, on twig under a limb, from 9 to 75 ft. up. *Eggs*, 2, white.

KINGFISHERS, etc.: *Order Coraciiformes*

KINGFISHERS: *Family Alcedinidæ*

WESTERN BELTED KINGFISHER. *Ceryle alcyon* [*caurina*]

The rattling cry of the Kingfisher as it flies off a limb overhanging some pool, or as its blue and white form comes winging down a mountain stream is familiar to all fishermen. Along the coast its bushy head, long

BELTED KINGFISHER

bill and white breast is a characteristic sight, on a pile in the harbor or on the railing of a boat house. When perched it stretches up its head and neck, and jerks its short tail nervously. When it is unable to fish from a perch above the water, it hovers directly over the water, its wings vibrating in rapid strokes, its tail held out behind and only slightly downward. In flight it often 'changes gear,' alternating slower wing-beats with a few more rapid strokes, and always it seems to be pushing its bill ahead of its body, its long stout bill and heavy head giving it an appearance of being overbalanced in front.

11–14½ Bill 2

Ad. ♂. — Upper parts blue; head with a loose crest, raised when the bird perches; white spot in front of eye; a *white collar encircling the neck;* a *white area in the* black of the *extended wing;* outer tail feathers black, narrowly barred with white; *band of blue across breast;* flanks washed with blue; rest of under parts white. Bill long, stout black (yellowish at base below); feet black. **Ad.** ♀. — Similar, but an *additional chestnut band* across belly, and chestnut along flanks. **Im.** ♂. — Blue collar and flanks mixed with chestnut.

Dist. — *Cal.*, *Ore.* } Common S.V. (Mar.–Nov.) throughout, less common in winter.
Wash. S.V. (Mar.–Nov.) east, casual in winter; R. west, less common in winter.

Nest, in a burrow, 6–8 ft. long, in a perpendicular bank of sand or clay, near water. *Eggs*, 5–7, white.

WOODPECKERS: *Order Piciformes*

WOODPECKERS: *Family Picidæ*

HAIRY WOODPECKER { CABANIS / HARRIS, etc. } *Dryobates villosus* subsp.

A loud metallic *chink* in heavy timber or a cry suggesting the rattle of the Kingfisher calls our attention to a medium-sized Woodpecker digging into the trunk of a tree or hitching up or around the trunk. It is an almost exact reproduction of the smaller Downy Woodpecker (see next species) with a broad white area down the middle of the back, black wings spotted with white and black and white markings on the side of the head. The only distinction in plumage is in the outer tail feathers, and is visible only if the bird allows a near approach; they are pure white in the Hairy, slightly barred with black in the Downy species. The Hairy's bill is distinctly longer and stouter. The *chink* notes are very similar in pitch but are heavier in the larger bird. The longer call is distinctive; in the larger bird it stays on the same pitch; in the smaller bird it goes down the scale toward the end like a whinny. The Hairy Woodpeckers all share the same habits, digging for larvæ, or flaking off layers of bark from decaying trees, excavating deep nesting cavities and drumming on resonant wood in the mating season.

9–10 Bill 1¼

Similar to Downy Woodpecker but outer tail feathers white.

Dist. — Cabanis Woodpecker. *D. v. hyloscopus.*
Cal. R. north to the central Sierras and Mendocino Co., chiefly on the lower slopes of the mountains, in winter more widely distributed.

Southwestern Hairy Woodpecker. *D. v. leucothorectis.*

Cal. White and Panamint Mts.

Harris Woodpecker. *D. v. harrisi.*

Under parts smoky.

Cal. Common R. in northwestern Cal.

Ore. }
Wash. } R. west of the Cascades and on east slope.

Sierra Woodpecker. *D. v. orius.*

Cal. R. in northeastern Cal.

Ore. R. in southeastern Ore. and along the Cascades, wandering in winter.

Wash. Fairly common R. in the southern Cascades north to Mt. Rainier and Lake Chelan.

Rocky Mountain Hairy Woodpecker. *D. v. monticola.*

Ore. R. in northeastern Ore.

Wash. R. in northern Cascades and in eastern Wash.

Nest, in holes in trees. *Eggs,* 3–5, white.

HARRIS WOODPECKER — WILLOW WOODPECKER

Downy Woodpecker. *Dryobates pubescens* subsp.

A sharp metallic *chink* from a willow thicket along a stream or stream bed, or from some oak or walnut in the adjacent lowland, attracts our attention to a small bird hitching up the trunk or limb, stopping frequently to hammer or dig out some grub from the wood. The head is black, often with a scarlet patch on the nape, the wings are black barred with white, but a broad line down the *middle of the back is pure white.* When the bird flies it pitches through the air in long undulations. Besides the sharp *chink* it often utters a series of rapidly descending notes suggesting in form the whinny of a horse. In spring the Downy Woodpecker finds some dry resonant stub, on which it raps out with surprisingly rapid strokes a long roll, apparently its mating call.

There are two birds from which the Downy Woodpecker must be carefully distinguished, the Hairy Woodpecker and the Nuttall Woodpecker. The white outer tail feathers in the Downy are barred with black and are pure white in the Hairy. The Downy is smaller, has a distinctly shorter bill and a lighter call note; moreover, the long call of the Downy descends in pitch toward the end, while that of the Hairy does not. The Downy is found in more open, deciduous timber; only in winter are the two species likely to occur together. The Downy is about the same size as the Nuttall and often in California frequents the same groves, but a back view at once distinguishes one bird from the other. The Downy's back has a white stripe down the middle, the Nuttall's is barred completely across. The single *chink* of the Downy is less hoarse and shorter than the *prrp* of the Nuttall; its 'whinny' descends in pitch and the Nuttall's long call does not.

$6\frac{1}{4}$–7 Bill $\frac{3}{4}$

Ad. ♂. — Upper parts black and white; a white bar from above the eye back along side of head, and one from below eye to back of neck; nape scarlet; *middle of back white,* showing when wings are closed; wings black, more or less spotted with white; inner tail feathers black, outer tail feathers white, inconspicuously barred with black; under parts white or smoky gray. Bill black; feet black. **Ad. and Im.** ♀. — Lack the scarlet nape. **Im.** ♂. — Scarlet extending well over the crown.

Dist. — Willow Woodpecker. *D. p. turati.*

Cal. Common R. chiefly in or near willow growth west.

Gairdner Woodpecker. *D. p. gairdneri.*

Wings wholly black or only slightly spotted with white; under parts smoky gray or brownish.

Cal. Fairly common R. in the extreme northern end of the humid coast belt.

Ore. / *Wash.* Fairly common in deciduous forests west.

Batchelder Woodpecker. *D. p. homorus.*

Cal. R. in the Warner Mts., Modoc Co.

Ore. / *Wash.* R. in deciduous timber east.

Northern Downy Woodpecker. *D. p. nelsoni.*

Wash. One record.

Nest, in holes in trees, ten to twenty-five ft. up. *Eggs,* 4–7, white.

Cactus Woodpecker. *Dryobates scalaris cactophilus*

In the mesquite thickets south of Palm Springs, in the gnarled tree yuccas of the Mohave Desert, and along the willow-bordered ditches of

Imperial County, a noisy little woodpecker suggests the Nuttall in its coloration and the Downy in its notes. Fortunately the desert in which the Cactus Woodpecker delights is a barrier to both the latter species so that there is hardly ever any possibility of confusion; from the San Gorgonio and Cajon Passes south and east any small woodpecker with black and white barred back is the Cactus. The common notes are a single high-pitched *tschik* or a longer rattling call with a slight fall toward the end. It often calls as it flies, and like the other woodpeckers drums in spring on dry limbs.

7–7¾

Ad. ♂. — Forehead black speckled with white, top and hind head red (more or less speckled with gray and black); sides of head white with black stripe from bill under eye joining another black stripe back from eye; *back and wings black barred and spotted with white;* outer tail feathers white barred with black, the rest black; under parts dirty white or tinged with smoky-brown. Bill dark gray; feet black. **Ad.** ♀. — Lacks red on head.

Dist. — *Cal.* Common R. in the southeastern deserts.

Nest, in holes in trees, or in cactus and tree yuccas. *Eggs,* 4–5, white.

Nuttall Woodpecker. *Dryobates nuttalli*

One cannot remain long near a grove of live oaks in the foothills of California without hearing from some tree a hoarse ringing call *prrip,*

NUTTALL WOODPECKER

often lengthened to a rattling *prrrrrrt.* It has the exclamatory quality of the Hairy Woodpecker's, but is less clear and metallic, with more burr. A moment later a medium-sized bird will launch from near the top of the tree and fly with deep undulations to some neighboring grove, often repeating its call as it flies. If the observer follows and finds the Nuttall Woodpecker at work, hitching up the dead limbs and hammering into them, he will note that the *back is barred with black and white* and lacks the broad stripe of white down the back which characterizes the Downy Woodpeckers. It is not unusual to find both the Willow and the Nuttall foraging at the same time in orchards or groves between the dry foothills or canyon slopes and the willow thickets, but neither often invades the characteristic domain of the other. It would be very difficult to distinguish the Nuttall from the Cactus Woodpecker, if the two were found together. Fortunately their ranges do not overlap. Like the other woodpeckers the Nuttall, particularly in spring, drums on resonant timber or telephone poles; it also gives at that season a rapid, squealing *quee quee quee quee.*

7

Ad. ♂. — Top of head black, back of head red; white stripe over and behind eye, and one from base of bill, separating two black lines; *back and wings black narrowly barred with white;* under side of outer tail feathers white, barred with black; under parts white or dingy white, barred on sides with black. Bill and feet dark brown. **Ad.** ♀. — Similar but no red on nape.

Dist. — *Cal.* Common R. of the foothills west of the Sierras except in the humid coast belt.

Nest, a hole in a tree. *Eggs*, 4–5, white.

White-headed Woodpecker. *Xenopicus albolarvatus* subsp.

A black woodpecker with a *white head* squealing shrilly from a low dead stub or hitching up a forest pine is so easily recognized that it is a relief to a bird student swamped by new and puzzling birds. When the bird flies, a *large patch of white in the wing* is conspicuous; when it is perched, the white shows as a narrow stripe on the bend of the wing. The White-headed Woodpecker often nests in the butts that are left standing when large trees have been broken off near the ground. It is not shy and may be easily observed flying to and fro from its nest opening, or clinging to the side of the trunk protesting shrilly with a single high-pitched *wick* or a shrill rattling cry similar to that of the Hairy Woodpecker. It drums on resonant wood like so many of its family.

$9–9\frac{1}{3}$

Ad. ♂. — *Top of head, throat and upper breast white;* narrow red patch on nape of neck; rest of plumage black except a *white patch in the wing.* Bill and feet blackish gray. **Ad.** ♀. — Without red on nape.

Dist. — Southern White-headed Woodpecker. *X. a. gravirostris.*
Common R. from the Cuyamaca Mts. to the San Gabriel Mts.
Northern White-headed Woodpecker. *X. a. albolarvatus.*
Cal. Common R. throughout the higher mountains from northern Ventura Co. north.
Ore. Not common R.
Wash. Not common R. east.

Nest, in holes in dead stubs, often near the ground. *Eggs*, 3–5, white.

Arctic Three-toed Woodpecker. *Picoides arcticus*

A medium-sized woodpecker with a solid black back is occasionally seen in deep coniferous forests of high mountain ranges from the Sierras northward, particularly in burnt-over areas. The male is at once distinguished from any other woodpecker by the golden yellow crown-patch, the female by the uniform black of the back. In the breeding season the Arctic Three-toed Woodpecker makes a very loud rolling sound by drumming on dry limbs and when concerned about the nest a shrill *kick-er-uck-a-kick*. The ordinary call is *tschick* or *tschuck*.

$9\frac{1}{2}$–10

Ad. ♂. — *Crown golden yellow;* white line below eye, and a black line on each side of throat; *back uniform black;* wings barred with small white spots; outer tail feathers white; under parts chiefly white, flanks barred with black. Bill and feet dark gray. **Ad.** ♀. — Lacks yellow crown-patch.

Dist. — *Cal.* *Ore.* *Wash.* } Not uncommon R. on the higher mountains from Calaveras Co., Cal., to the Canadian border, chiefly east.

Nest, holes in stumps or stubs, usually not above 8 ft. *Eggs*, usually 4, white.

American Three-toed Woodpecker. *Picoides americanus* subsp.

The American Three-toed Woodpecker may be distinguished from the preceding species by a narrow 'ladder' of black and white bars down the back. It is restricted in the Coast States to deep coniferous woods along the northern border. Brooks describes it as a 'usually silent bird, its tapping being usually the only sign of its presence.' The same writer speaks of its cry as 'a sharp cluck, without the insistent ring of its allies of the Dryobates group.'

$9\frac{1}{2}$

Ad. ♂. — Small crown-patch of golden yellow; back of head black separated from black side of head by narrow white line back from eye; a *narrow 'ladder' of black and white bars down middle of back*, wings barred with rows of white spots; tail black in center, outer feathers white; throat and middle of belly white; rest of under parts white barred with black. Bill lead-color, feet blackish. **Ad.** ♀. — Forehead speckled black and white, no yellow.

Dist. — Alaska Three-toed Woodpecker. *P. a. fasciatus.*
Ore. Wallowa Mts. (Subspecies undetermined).
Wash. Probably R. in high mountains.
Alpine Three-toed Woodpecker. *P. a. dorsalis.*
Wash. One taken in the Blue Mts., breeding.

Nest, in holes in trees. *Eggs*, usually 4, white.

Red-naped Sapsucker. *Sphyrapicus varius nuchalis*

Rings of small holes punctured in living trees are evidence that a Sapsucker has been drilling for sap, inner bark and the insects which are attracted by the sweet sap. In eastern Washington and Oregon and in northeastern California the bird which is found quietly clinging to the girdled trees shows a *black area between the red throat and the yellowish belly,* and a *broad black area on the nape.* These black areas and the white stripes on the side of the head distinguish the Red-naped from the Red-breasted Sapsucker. Both species show a broad white stripe along the bend of the wing, and utter a squealing cry, not loud and sharp like those of the other small Woodpeckers.

RED-NAPED SAPSUCKER

$8–8\frac{3}{4}$

Ad. ♂. — *Top of head crimson bordered all around by black;* narrow line of crimson across nape; back, wings and tail speckled with black and white; *conspicuous white stripe along bend of wing;* tail chiefly white through the middle; white line from base of bill bordering the throat; throat crimson; *breast black;* rest of under parts yellowish, streaked with black on the sides. Bill black; feet dark gray. **Ad.** ♀. — Less crimson on throat; black chest-patch duller. **Im.** — Black on breast wanting or obscure.

Dist. — *Cal.* S.V. in the Warner Mts., Modoc Co.; W.V. along the lower Colorado, irregularly west.

Ore. / *Wash.* } S.V. (Apr.–Sept.) east.

Nest, holes in trees, often in a live aspen. *Eggs,* 4–5, white.

RED-BREASTED SAPSUCKER. *Sphyrapicus ruber* subsp.

The incoming tide washes away the footprints of sandpipers and gulls on the beach, and the next wind covers with sand the tracks of Roadrunners in the desert, but the Sapsucker leaves on the trunks of trees a mark which lasts for years. Rows of holes circling the trunk an inch or so apart show where the bird has cut little wells to feed on either the sap or the inner layer of bark. When a Sapsucker is girdling a tree, his bill makes only a faint sound in the live wood, so that our first indication of the bird's presence is often a view of its *red head and breast* as it flies off. A *white stripe along the bend of the wing* is conspicuous both in flight and when the bird is perched. In the breeding season the Sapsucker drums with a definite beat which is characteristic, *trrup, tut-u-rut, tut tut.* The ordinary cry is a nasal squeal, *chée-arr*, somewhat suggesting the note of a Red-bellied Hawk. In California the Red-breasted Sapsucker breeds only in the mountains, nesting either in evergreen trees or in the poplars along streams. In winter it descends to the lowlands, drilling in pepper trees, walnut and apple orchards. In Oregon and Washington it occurs throughout the evergreen belt. The unbroken red of head, neck and breast, showing no black or white on the sides of the head or breast distinguish the Red-breasted from the Red-naped Sapsucker.

RED-BREASTED SAPSUCKER

$8\frac{1}{2}$–$9\frac{1}{4}$

Ad. — *Head, neck and breast crimson;* back and wings black, spotted with white; *stripe along bend of wing white;* rump whitish; tail white down the middle; belly yellowish. Bill dark gray; feet gray. **Im.** — Crimson dull and mottled with gray.

Dist. — Sierra Red-breasted Sapsucker. *S. r. ruber.*

Cal. Common S.V. in the higher mountains; in winter irregularly common in the lowlands.

Ore. R. in southern Cascades.

Northern Red-breasted Sapsucker. *S. r. notkensis.*

Cal. Common W.V. along the humid coast belt.
Ore. R. west.
Wash. S.V. west, occasional in winter.

Nest, in holes often in aspens. *Eggs*, 5–6, white.

WILLIAMSON SAPSUCKER. *Sphyrapicus thyroideus*

In nearly all woodpeckers the sexes are alike except that the females lack the red on the head or show less of that color. In the Williamson Sapsucker, however, the female looks so unlike the male that she was for some time considered a different species. The male is a striking bird; when flying the chief effect is that of a *black bird* with *white rump* and *white in the wings*. When a male is perched facing the observer, a small amount of red in the throat and the yellow belly are evident. Females and

WILLIAMSON SAPSUCKER (♂ and ♀)

young are brown with a conspicuous white area on the lower back. The Williamson Sapsucker is found only in coniferous forests in the higher portions of the mountains. It bores rings of holes around the trunks of trees, resorting commonly to pines, either for sap, inner bark or insects. Its common cry is a nasal *whée-yer* or *wháy-yer*. When it drums, the taps have a definite rhythm, like that of the preceding species, a long note followed by three or four shorter ones.

$9–9\frac{3}{4}$

Ad. ♂. — *Top of head, back and tail glossy black;* narrow white stripes from eye backward, and from bill under eye; *wings with large white patch; rump white;* chin red; belly yellow. Bill and feet dark gray. **Ad.** ♀. — *Head and throat brown; back,* wings and sides *barred with black and brownish white; rump white;* band of black across breast; belly yellow.

Dist. — *Cal.* Common R. of the higher mountains; in winter to lower levels.

Ore. R. in the Cascades, wandering to lower levels after breeding.

Wash. S.V. (May–Sept.) in high mountains east.

Nest, in holes in stubs. *Eggs,* 3–7, white.

Western Pileated Woodpecker. *Phlœotomus pileatus picinus*

In or near heavy timber from the Yosemite northward a bird as black as a crow but somewhat smaller flies with slow wing-strokes and steady flight across an opening. As it flies it shows a *large white patch* on the *under side of the wing.* When the Pileated Woodpecker lights, it shows a

PILEATED WOODPECKER

bright red head with a *pointed tuft of red* extending back from the top of the head and a white stripe down the side of the neck. When it clings to the trunk of a tree, the long head and slender neck are held back to give room for the powerful strokes of the heavy bill, which open large mortise-shaped holes in the trunk and pile up chips and flakes at the base of the tree. The sound of its strokes from the depths of the forest suggest a lumberman giving loud blows with a mallet. The Pileated Woodpecker frequently works over fallen logs and in the fall even swings on slender twigs to feed on the ripe berries of the dogwood (Grinnell and Storer).

The commonest call of the Pileated Woodpecker is a far-reaching *whĭ whĭ whĭ* which suggests the *wick wick* note of the Flicker, but the notes are not so sharp and the series is generally not so prolonged. This call is occasionally given on the wing. Other notes are *kak, kak, kak,* and when two birds are together a low *kyuck kyuck.*

17–18 Wingspread $2\frac{1}{3}$ ft.

Ad. ♂. — General color black; *whole top of head and pointed crest flaming red;* narrow white line above eye, another below eye and down side of neck and breast; red stripe back from base of lower mandible; *large white patch on under side of the wing,* lesser area of white above. Bill and feet lead-gray. **Ad.** ♀. — Similar, but crest shorter and fore part of head blackish brown; forehead and stripe from lower mandible brownish black. **Im.** — Crest salmon.

Dist. — *Cal.* Not uncommon R. in heavy timber from the central Sierras northward and northwest.

Ore. / *Wash.* Common R. in heavy timber.

Nest, in holes in trees, usually at a considerable height. *Eggs,* 3–5, white.

California Woodpecker. *Melanerpes formicivorus bairdi*

The California Woodpecker is a noisy, conspicuous bird of the oaks, travelling back and forth among the trees, or to the telephone poles if near a highway. When a bird lights on a pole or limb already occupied,

CALIFORNIA WOODPECKER

there is always mild excitement, fluttering of the wings, bowing and scraping, and always a lively interchange of harsh calls, like the syllables *chák-a, chák-a, chák-a chak,* dying off at the end. The California

Woodpecker's *white rump* and the *broad white patches* in the *black wings* are easy recognition marks when the bird is flying away; the yellowish white throat bordered below by black is conspicuous as the bird flies toward an observer; the *white forehead* and the *crimson nape*, and the black streaks forming a band across the breast are easily seen when the bird is perched. Acorns and nuts are taken from the trees to a post and opened; at other times the birds store enormous quantities of acorns in the trunks of trees or in poles, driving the tip of the acorn into a small hole. The California Woodpecker at times makes sallies from its perch and then dives back, after capturing some winged insect. The bird has the undulating characteristic flight of its tribe, but no other woodpecker in the lowland country has white patches in the middle of the wings.

$9\frac{1}{2}$

Ad. ♂. — *Forehead white* or yellowish, *crown red*, back and wings glossy black, *wings with large white patches; rump white;* tail black; chin black; throat and sides of head white or yellowish; breast crossed by a black band, from which black streaks run down; belly white. Bill black; iris generally white; feet dark gray. **Ad.** ♀. — Similar but red crown bordered in front by black band.

Dist. — *Cal.* Common R. of oak woods, throughout, up into the yellow pine belt in the mountains.
Ore. Locally R. in southern Ore.

Nest, in holes in trees and telephone posts. *Eggs*, 4–6, white.

Lewis Woodpecker. *Asyndesmus lewisi*

On first seeing a Lewis Woodpecker, one thinks rather of a small crow than a woodpecker; the *broad black wings* are almost continually flapped and the bird's flight is steady and easy. When the bird sails up to a tall dead stub and lights against the trunk, it is easy to recognize it as a woodpecker, but it often lights on the top of a bare limb or even, when acorn-hunting, among the upper foliage of a live oak. The Lewis Woodpecker is a skillful flycatcher, sallying out in any direction on set wings, turning and sailing back to its stub without a single stroke. After alighting it frequently bobs its head. It is particularly fond of fruit, coming into cherry and almond orchards.

The general appearance of the Lewis Woodpecker at a distance is black, but a near view shows a *gray collar* across the back of the neck and the *coarse red feathers* of the under parts. It is a great wanderer, appearing almost anywhere in the lowlands after the breeding season, especially where acorns are abundant. When it breeds in forested regions, it prefers rather open country, clearings and burns; it is common in open valleys in hilly country, using the fence posts and telephone poles as perches. For a great part of the year the Lewis Woodpecker is a silent bird, uttering not even a call note, but in the mating season it utters a harsh *chirrr* and a high-pitched squealing *chee-up*, repeated at rather long intervals. Adult birds utter near the nest a series of sharp metallic cries like the syllable *ick, ick, ick*, which when rapidly repeated become a rattle. The young in the nest utter the usual hissing sound of young woodpeckers.

$10\frac{1}{2}$–$11\frac{1}{2}$ Wingspread $1\frac{3}{4}$ ft.

Ad. — Upper parts black (greenish in strong light); a *gray collar across the nape;* forehead and sides of head dark red; upper and under surface of wings black; upper breast gray, passing into *rose, brightest on belly,* feathers of under parts coarse and wiry. Bill blackish; feet gray. **Im.** — Lack the gray collar or have it less developed; less rose below.

LEWIS WOODPECKER

Dist. — *Cal.* R., locally in central Cal., and commonly along both slopes of the Sierras from Kern Co. north; scatters widely in winter.

Ore., *Wash.* Common R. in open timbered country throughout; scatters widely but irregularly in winter.

Nest, in holes high or low. *Eggs*, 6–8, white.

GILA WOODPECKER. *Centurus uropygialis*

In the willows and cottonwoods along the Colorado River bottoms, a high-pitched nasal squeal calls attention to a woodpecker with brown head and neck, and *back narrowly barred with white.* When the Gila Woodpecker flies from one cottonwood to the next with undulating flight, *two whitish patches* show each time it opens its wings. It is an active as well as noisy bird, calling as it flies, hammering on dead stubs and jerking its head when perched. Besides its ordinary high-pitched squeal, the Gila Woodpecker has an excited trill, uttered when a bird welcomes

GILA WOODPECKER (♂)

its mate, and a harsh low *churr churr*. Where the country has been brought under cultivation, it has adapted itself to the presence of man, frequenting the cottonwoods about the ranches and persistently visiting the fig trees and date palms when the fruit is ripening.

8–10

Ad. ♂. — Head grayish brown; crown red, bordered in front by pale buff; *back and rump narrowly barred with black and white; white patch on outspread wing;* tail black, middle and outer feathers barred with white; under parts grayish brown. Bill blackish; feet light gray. **Ad.** ♀. — Similar but without red crown.

Dist. — *Cal.* Common R. along the lower Colorado.

Nest, in holes in trees or giant cactus. *Eggs,* 3–5, white.

The Boreal Flicker (*Colaptes auratus borealis*) has a *red band across the nape, yellow shafts* and *under sides of wing and tail feathers* and lacks the red stripe on the side of the head. Otherwise in color, habits and notes it resembles the following species.

Dist. — Casual or accidental as far south as Los Angeles Co., Cal., occurring more frequently northward.

Flickers are not infrequently seen with more or less yellow on the under sides of wings and tail, but with other characters of the Red-shafted Flicker. These may be hybrids between the Boreal and Red-shafted Flickers or aberrant individuals of the latter species.

Red-shafted Flicker. *Colaptes cafer* subsp.

Wherever there are trees either in natural groves on hillsides or along streams or in orchards or windbreaks, the brown figures of Flickers flying to and fro constantly cross the sky. Even when no color or markings are distinguishable, a trained observer can identify them at once by

RED-SHAFTED FLICKER

the undulating flight and the contrast of the narrow head and neck with the broad wings. If the light is favorable and the colors show, the flash of *red* as the wings open and close, and the *white rump* are unfailing recognition marks. When a Flicker alights, it generally bobs the head vigorously. On the ground, where they spend much time probing for ants, Flickers hop ungracefully but energetically, or stand with head erect, watchful. The back view is then all brown but from in front the *black crescent* is conspicuous *against the gray breast.* When they alight in trees, they either cling against the main trunk or large limbs, or perch in the topmost twigs of dead limbs. In the mating season when several birds are together, the male spreads his wings and tail, and bobs and turns to display them. At this time their notes resemble the syllables *yuck-a, yuck-a.* When startled a Flicker gives a curious *whurroo* as it flies off. The ordinary call is a loud *tí-err*. The mating call, heard occasionally even in the fall, is a vigorous, resounding *wick-wick-wick-wick*, often long continued. As soon as the winter rains have freshened the dry fields, or in the North after the first mild days of spring, this cry rings from all the groves.

$12\frac{3}{4}$–14

Ad. ♂. — Head brownish (cinnamon-brown on forehead); back and wings brown barred with black; *rump white;* tail black; stripe down side of head red; under parts whitish; *black crescent across breast;* belly marked with round black spots; *under sides and shafts of wings and tail red.* Bill blackish; feet dark gray. **Ad.** ♀. — Similar to male but stripe on sides of head faint, brown or buffy instead of red. **Im.** — Lacks the stripe entirely.

Dist. — Red-shafted Flicker. *C. c. collaris.*

Cal. Common R. in open timbered country at lower levels throughout, more widely scattered in winter.

Ore. / *Wash.* } Common R. east.

Northwestern Flicker. *C. c. cafer.*

Cal. Common R. in the northwestern portion of the State.

Ore. / *Wash.* } Common R. west, less common in winter.

Nest, in holes in trees, occasionally in buildings, posts or even banks. *Eggs*, 5–10, white.

Gilded Flicker. *Colaptes chrysoides mearnsi*

The round holes which are evident even in photographs of the giant cactus are made and inhabited by the Gila Woodpecker and by the Gilded Flicker. This cactus, common in southern Arizona, is found only in one locality in California on the Colorado River a few miles above Yuma. Here the Gilded Flicker also makes its westernmost appearance. The appearance of the Gilded Flicker is very much like that of the common Red-shafted Flicker with one very striking difference. The color of the *under sides of wings and tail* is *yellow.* Its notes and habits are practically the same as those of other Flickers. It calls *tí-err* from its perch on a tall cactus, feeds often on the ground and utters the *whurroo, yuck-a* and *wick wick wick* notes of the other Flickers.

11–12

Similar to the Red-shafted Flicker, but smaller, head lighter brown, back grayer, belly whiter and *shafts and under surface of wing and tail feathers yellow.*

Dist. — *Cal.* Fairly common R. in stands of giant cactus, occasionally in cottonwoods, on the Colorado R. above Yuma.

Nest, in holes in giant cactus. *Eggs*, 2–5, white.

PERCHING BIRDS: *Order Passeriformes*

FLYCATCHERS: *Family Tyrannidæ*

Eastern Kingbird. *Tyrannus tyrannus*

In eastern Oregon and Washington on the borders of broad natural meadows or along lowland streams, a Kingbird flies out from a fence or dead branch of a tree, and as it wheels back to its perch, shows a *black tail* entirely and *broadly tipped with white.* Its *under parts* as it sits facing the observer are *pure white,* with none of the yellow that shows on the lower belly of the Western Kingbird. The Eastern Kingbird is notorious for its habit of pursuing crows and hawks, darting at them from above with vicious jabs, often following them for a long distance and returning at last with a shrill *kip-per kipper.* Its mating performance consists in flying upward, and then tumbling suddenly in the air, repeating the manœuvre again and again, all the time uttering its shrill cry. Another common note is a sharp *bzt.* Where the Eastern Kingbird occupies the same general region as the Western Kingbird, the former is more often found near water and the latter in the drier country. The flight of the Kingbird is steady and at about the same level.

EASTERN KINGBIRD

8–9

Ad. — Top of head blackish with a concealed patch of orange-red; back gray; wings brown; *tail black,* tipped *with white; under parts white,* washed with gray across the breast. Bill and feet black. **Im.** — Tip of tail and breast tinged with pale brownish buff.

Dist. — *Cal.* Rare straggler.
Ore. Fairly common S.V. in valleys and meadows from Wasco, Sherman and Grant Cos. eastward.
Wash. Common S.V. east. (May–Sept.), sparingly M. and S.V. west.

Nest, of plant stems, wool, etc., in trees or bushes, with little effort at concealment. *Eggs,* 3–4, white or creamy white, boldly marked with reddish brown or lilac.

Western Kingbird. *Tyrannus verticalis*

If one has camped in a grove where a pair of Western Kingbirds were nesting, or lived in a ranch house under the eucalyptus where their young were being fed, one will agree that it is impossible to represent in human speech the intricate and varied calls of this loquacious bird. At early dawn the twittering musical cries begin, and all through the day when the pair come together or when an intruder of the same species appears there is a flutter of wings and an outburst of shrill notes. The Western Kingbird's commonest note is a sharp *whit,* often elaborated to a liquid *whit ker whit*. At the height of the mating season the male indulges in a flight performance during which repeated jerky flights are accompanied by continual twittering, and before dawn he opens the morning chorus by repeating over and over a call like the syllables *kit, kit, feedle-di-di*. Wire fences, especially where trees are scarce, are a favorite perch. The ashy gray head and sulphur-yellow belly show as the bird faces the observer; if the bird flies off in pursuit of a winged insect the black tail when widely spread shows the white edging of the outer feathers. The bird often flies upward and then after a capture sails gracefully down to the perch.

8–9½

Ad. — Head, neck and back light ashy gray; (male with concealed crown-patch of scarlet); wings brown; *tail black, outer feathers conspicuously edged with white;* breast light gray, throat paler (but not sharply defined from surrounding portions); *belly* and area under base of tail *sulphur yellow*. Bill and feet black.

Dist. — *Cal.* Common S.V. (Apr.–Sept.) to lower levels, especially common in the interior valleys, rare or absent in the northwest; common M.

Ore. Common S.V. (Apr.–Sept.) east, rare west.

Wash. Common S.V. (Apr.–Sept.) east, rare M. or S.V. (Mar.–Oct.) west.

Nest, of twigs, grasses, wool, etc., in trees or bushes, or on beams of buildings or cross-bars of posts. *Eggs*, 3–5, white or creamy white, boldly marked with reddish brown or lilac.

Cassin Kingbird. *Tyrannus vociferans*

As one drives in winter through the open country in San Diego and Riverside Counties, a stocky, heavy-shouldered bird with yellow belly and dark gray back flies out from a wire, showing as he turns a *black tail* with *no outer white feather*. When he lights and faces the observer a *white chin* is conspicuous against the dark gray neck and breast. In summer the Cassin Kingbird is found throughout southern California, as far north as San Luis Obispo on the coast and at least to Kern Co. in the interior. Except possibly in San Diego Co. it is nowhere common and is generally outnumbered by the Western Kingbird. It has none of the musical and complicated utterances of the latter; its common call is a harsh, low-pitched *cherr*, followed by a *ke-déar*, which suggests the Ash-throated Flycatcher. In the breeding season it utters a series of high, petulant notes, *ki-dee-dee-dee*. To distinguish the two Kingbirds in the country where both occur, chiefly in southern California, note the distinct white throat of the Cassin contrasting with its dark breast. The light gray of the Western Kingbird fades to an almost white throat directly under the bill, but does not offer a marked contrast to the surrounding gray. The back of the Cassin Kingbird is also darker gray with an olive cast. The Cassin in winter and spring shows a very narrow light edging at the tip of all the tail feathers, evident when the bird sits low on a wire with its back to the observer; later in the season the edging becomes worn and is not conspicuous. If a Kingbird shows

Above: WESTERN KINGBIRD (LEFT); CASSIN KINGBIRD
Below: SAY PHŒBE; ASH-THROATED FLYCATCHER

a prominent white outer tail feather in the outspread black tail, it is a Western.

$8\frac{3}{4}$–9

Ad. — Upper parts dark gray (back olivaceous in strong light); (male with concealed crown-patch of reddish orange); wings brown; tail black (showing in winter and spring a slight grayish edging of the outer tail feathers and a grayish tip of tail); *chin white*, contrasting with dark gray of throat and breast; *belly sulphur-yellow*. Bill and feet black.

Dist. — *Cal.* Fairly common R. locally in the lowlands of southern Cal., breeding as far north as San Luis Obispo and San Benito Cos.; winters in small numbers as far north as Santa Cruz, commoner from Los Angeles Co. southward.

Nest and Eggs, similar to those of preceding species.

The Arizona Crested Flycatcher (*Myiarchus magister magister*) has been taken on the California side of the Colorado River above Yuma. It is slightly larger than the following species but can hardly be distinguished in the field.

Ash-throated Flycatcher. *Myiarchus cinerascens cinerascens*

When a pair of Ash-throated Flycatchers choose a hollow in a dead limb for a nesting site the whole neighborhood becomes aware of their presence. Besides the common call notes, *pwit, chi-wit* and *pe-whéurr*, they have a long rolling *prrip*, and when a rival appears the tree-tops resound with harsh bickering cries. Ordinarily the Ash-throated Flycatcher is a rather quiet, dignified bird, sitting upright on a low limb or in treeless country on a bush, sallying out after a bee or other large insect, spreading its *long reddish brown tail* as it turns. When the bird faces the observer the bushy head and whitish throat are conspicuous. Its sharp eye often detects a caterpillar on the under side of a leaf, which it captures by an upward flight and an instant's hovering in the foliage.

The Ash-throated Flycatcher at a distance might be confused with either the Western or the Cassin Kingbird, particularly on migration when it frequently perches on fence-wires along the road. Its proportionally longer tail distinguishes it even before the dark brown head and *reddish brown tail* are evident; both the Kingbirds have black tails. The yellow on the belly of the Flycatcher is paler and less conspicuous than in the Kingbirds. The characteristic *pe-whéurr* of the Flycatcher might easily be confused in southern California with the harsh *ke-déar* of the Cassin Kingbird.

8–$8\frac{1}{2}$

Head, bushy, brown; back and wings grayish brown; two whitish wing-bars; wings *show* when spread an area of reddish brown; tail *showing reddish brown when spread;* throat whitish; chest gray; belly pale yellow. Bill blackish; feet black.

Dist. — *Cal.* Common S.V. (Apr.–Sept.) in canyons, dry washes and wooded slopes at low levels; common M. Fairly common W.V. along the lower Colorado R.
Ore. Uncommon S.V. (June–Aug.) east.
Wash. Casual S.V. (late May–late July); one record west.

Nest, in holes in trees or stumps, lined with rootlets, grass, hair, feathers, occasionally cast snake-skins, etc. *Eggs*, 3–6, creamy or buff, marked with streaks of purplish brown.

Say Phœbe. *Sayornis sayus*

Sometime in September the sweet, plaintive *pée-ee* of the Say Phœbe from a telephone wire or fence post announces the return to southern California of the winter birds. After the breeding season, a pair of Phœbes no longer keep together; each bird has its own domain and its own lookout posts. In the breeding season the Say Phœbe is a bird of rocky canyon mouths at the edges of the desert or of the gray sage-brush plains. Rich cultivated lands and the humid coast belt are left to the Black Phœbe; the Say Phœbe at all times prefers flat open spaces. When hunting over open spaces it often hovers, but not vigorously like the Mountain Bluebird; its efforts are weaker and it varies its position. The Say Phœbe in the mating season utters repeatedly a swift *pit-tsée-ar*, finally fluttering about in the air repeating a rough trilling note. Even in the winter this mating song is occasionally heard. The Say Phœbe shows no marked contrast of black head and white belly; the general color is brown with a *reddish brown belly;* this rusty shade on the belly readily distinguishes it from either of the yellow-bellied Kingbirds. A trained eye can distinguish the Say from the Black Phœbe in flight even at long range; the Say has a more powerful wing-stroke which sends it through the air with a more buoyant flight, and from behind its flight is seen to be somewhat zigzag. At close range its black tail shows in contrast to the brown back. The bird shares with the Black Phœbe the habit of flirting its tail after alighting, generally spreading it at the same time.

7

Ad. — Top and back of head dark brown; back grayish brown; *tail blackish;* throat and breast brownish gray; *belly and area under tail rusty brown.* Bill and feet black.

Dist. — *Cal.* R. in the deserts and in the drier portions of the San Joaquin Valley, and locally in the coastal ranges north to San Benito Co.; M. throughout except in the humid coast belt; W.V. (Sept.–Apr.) north to San Francisco and the northern portion of the Sacramento Valley.

Ore. / *Wash.* Common S.V. (Feb.–Sept.) east; casual M. and possibly S.V. west. A few winter west.

Nest, of grasses, wool and other soft material, placed in outbuildings, under bridges and on ledges. *Eggs*, 3–6, white, occasionally dotted with reddish brown.

Black Phœbe. *Sayornis nigricans*

One of the first birds on the Coast to adapt itself to the presence of man and to adopt his buildings as its home was the Black Phœbe. The trim black figure of this bird is a common sight throughout the winter, perched on the ridgepole of an outbuilding or flying to some garden stake, flirting its tail after alighting and uttering a sharp, energetic *chip.* Often it doubles and turns in hot chase after some insect till the sharp click of the bill announces its capture. In winter it is solitary, each bird keeping its own game preserve. Even at that season on mild days it often indulges in a soft *tsee, tsee* often repeated or even utters its spring song of four syllables, the first two *ti wee* with an upward inflection, the last two *ti wee* with a downward inflection. In the mating season the male often makes a song flight, fluttering about in the air, repeating *ti-ti-ti* for a few seconds and then slowly descending. In April the single birds pair off and build in farm yards, under bridges or in their original position on ledges along streams. The same site is used year after year. The plain black of the head, neck and upper parts, contrasting with the pure white area of the belly, easily distinguishes the Black Phœbe from any other Flycatcher.

BLACK PHŒBE

6½

Ad. — *Head, neck, breast and upper parts black;* edges of wing feathers whitish; outer web of outer tail feathers (not conspicuously) white; *belly white,* cut off sharply in somewhat V shape from black breast. Bill and feet black. **Im.** — Head and neck brownish black; wing-bars buffy white.

Dist. — *Cal.* Common R. at lower levels as far north as Trinity Co., less common along the northwest coast, occurs sparingly east of the Sierras north to Bishop.

Nest, a shelf of dried mud, mixed with grass, etc., placed on ledges of cliffs or sides of sheds or other buildings. *Eggs,* 3–6, usually white, sometimes sparingly dotted with reddish brown.

Olive-sided Flycatcher. *Nuttallornis borealis*

High on a dead stub toward the top of a tree a bird sits in flycatcher fashion, almost upright, or sallies out or up and, after the capture of a flying insect, drops back to its post of observation. Its cry, *pi-pée* or *pi-pée-pa,* heard in the breeding season from the pine, or fir-covered slopes of the mountain, has a wild character suited to the surroundings. Olive-sided Flycatchers have besides a short *pil-pil* which they repeat over and over as they sit on their vantage posts of dead twigs. If the bird is seen from behind at close range, two cottony patches on the flanks are evident, especially when the wings are opened. These white patches and its greater size distinguish the Olive-sided Flycatcher from the smaller Wood Pewee. Both birds, when breast on, show light under parts washed with a darker shade on the sides and with a still lighter line down the middle.

OLIVE-SIDED FLYCATCHER

Olive-sided Flycatchers occur frequently in the lowlands in migration in spring and fall. In spring their call helps to identify them, but in the fall they are usually silent and it is only by their size that a trained observer can distinguish them from Wood Pewees.

7–8

Ad. — Upper parts dark brownish gray; two white tufts on sides of the rump which show in flight; throat whitish, under parts brownish on the sides, with a whitish stripe down the middle; no wing-bars, except in young birds. Bill black above, yellowish below; feet black. **Im.** — Throat and belly whitish, somewhat streaked with dusky; two indistinct buffy wing-bars.

Dist. — Common S.V. (Apr.–Sept.) in coniferous forests throughout the Coast States; in California confined to the mountains except in the humid coast belt from Monterey northward.

Nest, of twigs in trees (usually conifers), generally 25 ft. from the ground. *Eggs*, usually 3, creamy white or buff, spotted or wreathed about the larger end with brown.

Western Wood Pewee. *Myiochanes richardsoni richardsoni*

A harsh *pée-ee* repeated monotonously all day from May till August is a characteristic sound in the evergreen belt on all the mountains. The singer, if we call the note a song, is a slender gray bird generally sitting fairly upright on an exposed stub. Each vocal effort shows in a forward movement of the head and a backward jerk of the tail. The restless movement of the head to one side or the other shows that the Wood Pewee has chosen his perch with a purpose. A quick upward launch or downward dash after a passing insect ending with an audible click of the bill is followed by a rapid, twisting sweep back to the perch; after alighting the bird quivers wings and tail. When a

WESTERN WOOD PEWEE

pair are together in the mating season they utter a hoarse, gurgling note, *chée-up chée-up*, and the male encourages the female during the nest-building by a musical *pip, pip, pip, pip, peé-a*, or at times mounts into the air and flies about calling *pit, pit, pit.* On the breeding ground before sunrise and after sunset, the male repeats over and over a song made up of two phrases, first the usual hoarse *pee-ee* followed by the same phrase in a softer tone with a downward inflection.

The Wood Pewee is only slightly larger than the smaller Flycatchers, but even when it is silent, it can be distinguished by a practiced eye. The dark sides of the breast are divided by a narrow lighter-colored line, and the eye lacks the light-colored ring that sets off the eye of a small Flycatcher.

6–6½

Ad. — Upper parts dark brownish gray; two not very conspicuous white wing-bars; wings and tail dusky; under parts dark gray, lighter on throat and belly, dark sides often separated by an indistinct lighter line down the middle of the breast. Bill black above, light brown below, feet black.

Dist. — *Cal.* Common S.V. (end of Mar.–end of Aug.) in wooded regions throughout; common M. elsewhere.
Ore. Common S.V. (Apr.–Sept.) in wooded regions throughout.
Wash. Common S.V. (Apr.–Sept.) in wooded regions east, less common west.

Nest, neatly made of grasses and fibers, often covered with spider's web and saddled on a limb. *Eggs*, 3–4, white, wreathed around the larger end with spots of dark brown and purple.

WESTERN FLYCATCHER. *Empidonax difficilis difficilis*

From under live oaks in a canyon, from deciduous trees near a stream or even from shady plantations about dwellings from April to July a single sharp note, *pee-íst*, like the expiration of wheezy breath, catches the ear of an attentive listener. The small bird that utters the note is perched in the shadows and is seen only when it flies rapidly out, catches an insect on the wing and returns to its recess in the leaves. Besides the *pee-íst* note, almost but not quite two syllables, the Western Flycatcher utters a low *whit.* In the breeding season the male repeats, often for long periods from the same perch, three syllables which constitute his attempt at song, *ps-séet ptsick*, and after a slight pause *sst.* Like the other small flycatchers the Western Flycatcher quivers its tail on alighting and often jerks it upward when perched. By learning the

WESTERN FLYCATCHER

wheezy call a student can readily distinguish the Western Flycatcher. When the bird is seen in good light it shows a decided yellow tinge over the under parts, but there are three other small flycatchers which have a certain amount of yellow on the under parts. For a discussion of the Hammond and Wright Flycatchers, which resemble the Western closely, see pp. 207 and 208. The Traill Flycatcher is very similar in appearance to the Western, but though often found in the same general region, is restricted to willow thickets and to bushy places in wet mountain meadows. Its song is quite different from that of the Western Flycatcher (see below). The Wood Pewee is also common in groves and thick plantations; it is slightly larger than the Western Flycatcher and has no yellowish wash on its under parts.

$5\frac{1}{2}$–6

Ad. — Upper parts brown (olivaceous in strong light); eye-ring white; two dull whitish wing-bars; breast yellowish, tinged with brown; belly brighter yellow. Bill dark above, flesh-colored below; feet brownish dusky. **Im.** — Wing-bars yellowish brown; belly whitish.

Dist. — *Cal.* Common S.V. (Mar.–Oct.) in cool shade in lowlands and in the foothills; common M.

Ore. / *Wash.* Common S.V. (Apr.–Sept.) in moist woodland; less common east.

Nest, of moss, rootlets, etc., on ledges or in crannies of rock, in stumps or trees, and even on boards of bridges or buildings, generally near a stream. *Eggs*, 3–4, white or buffy, marked with reddish brown.

Traill Flycatcher. *Empidonax trailli trailli*

From the banks of the muddy Colorado at Yuma along every willow-bordered watercourse in the lowlands as far north as the Canadian border, an explosive *weeps-a-pi-dēea* marks from May to August the presence of the Traill Flycatcher. In open mountain meadows, as in the Yosemite, its song mingles with that of the Lincoln Sparrow, while in the lowlands it is the companion of the Chat and the Least Vireo. The bird keeps well hidden in thick foliage, but by watching patiently we get a glimpse of an olive-gray figure perched upright on a willow spray, and note the *pale wing-bars*, the *whitish eye-ring* and perhaps the shade of yellow on the lower belly, before the bird darts out to capture a passing insect. The vigorous four or five syllabled song, given in one utterance, with the characteristic emphasis at its close, is quite unlike that of any of the other small flycatchers. The song is occasionally shortened to the last two syllables, *pi-dēea* and is often preceded by an explosive *prrit*. Besides the song the Traill Flycatcher utters constantly a sharp *whit* and, when two birds quarrel, a grating twitter. The Traill Flycatcher so closely resembles two other small Flycatchers that may occur in the same general region, the Western in the lowlands and the Wright in the mountains, that it is only by its notes and by the nature of its breeding haunts that a student can make sure of its identity. The Western Flycatcher, though it also affects the neighborhood of streams, demands for its hunting a certain amount of open space in the shade of tall trees of mixed growth; neither the Western nor the Wright would be found regularly in the dense willow thickets which the Traill prefers.

$5\frac{1}{2}$–6

Ad. — Upper parts brownish gray; under parts light gray, washed with yellowish on the belly; *eye-ring whitish;* upper surface of wings crossed by two *whitish gray bars*. Bill dark above, horn-colored below; feet brownish black. **Im.** — Wing-bars buffy.

Dist. — Common S.V. (May–Sept.) in extensive willow thickets the whole length of the Coast; also up the mountain streams and on the borders of mountain meadows as high as 5000 ft.

Nest, a cup of grasses, fibers, etc., low in the crotch of a bush or small tree near water. *Eggs*, 3–4, creamy white or buff, marked with brown chiefly about the larger end.

Hammond Flycatcher. *Empidonax hammondi*

When Theodore Roosevelt first met John Muir, it is reported that his first question was, 'How can one tell the Hammond from the Wright Flycatcher?' It is doubtful whether any future President of the United States will have the slightest interest in the problem. There are probably surprisingly few ornithologists who would attempt to distinguish the two species unless they had the dead birds in the hand. The only way to tell them apart is by their songs, which are sufficiently distinct. In dense forests of Douglas fir (locally known as red fir), in Washington and Oregon and along the Sierras from the Yosemite northward, one hears from far up in the lofty trees, a series of three notes, emphatic but not carrying at all far, often in this series *sewip, tsurp treep;* the order is often changed or one note is repeated without the others. After craning the neck for some time, an observer will catch sight of a very small brown bird flying to an exposed stub, where, after alighting in the perpendicular flycatcher fashion, it quivers its tail several times. Besides this characteristic and common three-syllabled song, the Hammond Flycatcher occasionally utters a very different series of notes, *pee, pee, pée-wit, pée-wit.* On the rare occasions when a Hammond Flycatcher perches low enough for observation, one sees gray under parts and brownish upper parts with dull whitish wing-bars. One can be sure that it is not a Western or a Traill Flycatcher if the bird is found in a stand of tall conifers, but the Wright also occurs in openings in such timber and is so like in appearance that the task of distinguishing them is hopeless, unless they are singing (see p. 208). A small Flycatcher in tall firs singing a series of three notes which includes the low note, *tsurp,* anywhere from the central Sierras northward may safely be recorded as a Hammond. The Hammond Flycatcher is a common but generally overlooked migrant in southern California, both in spring and fall, but at this time it rarely says enough to make identification possible.

$5\frac{1}{2}$

Ad. — Upper parts brownish gray (olivaceous in strong light); two whitish wing-bars; throat grayish; breast dark gray; rest of under parts yellowish. Bill dark above, light below; feet dark. **Im.** — Wing-bars yellowish.

Dist. — *Cal.* S.V. (May–Sept.) in forests of red fir or lodge-pole pine in the Sierras from at least the Yosemite northward; M. through the rest of the State.

Ore. / *Wash.* S.V. (May–Sept.) in coniferous forests both east and west.

Nest, a cup of plant fibers, 15–50 ft. or more high, generally on horizontal limb. *Eggs*, 3–4, creamy white occasionally speckled with reddish brown.

Wright Flycatcher. *Empidonax wrighti*

A small gray bird flies out in summer from a low limb of a pine or from the thick chaparral of a mountain slope, captures a passing insect, wheels back to its perch, quivering its tail as it lights, and then utters a series of thin unmusical notes, given without vigor or enthusiasm. The bird itself has the upright carriage on its perch, the whitish eye-ring and the pale wing-bars that characterize four or five of the small Flycatchers. The song of the Wright Flycatcher is a little more vigorous and much more varied than that of the Hammond. It is commonly built up of three notes, *psit hreek pseet*, the last note the highest, but these are often grouped in series of fours, *psit hreek psit pseet*, or otherwise varied. Even when the song is made up of a series of three, it may be distinguished from that of the Hammond by the absence of the low *tsurp* characteristic of the latter. The Wright Flycatcher also utters, particularly toward dusk, a quite different series of notes, *tee, tee, tee-hick*. The common call note, used by both sexes, is a soft *pit*, heard constantly from the bushes in which the bird nests.

The Wright Flycatcher is not so yellow below as the Western Flycatcher, which, moreover, hardly reaches the altitude at which the Wright Flycatcher generally breeds. Its notes distinguish it at once from the willow-loving Traill Flycatcher. There remain the Hammond and the Gray Flycatcher from which the Wright Flycatcher must be distinguished. The Gray Flycatcher is confined to the sage-covered plains and slopes of northeastern California, eastern Oregon and western Nevada; moreover its notes are distinct (see p. 209). The Hammond Flycatcher overlaps the Wright to a considerable extent but as a rule prefers denser, cooler forests, and does most of its hunting from a height of over thirty feet from the ground. The Hammond Flycatcher is absent in breeding season from the region south of the Sierras and even there is confined to the red firs on the west side; the only small Flycatcher in the mountains of southern California in summer (outside of willow-bordered streams and cool canyons) is therefore the Wright. Wright Flycatchers are occasionally common on migration in the lowland but it is impossible even for the practiced eye to distinguish the species, when silent, from its congeners.

$5\frac{1}{4}$

Upper parts brownish gray; under parts light gray, tinged with yellow on the belly; *eye-ring whitish;* upper surface of *wings* crossed by *two whitish bars*. Bill dusky, paler below; feet dark.

Dist. — *Cal.* S.V. (May–Sept.) in all the higher mountains from the San Jacinto and San Bernardino Mts. northward; M. at lower levels.

Ore. ⎱ S.V. (May–late Aug.) in mountains throughout; M. at
Wash. ⎰ lower levels.

Nest, a cup of fibers and strips of bark, in bushes or saplings not over 15 ft. from the ground, generally in a crotch. *Eggs*, 3–5, creamy white.

Gray Flycatcher. *Empidonax griseus*

As late as 1913, the summer home of the Gray Flycatcher was unknown or confused with that of its near relative the Wright Flycatcher. Now we know that it nests in the wide expanse of gray sage (*Artemisia tridentata*) that extends from northeastern California through western Nevada and eastern Oregon. It shares this domain with the Sage Thrasher and the Brewer Sparrow; the latter glean their food from the ground or the bushes themselves, but the Gray Flycatcher, perched on the top of a tall sage-bush, watches the air for its prey. When a Gray Flycatcher is startled, it dives from its perch and in its flight keeps well down among the brush. Its song is more emphatic and less varied than either the Hammond's or the Wright's. It has only two elements, a vigorous *chí-wip* and a fainter *cheep* in a higher pitch. These two notes are used in a variety of combinations, but when once they are heard, the Gray Flycatcher can be instantly recognized. The call notes are a sharp *whit*, like a Traill's, and a liquid *whilp* which passes into a gurgling note, similar to that of several of the other small Flycatchers. The Gray Flycatcher nests chiefly in stands of pure sage, where the older bushes grow to a height of six feet or more, but also breeds in open woods or yellow pine, where sage and other bushes grow among the trees. In winter it is not uncommon in southern California, especially along the Colorado River. In migration it passes through central California, but only a trained observer under very favorable conditions can distinguish it when not in song. When on its breeding ground the character of its song and the nature of its habitat are safe guides to any one who already knows the Wright Flycatcher and its song.

$5\frac{1}{2}$

Similar to the preceding, but slightly larger and grayer (hardly any yellowish on under parts); bill black above, lower mandible noticeably flesh-colored toward base, but not showing often in life; feet dark.

Dist. — Locally common S.V. (May–Aug.) in sage-brush country from Inyo Co., Cal., north, through Modoc Co., Cal., as far north and west as Crook, Wasco and Union Cos., Ore. Not uncommon M. in central Cal. and W.V. in southern Cal.

Nest, a deep cup of grasses, fibers, etc., in high sage-bushes or greasewood. *Eggs*, 3–4, creamy white.

Vermilion Flycatcher. *Pyrocephalus rubinus mexicanus*

From March to June in the cottonwoods and willows along the Colorado north of Yuma or in the shade trees in the lower Imperial Valley, a small Flycatcher with bright red head and body, set off by blackish wings and tail, flies from a low perch forty or fifty feet into the air and flutters about like a huge butterfly. While in the air he continually utters a slight call of two or three notes, *pítt-a-see, pítt-a-see,* jerking his head upward at each utterance. At other seasons the bright-colored males or the brown females are seen on the low limbs of trees along roadsides or ditches or on fences, twitching and spreading their tails after alighting, flying out after passing insects and usually returning to a different perch from the one they have left. The brown female may be recognized by a wash of red on the lower belly. Besides the notes uttered by the male in flight, both sexes utter a sharp *pisk.*

$5\frac{1}{2}$–$6\frac{1}{4}$

Ad. ♂. — *Top of head* (often raised as a crest) *bright scarlet;* line from bill through eye to back of head blackish; rest of upper parts dusky brown; *entire under parts scarlet.* Bill and feet black. **Ad.** ♀. **and Im.** ♂. — Top of head, back and wings brown; tail blackish; two inconspicuous whitish wing-bars; *under parts* white, streaked with dusky on breast and belly, and *tinged with salmon on lower belly.* **Im.** ♀. — Belly yellow.

Dist. — Fairly common R. along the lower Colorado R. from Yuma to Needles, less common in the Imperial Valley and north to Mecca. Occasional in winter from San Diego to Santa Barbara.

Nest, of twigs on limbs from 6 to 50 ft. above the ground. *Eggs,* 2–3, white or buff, boldly marked chiefly about the larger end with spots or blotches of brown and purple.

LARKS: *Family Alaudidæ*

Horned Lark. *Otocoris alpestris* subsp.

Almost from under one's feet in bare fields or hillsides of short grass, a brown bird rises and flies a little distance with comparatively powerful strokes of long-pointed wings. When it lights, if it faces the observer, it shows a very *conspicuous pattern of yellow and black on the head.* The throat is yellow, brighter in the male, paler in the female, and there is a broad bar of the same color over the forehead. This yellow is framed by sharply contrasting black. The nape of the neck and the upper back are a warm reddish brown, varying in intensity in the different subspecies. A close view of the male shows the black of the head extending in tiny points backward toward the nape, the so-called horns; as a rule these lie flat but they are erected in courtship. The black tail is an easy mark,

CALIFORNIA HORNED LARK

as the bird flies before one or overhead. When a flock wheel and show the under sides, the chief effect is white, almost as in small sandpipers. The birds walk and are generally rather sedate, stopping often and rarely taking more than a few steps at a time; occasionally they run. The common note of the Horned Lark is a shrill *tsee*, or *tsée-de-ree*, and a still sharper double-syllabled *tí-sick*. (See under Pipit, p. 266.) The song is thin and unmusical, suggesting the syllables *tsip, tsip, tsée-di-di*. It is often given from a clod of earth or other low perch, but in the height of the mating ardor the singer mounts aloft like his cousin the European Skylark and repeats his feeble effort over and over during a protracted circling flight.

$7\frac{1}{2}$–8

Ad. ♂ in breeding plumage. — *Forehead yellow* (or pale yellow), *bordered above by a broad black stripe* between forehead and top of head extending back into black tufts or 'horns'; rest of upper parts pinkish brown (or brownish gray), most conspicuous on nape and shoulders; outer tail feathers black, showing in flight, with more or less white edging on the outer feather (often not conspicuous); *throat bright yellow*, almost entirely *framed by black borders;* a *black shield-shaped area across the breast;* flanks shaded with pinkish brown; rest of under parts white. Bill dusky above, light gray below; feet black. **Ad. ♀.** — Similar but smaller and duller. **Ad. ♂ in winter.** — Lacks the black 'horns'; colors duller. **Im. in early summer.** — Upper parts pale brown, *heavily spotted with white;* under parts white, except upper breast, which is washed with light brown; no pattern of black or yellow on head and throat.

The Horned Lark varies in different parts of its range, in size and color. The different races cannot be distinguished in the field but the breeding bird can be fairly accurately determined for any one locality by the ranges given below.

Dist. — Yuma Horned Lark. [*O. a. leucansiptila.*]
Cal. R. on the deserts southeast, from Mecca to Yuma.
Mohave Horned Lark. [*O. a. ammophila.*]
Cal. R. on the Mohave desert and north to Owens Valley.
Desert Horned Lark. *O. a. leucolæma.*
Cal. W.V. to southeastern Cal., breeding on the White Mts., Inyo Co.
California Horned Lark. *O. a. actia.*
Common R. west of the desert divide from San Diego north to Stockton and San Francisco Bay region.
Island Horned Lark. *O. a. insularis.*
Common R. on all the Channel Is.
Ruddy Horned Lark. *O. a. rubea.*
Common R. in the northern Sacramento Valley.
Dusky Horned Lark. *O. a. merrilli.*
Cal. Common R. in northeastern Cal.
Ore. Common R. east.
Wash. Common S.V. (Mar.–Sept.) east; irregular in winter.
Streaked Horned Lark. *O. a. strigata.*
Ore. Common R. west.
Wash. Common S.V. (Feb.–Oct.) in southwest; casual in winter.
Pallid Horned Lark. *O. a. arcticola.*
Ore. Fairly common W.V. in the northeast.
Wash. Common S.V. at or about 7000 ft. on the Cascades, south at least to Mt. Rainier; W.V. to plains east.

Nest, in a depression on ground where vegetation is scanty, of grasses, weed stalks, etc. *Eggs*, 3–4, gray, dotted with olive and brown, and often wreathed about larger end.

SWALLOWS. *Family Hirundinidæ*

Western Purple Martin. *Progne subis hesperia*

The cornice of a building above the traffic of a city street and the hollow limbs of tall trees in mountain glades seem such opposite conditions that it is a surprise to find the same bird in both localities. Both, however, offer nesting holes and the sky above each has insect food, so that Purple Martins drop their liquid notes impartially over Seattle and Santa Barbara, and the forest trees of Mount Wilson. In Washington they have become almost exclusively city dwellers, and are found in all the large cities about Puget Sound. The blue-black males with their long wings and deeply forked tails utter their deep rich notes either from the edge of the nest or from the air. The commonest note is a deep, musical *pew, pew, pew*, but the full song ends with an indescribable run of rich guttural notes. The males return to the nesting site ahead of the females, take possession of their respective holes or crevices and await their tardier mates. Martins hunt at times low over bodies of water, but often circle two or three hundred feet in air.

WESTERN MARTIN

$7\frac{1}{4}$–$8\frac{1}{2}$

Ad. ♂. — *Entire body blue-black;* wings and tail blackish. Bill black; feet blackish. **Ad.** ♀ **and Im.** — Upper parts, wings and tail brown, glossed on the head and back with purple; forehead, throat, breast and flanks grayish white. Breast brown; belly white.

Dist. — *Cal.* Local S.V. (late Mar.–Aug.) in colonies scattered through the lower mountains and in a few cities.
Ore. Local S.V. (late Mar.–Aug.).
Wash. Fairly common S.V. (late Mar.–Sept.) in western Wash.

Nest, in hollows in trees, or in cornices of city buildings. *Eggs*, 3–5, white.

Cliff Swallow. *Petrochelidon lunifrons lunifrons*

A company of Cliff Swallows, gathering mud for their nests over a puddle, hold their tails daintily up and flutter their wings like a swarm of gigantic bees. When each has a bill full of mud, it adds the load to a mud nest under the eaves of a neighboring shed or in niches on walls of rock, showing as it flies off a *pale reddish brown rump.* When the eggs are laid, the female's cream-colored forehead is poked out of one or another of the long row of bottle-shaped nests, or the reddish brown rump of the male is conspicuous as he clings for a moment to the nest with food for the young. When nesting birds are alarmed, the place resounds with their piteous *keer, keer*. As the birds fly over the feeding grounds, they utter a single low *churr*. The song consists of a squeaking note, followed by a curious guttural sound that suggests the rolling of rubber. This song often issues from the bill of a bird whose head projects from the nest. In calm weather Cliff Swallows often hawk well up in the air, at other times they fly low over the fields or over water, but at all times like the Tree Swallows they set their wings and poise, or take a little upward flight. A close observer can distinguish these two species from all other swallows by this habit. *The cream-colored frontlet, dark throat* and reddish brown rump are the unmistakable field marks of the Cliff Swallow.

CLIFF SWALLOW

5–6

Ad. — *Forehead white or creamy;* top of head and back steel blue, collar across nape grayish; *rump reddish brown;* wings and tail dusky; chin, throat and sides of head rich reddish brown, a spot of blue in the throat; rest of under parts light gray. Bill black; feet brown. **Im.** — Lack the blue and have little or no reddish brown on throat.

Dist. — *Cal.* Abundant M. and S.V. (Mar.–Sept.) nearly throughout; winters sparingly in the Imperial Valley.

Ore. / *Wash.* } Common S.V. (Apr.–early Sept.) throughout.

Nest, gourd-shaped structure of mud pellets, under eaves or against cliffs. *Eggs*, 3–5, white, speckled or spotted with brown and lilac.

Barn Swallow. *Hirundo erythrogastra*

Southern California lacks the familiar figure of the Barn Swallow darting in and out of wide-open barn doors, but in Washington and Oregon the cheery twittering of the bird resounds under the high barn rafters as it does through the farms of the Middle West and the East. In the interior valley of California where irrigation ditches cross and recross the low land, Barn Swallows nest under the planks that serve as bridges wherever the roads or trails cross a ditch. As a rule Barn Swallows fly low, often just skimming the tops of the grass or the surface of the water. An observer readily makes out the *dark steel blue of the upper parts* and the *long outer tail feathers* as the bird dashes past. Young birds are pale below but old birds show *rich chestnut* over the *entire under parts*, deepest on the throat. The Barn Swallow, besides being the most distinctly marked of all our swallows, is by far the most musical; the full song, often given from the ridgepole of a barn or other perch, consists of cheerful twittering sounds ending in a run of guttural notes like rubber being rolled. When flying in friendly companies, Barn Swallows utter a gentle twitter, but when they become excited, this changes to an em-

BARN SWALLOW

phatic *kit-tic.* When concerned about the nest, they utter a high-pitched *keet.*

$5\frac{3}{4}$–$7\frac{3}{4}$

Ad. — Forehead reddish brown; rest of upper parts steel blue; *under parts reddish brown,* deepest on throat and upper breast; throat separated from breast by an imperfect blue collar; wings and tail dusky; *outer pair of tail feathers two inches longer than innermost,* all but central pair with white spots showing when tail is spread. Bill black; feet brown. **Im.** — Colors duller; outer tail feathers much shorter than in **ad.**

Dist. — *Cal.* Common M. throughout; S.V. (Mar.–Sept.), rare in southern Cal., common in the interior valleys. Winters sparingly in the Imperial Valley.

Ore. / *Wash.* Common S.V. (late Apr.–late Sept.) throughout.

Nest, of mud mixed with straw and feathers, on niches in caves along the ocean, on beams of buildings or under bridges inland. *Eggs,* 3–5, white, speckled with brown and lavender.

Tree Swallow. *Iridoprocne bicolor*

One of the first indications of the returning wave of birds in the spring migration is the appearance of swallows over the marshes along the coast, or over the lakes of the interior valleys. In southern California the first scattered flocks appear in February, flying in a general northerly direction, but stopping to feed as they go. The earliest are generally the Tree Swallows. As they pass over, their pure white under parts distinguish them from either the Cliff or Barn Swallows, and when the sun shines on the uniform *steel blue or green* of their *heads and backs* they are readily distinguished from Violet-green Swallows. When feeding, Tree Swallows sail more than Violet-greens; like the Cliff Swallows they often mount a little on set wings, poising at the top of the curve with back slightly arched and tail depressed, and then sail downward before taking another series of strokes.

TREE SWALLOW

Tree Swallows sun themselves on dead twigs, twittering gently from their perches; the same notes *killy killy tsiti killy*, not sweet or musical but yet pleasing to the ear, are uttered as they fly about feeding. In the breeding season the male flies about near the nest even before dawn, steadily repeating the phrases *chilp wheat*, or *chilp tsip wheat*. When the young are hatched, immense flocks assemble along the telephone wires in the low country or in low trees or reeds. The young lack the greenish color of the head and back, and have a wash of brownish on the sides of the breast, but can readily be distinguished from Bank Swallows, which have a dark band completely across the breast.

5–6¼

Ad. ♂. — Entire *upper parts greenish blue;* under parts pure white. Bill black; feet brown. **Ad.** ♀. — Upper parts usually duller, almost brown. **Im.** — Upper parts brown, an incomplete dusky collar across the breast.

Dist. — *Cal.* Common M., and S.V. (Feb.–Sept.) in the interior valleys and near large bodies of water; winters irregularly in central and southern Cal.

Ore. / *Wash.* } Fairly common S.V. (late Feb.–Sept.), commoner west.

Nest, in holes in trees, in nest boxes or holes in buildings. *Eggs*, 4–7, white.

NORTHERN VIOLET-GREEN SWALLOW. *Tachycineta thalassina lepida*

In California the Violet-green Swallow is generally seen darting about the crevices in steep canyon walls or sailing about tall pines, perching on dead stubs far up in the trees, filling the mountain glades with cheery twittering. From southern Oregon northward the bird has thrown in its lot with man. In every village street and even in moderate-sized cities the metallic violet and purple backs and snow-white breast flash past.

VIOLET-GREEN SWALLOW

Before dawn when the Robin chorus is in full swing, Violet-green Swallows fly about in the darkness repeating over and over two or three slight notes, *tsip tseet tsip*. Their ordinary notes are a rapid twitter. Violet-green Swallows take more rapid wing-strokes than Tree Swallows and sail less. As the bird turns, the white feathers almost meeting over the rump show even when the observer is below, and there is white on the sides of the neck. If seen from above, the different shades of green, violet and purplish distinguish the bird at once from the Tree Swallow, whose upper parts are all the same shade of greenish blue.

5½

Ad. ♂. — Top of head bronze, with bronzy reflections; rump violet or purplish; wings and tail dusky; sides of neck and under parts white, the *white nearly meeting over the rump.* Bill black; feet brownish black. **Ad.** ♀. — Like ♂ but duller. **Im.** — Upper parts gray; under parts whitish.

Dist. — *Cal.* Abundant M. and common S.V. on the lower slopes of the mountains (yellow pine belt), almost reaching the coast along the coast range; winters irregularly from Santa Barbara Co. southward.

Ore. / *Wash.* } Common S.V. (Mar.–late Sept.).

Nest, in holes in trees, crevices in cliffs, holes in buildings or nest boxes. *Eggs*, 4–6, white.

BANK SWALLOW. *Riparia riparia*

If small brown swallows are seen flying in and out of holes in a steep bank overhanging a river or lake, or in a cliff of clay fronting the ocean, they are either Bank or Rough-winged Swallows. If the colony is numerous, inhabiting many holes along the bank, let the observer watch carefully for a *brown band across the breast of the bird.* The presence of this band distinguishes the Bank Swallow from the Rough-winged Swallow; in the latter the whole throat and breast are gray. Bank Swallows, moreover, usually congregate in one breeding place, while Rough-wings are scattered in single pairs or small companies. Bank Swallows, both as breeding birds and in migration, are far outnumbered by Rough-winged Swallows. In migration Bank Swallows occur over low ground, meadows and marshes, along the beaches or over lakes and streams, often in company with other swallows. In flight the Bank Swallow rarely rests its wings and poises, or takes an upward flight like some of the other species; it flies low and swiftly. Its ordinary note is a harsh but slight *brrit.* Immature Tree Swallows have brown backs and a wash of brown on the sides of the breast but not entirely across as in Bank Swallows.

BANK SWALLOW

4¾–5½

Ad. — Upper parts grayish brown; under parts white, a *dark brownish band* across the breast, separating white throat from white belly. Bill black; feet brown.

Dist. — *Cal.* Fairly common M. throughout; S.V. (Mar.–Aug.) locally in colonies in sea cliffs or in banks of clay or sand along streams or on lakes.

Ore. / *Wash.* } Local S.V. (Apr.–Sept.).

Nest, of straw and feathers in a hole in banks. *Eggs*, 3–6, white.

ROUGH-WINGED SWALLOW. *Stelgidopteryx serripennis*

Early in March a pair of grayish brown swallows appear about some bank which a stream is under-cutting, or a stone bridge, or scattered flocks hawk about ponds or over marshes. As they turn Rough-winged Swallows show a gray throat and breast. They nest either in crevices of banks or masonry, or in holes in sand or clay. In migration Rough-winged Swallows are rather silent and may be easily overlooked but where several pairs are occupying holes in a bank, they play about with graceful flight, constantly uttering a slight harsh *prrit* or higher *preet*. The Rough-winged Swallow can be distinguished from the Bank Swallow by the absence of the dusky band across the breast.

ROUGH-WINGED SWALLOW

5–5¾

Ad. — Upper parts brown; *throat and breast brownish;* rest of under parts white. Bill and feet black.

Dist. — *Cal.* Common M. and fairly common S.V. (Feb.–Sept.) locally throughout, rare along the north coast.

Ore., *Wash.* } Common S.V. (Apr.–Sept.) throughout.

Nest, of rootlets in a bank, side of cut, or in masonry. *Eggs*, 3–6, white.

MAGPIES, JAYS, CROWS, etc.: *Family Corvidæ*

MAGPIES and JAYS: Subfamily Garrulinæ

BLACK-BILLED MAGPIE. *Pica pica hudsonia*

The striking black and white of the Magpie as it flies with level flight across an open field becomes a frequent sight when one enters the sage-brush country east of the Cascades. The long tail extending straight out behind in flight, or elevated when the bird walks on the ground, and the *white patches on the wings*, appearing and disappearing as the wings are opened or closed, make identification easy. The Yellow-billed Magpie comes within seventy or one hundred miles of the Black-billed at the western base of the Sierras in California, but the two species have never yet been found in the same locality. The Black-billed Magpie spends much of its time in bushes and low trees near water, generally in small companies. Its notes are a rapidly repeated *chek, chek, chek*, and a single nasal *maag*, but when a number are together, they indulge in much conversation in low clucking or whistling notes. About ranches Magpies if not molested become very tame and feed in the corrals and hogpens. In winter they gather in large flocks.

$17\frac{1}{2}$–$21\frac{3}{4}$

Ad. — General effect *black and white,* the wings showing greenish blue at the right angle and the tail bronzy green; large *patches of white* on the shoulder and *in the outspread wings;* belly white, sharply cut off from the black breast; *middle tail feathers very long,* each outer pair shorter. Bill and feet black.
Im. — Like **ad.** but without metallic reflections.

Dist. — *Cal.* Fairly common R. along the eastern border from Independence and Mono L. to the Oregon line and west to Susanville and Shasta Valley.

Ore. / *Wash.* } Common R. east; irregular in winter west.

Nest, a bulky structure of twigs in trees and large bushes from 4 to 50 ft. from the ground, canopied with twigs, with an entrance on each side. *Eggs,* 6–9, gray green, streaked and speckled with brown.

Yellow-billed Magpie. *Pica nuttalli*

If all birds were as easily identified as the Yellow-billed Magpie, bird-study would lose much of its interest. No other bird (except the preced-

YELLOW-BILLED MAGPIE

ing species) has, in addition to its striking pattern of apparent black and white, a tail longer than the rest of the body. In the valleys of the San Joaquin and Sacramento Rivers, and east of the Coast Range from Santa Cruz County to the Santa Inez Valley, wherever groves of the deciduous oaks line the streams or cover the slopes of the hills, Magpies are still found in large or small colonies. Their bulky nests, many in each tree, may first attract our attention, but almost at once one or two birds will be seen flying evenly across the fields, the *long narrow tail straight out behind*, and the *large white patches in the wings* contrasting with the black of the head, back and tail. On the ground Magpies walk like crows, or occasionally in long grass hop like jays. When the bird is walking, the tail is held straight out behind, the tip curved slightly upward, but when perched it hangs down straight below like a macaw's. When a Magpie lights the tail is jerked upward, sometimes so sharply as to threaten apparently to overturn the bird. Magpies are always in groups and are talkative, but not particularly noisy. The common note is a single *eck*, or *erk*, with little emphasis or resonance, sometimes repeated in a series of from four to seven, *eck*, *eck*, *eck*, etc., suggesting a little the cries of California Woodpeckers, but not so harsh. The Magpie also has a much lower *charr*. Even if the yellow bill is not seen, one can be sure that a Magpie seen west of the Sierras is the Yellow-billed.

16—18

Similar to preceding species, but bill yellow.
Dist. — Common R. locally from Santa Barbara Co. to Santa Clara Co. and in the Sacramento and San Joaquin Valleys.
Nest, like that of the preceding species. *Eggs*, usually 5–8, gray, speckled and streaked with pale brown or buff.

Crested Jay { Steller Jay / Blue-fronted Jay / Coast Jay } *Cyanocitta stelleri* subsp.

Wherever there are conifers, either in the mountains or along the humid coast belt, the loud harsh *tchek*, *tchek*, *tchek* of the Crested Jay rings through the forest aisles, or we get a flash of shimmering blue as the bird scales across an open space on set wings. The Crested Jay is a noisy, inquisitive bird, hopping about a camp in search of bits of food, or screaming an alarm at our approach. It is one of the first birds to discover a hawk perched in a tree, or an owl in its hiding place, and to proclaim its discovery with angry cries. Besides the ringing *tchek*, a little lower in pitch than the cry of the California Jay and generally given in flight, the Crested Jay utters from its perch a loud *kweesch*, *kweesch*, *kweesch*. It has besides a deeper *chu-chu-chu* and a note resembling a squeaking wheelbarrow, *kée-lu*, *kée-lu*. It also utters screams so like those of the Red-tailed and Red-bellied Hawks as to deceive the listener. Occasionally from the cover of dense foliage, it utters a formless succession of liquid, pleasing notes quite unlike its usual discordant notes, or a purring or rolling note. When a Jay alights in the lower branches of a tree, it usually hops vigorously up the ladder of higher branches. The Crested Jay is a destructive poacher in the breeding season, searching out and devouring the eggs and young of smaller birds. While engaged in egg-hunting it can be as silent and secretive as it is ordinarily bold and

BLUE–FRONTED JAY

noisy. A glimpse of the *solid blue lower back and long blackish or dark brown crest* distinguishes any form of the Crested Jay from the brown-backed crestless California Jay. The two species overlap where the chaparral and forest meet, but the California Jay keeps chiefly to the oaks and scrub, the Crested Jay to the pines.

12–13½

Ad. — *Head, long crest and upper back blackish or dark brown;* lower back greenish blue; wings and tail purplish blue, crossed with narrow black bars; throat and upper breast blackish or brownish, passing into blue on the rest of the under parts. Bill and feet black. **Im.** — Duller.

Dist. — Blue-fronted Jay. *C. s. frontalis.*
Two vertical lines of faint blue on forehead.
Cal. Common R. in the mountains from San Diego to Ventura and Santa Barbara Cos. and along the Sierras.
Coast Jay. *C. s. carbonacea.*
Cal. Common R. of humid coast from Monterey Co. north.
Ore. Common R. of conifers west.
Wash. R. in timber of southern Wash. west.
Black-headed Jay. *C. s. annectens.*
Ore. } *Wash.* } Common R. of conifers east.
Steller Jay. *C. s. stelleri.*
Wash. Fairly common R. northerly in western Wash.

Nest, a structure of twigs, often including a cup of mud, and lined with rootlets, in trees. *Eggs,* 3–5, greenish, speckled with olive-brown.

Woodhouse Jay. *Aphelocoma woodhousei*

In appearance and habits the Woodhouse Jay is so like the California Jay (see next species) that it would be hard to distinguish the two birds in the field, if their ranges overlapped. As it is, the eastern slope of the Sierras roughly separates the California Jay on the west and the Woodhouse Jay on the east. The notes of the Woodhouse Jay are to the writer's ear indistinguishable from those of the California Jay. It has the same pitching flight over the chaparral, jerks its head after alighting and hops in the same way on the ground. Under favorable conditions the grayer tone both of the under parts and of the middle of the back is evident.

$11\frac{1}{2}$–$12\frac{3}{4}$

Ad. — Top of head, upper back, wings and tail dull blue, middle of back washed with brown (*but not clearly marked off from the blue*); sides of head brownish; narrow white line over eye; throat and upper breast whitish, streaked with dark gray and bluish; rest of under parts gray. Bill and feet black.

Dist. — Fairly common resident locally in the desert ranges of extreme eastern Cal. and in the Steens Mts., Harney Co., Ore.

Nest, of sticks in a bush. *Eggs*, 3–6, pale green, marked with brown and lavender.

California Jay. *Aphelocoma californica* subsp.

A long-tailed, blue-winged bird flies down a bush-covered hillside or from one live oak to the next, flapping vigorously a number of times and

CALIFORNIA JAY

then setting outspread wings and tail stiffly and pitching forward in a long shallow curve. At the same time the California Jay utters a succession of harsh cries like the syllable *tschek, tschek,* slightly higher pitched than those of the Steller Jay. Another note commonly uttered when the bird is perched is a very harsh *ker-wheek.* When a Jay alights it bobs its head emphatically; on the ground it hops. A common sight is a Jay with an acorn in its bill, flying to a limb where it can hammer it open. Too common also is a piteous outcry in the nesting season from a pair of smaller birds, fluttering about the nest where a Jay is stolidly taking one shrieking nestling after another. When a pair of Jays are together in a thick tree, they utter a number of low warbling notes, and occasionally a peculiar rolling *burrr.*

$11\frac{1}{2}$–$12\frac{1}{4}$

Ad. — *Top of head rich blue;* wings and tail duller blue; line over eye white; sides of head blackish; middle of back grayish brown; *throat* and upper breast *whitish,* with dusky streaks; sides of breast blue, forming almost a collar across the breast; rest of under parts light gray. Bill and feet black. **Im. in summer.** — Head and neck streaked with brown.

Dist. — Interior California Jay. [*A. c. immanis.*]

Cal. R. in the San Joaquin and Sacramento Valleys, and through the lower slopes of the Sierras northward.

Ore. R. in the valleys between the Coast Ranges and the Cascades, rarer northward.

Wash. R. in the extreme southern portion.

Swarth California Jay. [*A. c. oöcleptica.*]

R. in the coast region of northern Cal. west of the Coast Ranges, from the east side of San Francisco Bay north to Humboldt Bay.

California Jay. *A. c. californica.*

R. from San Diego to San Francisco Bay west of the southern Sierras and the Coast Ranges.

Nest, of twigs lined with rootlets usually in bushes or low trees. *Eggs,* 3–6, varying greatly, buffy spotted with brown, or green spotted with deeper green.

SANTA CRUZ ISLAND JAY. *Aphelocoma insularis*

A bird student on his first visit to Santa Cruz I., twenty-five miles out from Santa Barbara, looks with especial interest for the Jay that is found only on this island. In voice, habits and general appearance it resembles very closely the California Jay of the mainland, but it is appreciably larger, the blue of the upper parts is richer and its voice is a trifle harsher.

WHITE-HEADED JAY. *Perisoreus canadensis capitalis*

The 'Camp-Robber' of eastern Washington and Oregon, though similar to the next species in general appearance and habits, is a distinct species. The chief difference in the field is the *white head* and the *white-tipped tail.*

$11\frac{1}{4}$–13

Ad. — *Head whitish,* except a dark patch about and behind the eye, and dark gray hind-neck; rest of upper parts light gray; *tail tipped with white;*

throat whitish; rest of under parts brownish gray. Bill and feet black. **Im.** — Uniformly dark gray, lighter on top of head.

Dist. — *Ore.* R. in the mountains of the northeastern portion of the state, west to Crook Co.

Wash. R. in the forests up to the limit of trees in extreme northern portion of Cascades, Okanagan Hds. and the Blue Mts.; in fall and winter irregularly to lower levels.

Nest, of twigs, shreds of bark and fibers, with a heavy lining of feathers. *Eggs*, gray, speckled with brown.

Oregon Jay / Gray Jay } *Perisoreus obscurus* subsp.

A bird with a *white forehead* and a *white collar across the hind neck*, a blackish hind head and a brown back, flits noiselessly out of the forest and starts to investigate the camp. With a soft *whee-oo* another follows, flying to the ground, hopping about or carrying back a scrap of refuse to a limb. A flock keeps constantly drifting on through the trees, flying now to the ground, then to a branch or even clinging to the side of a tree trunk. The soft, fluffy plumage gives the bird a gentle look in keeping with its fearlessness and soft voice. Let a hawk appear, however, and the Oregon Jays will mob him with loud screaming cries, *ke-wéep, ke-wéep.* Besides the soft whistled *whee-oo* with which a flock keeps in touch, the Oregon Jay utters a low *chuck* somewhat like a Robin's.

OREGON JAY

$9\frac{1}{2}$–11

Ad. — *Forehead white;* back of head and *nape* blackish, *separated from back by whitish collar;* back, wings and tail brown; under parts white. Bill and feet black. **Im.** — Upper parts sooty gray, darkest on head; under parts dark gray, paling on belly.

Dist. — Oregon Jay. *P. o. obscurus.*

Cal. Fairly common R. in the northern coast belt from Mendocino Co. northward.

Ore. / *Wash.* } R. in the forests west.

Gray Jay. *P. o. griseus.*
Cal. Fairly common R. in high forests in northern Cal. east of the humid coast belt, south regularly to Mt. Shasta, casually to L. Tahoe.
Ore. } R. in forested regions east; wanders after the breeding
Wash. } season.
Nest, of twigs, moss, etc., in trees, generally conifers. *Eggs*, 3–4, gray or greenish gray, thickly spotted with lavender and gray.

RAVENS, CROWS, etc.; *Subfamily Corvinæ*

Raven. *Corvus corax* subsp.

In the broken foot-hills of the inner Coast Ranges of southern California, in the deserts, and throughout the cattle country of eastern Oregon and Washington a single large black bird with long, pointed wings drops a hoarse *cruck* from some quarter of the sky. If a Raven passes overhead the shape of the tail is evident, longer and more wedge-shaped than that of a crow. Besides the low *cruck*, the Raven utters a resonant *cark, cark* and a hoarse *cor cor*, lower than the *karr* of a crow. Ravens are extremely skillful aviators, often soaring or sailing like hawks with their long, pointed wings stiffly set. They are playful in the air, pairs or small companies indulging in spring in much swooping and falling, frequently rolling halfway over so that their claws are directed upward and then quickly righting themselves. Except when some carcase has attracted a little company of Ravens, they are usually seen singly or in pairs. On the ground Ravens walk or hop awkwardly. Ravens often fly up from carcases of jack rabbits that have been run over by motor cars on desert highways.

The Raven is a distinctly larger bird than a Crow, but unless there is some standard of comparison, size is extremely difficult to gauge in the field. The long, pointed wings, the wedge-shaped tail and the quality of the voice must confirm the first impression made by the size.

$21\frac{1}{2}$–26 Wingspread 4–$4\frac{1}{2}$ ft.

Entire plumage black, with a purplish gloss in strong light; wings long, pointed; tail long, wedge-shaped. Bill and feet black.

Dist. — Raven. *C. c. sinuatus.*
Cal. Common R. locally, on deserts, in the foothills, along the northern coast and on the Channel Is.
Ore. R. locally along the coast and common on the plains east.
Wash. R. on the plains east.
Northern Raven. *C. c. principalis.*
Wash. R. west, especially along the coast.
Nest, a structure of twigs, usually on cliffs or trees. *Eggs*, 5–7, green, olive or drab, spotted and blotched with brown, lavender and drab.

Western Crow. *Corvus brachyrynchos hesperis*

In a book that attempted to give the life-histories of birds, the Crow would occupy much space; few birds show greater intelligence or have more varied and interesting activities. In a book whose chief aim is to make it possible to distinguish one bird from another, there is no need to say much about the Crow, probably our best-known and most easily recognized bird. No other large bird except the Raven shows a completely black plumage; no other call except the Raven's can be mistaken for the Crow's familiar *karr*. In farming country, particularly in the valleys of willow-bordered streams, long lines of Crows pass in late afternoon or early morning to and from some grove in which they roost at night. During the day they alight in open fields or in walnut groves and walk sedately about. On the neighboring trees or fences, individuals are perched whose heads and necks bob vigorously forward when they give the cry of alarm. In spring and less often in fall a flock of Crows indulge in aërial antics, falling and rolling from side to side as they drop. A company of Crows frequently raise a noisy clamor about a tree where a large hawk is perched or in which an owl is hidden, or if the victim flies, stream after it with corvine objurgations. The quality of the *caw* is then much harsher and angrier. Besides the common *caw* or *karr*, which varies in pitch, the Crow utters, particularly in the mating season, a gobble and a high 'gargling' note.

Crows are often seen in very large flocks; Ravens usually singly or in pairs. Crows frequent for the most part cultivated land or its immediate vicinity, especially willow-bordered streams; Ravens inhabit barren mountain ranges, high sea cliffs or the desert. For the distinction between the Raven's cut of wing and tail and its calls, and those of the Crow, see the preceding species.

17–20

Entire plumage black, with purplish gloss in strong light. Bill and feet black.
Dist. — *Cal.* / *Ore.* / *Wash.* } R. in open country, particularly in valleys throughout, but replaced on the coast of *Ore.* and *Wash.* by the next species, and in arid country by the Raven.
Nest, a bulky structure of twigs in trees. *Eggs*, 4–8, greenish or buff, spotted and blotched with gray and brown.

Northwestern Crow. *Corvus brachyrhynchos caurinus*

The Northwestern Crow, or Fish Crow, is almost as much of a shore bird as its fellow scavengers, the gulls. Along the many miles of shoreline around the innumerable arms of Puget Sound, the small black forms and hoarse cries of this crow are characteristic features of the landscape. A trained ear can usually detect the difference in their notes from those of the Western Crow; they are usually slightly hoarser and lower in pitch but vary in pitch and quality and are at times very close to the Western Crow's. In the mating season they have a 'gargling' note similar to that of the Western Crow. In actions and habits, the birds are much the same. They are very conspicuous in the Indian fishing villages along the coast of Washington, walking about in the streets and back yards, perching and cawing on the ridgepoles and gathering along the shore when fish are cleaned. Their small active bodies and quick wing-strokes often suggest European Jackdaws. The differences in size and voice are so slight between the Northwestern Crow of the coast of Washington and Oregon and the Western Crow of the middle and eastern portions that it would be rash to attempt to distinguish the two along the border line between the species.

16–17

Entire plumage black. Bill and feet black.

Dist. — *Ore.* Range not determined, but at least as far south as the northwestern coast.

Wash. Common R. from the mouth of the Columbia R. northward along the coast and on the tide flats of Puget Sound.

Nest, of twigs, deeper than the Western Crow's, with less rim, often in small trees. *Eggs*, like the Western Crow's.

Clarke Nutcracker. *Nucifraga columbiana*

Where the trees on the higher mountain peaks and crests begin to thin out near the timber line, a long grating *kr-a-a-a*, higher pitched than the

CLARKE NUTCRACKER

Jay's notes heard on the lower slopes, sounds from some pine among the rocks and is answered from the neighboring trees. Presently a stoutly built bird, a little smaller than a crow, gray and white, *with black wings and white tail,* flies across the open space with a leisurely crow-like flight, pitching once or twice just before it alights. Clarke Nutcrackers are generally seen in straggling companies which keep up a constant interchange of harsh cries, some like the snarling of a cat, some high and squealing, but usually including the characteristic *kra-a-a,* varying in pitch and loudness. The birds are restless, moving from one tree to another, often lighting in the tops of the branches, making no effort at concealment. The harsh cries, the contrast of black and white, and the familiarity of the Clarke Nutcracker readily distinguish it from any other bird of the high mountains.

12–13

Ad. — Forehead white, rest of head, back and under parts light gray: wings *black with large white patch* along after portion; *tail white* except black central feathers. Bill black, slightly decurved; feet black. **Im.** — Browner.

Dist. — Common R. near timber line, and about open spaces high up in the mountains, in coniferous forests throughout the Coast States; in fall and winter often appearing at lower levels and casually even to the coast.

Nest, of twigs and bark in trees, generally conifers, from 8 to 40 ft. from the ground. *Eggs,* 2–3, pale green, sparingly marked with brown, gray and lavender.

PIÑON JAY. *Cyanocephalus cyanocephalus*

On the eastern slopes of the Sierras, where gray piñon pines alternate with dark green junipers, a loose flock of medium-sized dull blue birds pass in straggling flight with nasal, mewing calls. The flight of the Piñon Jay is crow-like, not pitching like a California Jay's. Piñon Jays feed much on the ground as well as in trees, hopping or walking like crows. Besides the mewing call *quéh-a-eh,* given in flight, they utter, when perched, a continual *queh, queh, queh.* Piñon Jays are great wanderers, appearing at times far out of their regular range. The general dull blue color, the sharp straight bill and their characteristic notes readily identify them.

PIÑON JAY

10–11¾

Ad. — General color dull blue, brightest on head; throat streaked with white. Bill and feet black.

Dist. — *Cal.* Common R. locally along eastern base of Sierras and southward; wanders occasionally in fall and winter, even to the coast.

Ore. Locally common R. on the east slope of the Cascades; casual west.

Wash. One record.

Nest, a bulky structure of twigs, in trees, usually piñons or junipers. *Eggs,* 3–5, bluish white, either minutely speckled, or wreathed around larger end, with light brown and purple.

TITMICE, CHICKADEES, etc.: *Family Paridæ*

TITMICE and CHICKADEES: *Subfamily Parinæ*

PLAIN TITMOUSE. *Bœolophus inornatus* subsp.

Spring comes to the brown hillsides of California as soon as the first rains break the long autumn drought; the cuckoo-flower and ferns push up through the mould, the gooseberries blossom and the Plain Tit begins his lively if monotonous refrain from the live oaks. Different birds have various forms of this spring song, *witt-y, witt-y, witt-y* or *tí-wee, tí-wee tí-wee.* It is always a high clear whistle with a marked accent, and a persistence that shows the relationship of the bird to the Tufted Tit, with its *pée-to*, in the river bottoms of the Middle West. The rest of the year, when the Plain Tit is hunting leisurely through the oaks, his commonest note is a scratchy *tsíck-a-dee-dee* or *tsíck-a-dear*, which has to make up to a California bird lover in the lowlands for the absence of the Black-capped Chickadee. The Plain Tit is not an obvious bird; most people entirely overlook it, because the average individual pays no attention to its squeaky little notes. If one does follow the sound, one sees a rather trim brown bird with a marked crest and a bright black eye hammering a seed energetically against a limb, gleaning among the foliage, and frequently hopping about at the base of the tree, but almost always in or near oaks. The plain gray-brown coloration and the distinct tuft distinguish this bird from all others.

PLAIN TITMOUSE

5–5½

General plumage brownish gray above, light gray below; a *crest on head*, which may be flattened back. Bill dusky above and below, sides light gray; feet dull bluish gray.

Dist. — San Diego Titmouse. [*B. i. murinus.*]
Cal. Common R. of oaks west of the desert divides north to Ventura Co.
Plain Titmouse. *B. i. inornatus.*
Cal. Common R. in oaks and digger pines west of the Sierras, north of Ventura Co.
Ore. Local R. in valleys in southwestern Ore.
Gray Titmouse. *B. i. griseus.*
Cal. Not common and local in cedar and juniper east of the Sierras.

Nest, of fur or other soft material in holes in trees or even in knot-holes in buildings. *Eggs*, 6–8, white, plain or lightly spotted with reddish.

Black-capped Chickadee. *Penthestes atricapillus* subsp.

A band of foraging Chickadees lisping and calling is characteristic of the winter woods of Washington and Oregon even in the lowlands. If we stop to watch the little acrobats clinging to the tips of the twigs, or call them nearer by imitating their whistled *tee dee,* we become aware of other lisping notes, the fine wiry screep of a Creeper as he works up the trunk of a fir, the *ank* of a Nuthatch or the whispered syllables of Kinglets. It is easy to excite the curiosity of Chickadees either by whistling their song or by making a squeaking noise by kissing the back of the hand. They begin to utter excited little notes, *dee-dee-dee* and come nearer. Meanwhile the excitement has aroused the other birds in the neighborhood; the smack of a Junco and the drawling *quee* of an Oregon Towhee is added to the chorus. Finally the excitement dies down and the troop goes on. Besides the note from which the bird derives its name, it has a little gurgling call, suggesting the syllables *sisk-a-dee* delivered rapidly, and the song, two very sweet clear notes, the second an interval lower than the first *tee dee.*

The Black-capped Chickadee is commonest along streams, and is replaced in drier and more heavily wooded regions by the Chestnut-backed Chickadee. The two often occur in the same region but can readily be distinguished, if the back can be seen, gray in the Black-capped, chestnut in the other species. The call notes of the Black-capped are clearer, less hoarse than those of the Chestnut-backed.

$5\frac{1}{4}$–$5\frac{1}{2}$

Top of head black; sides of head white; back light or dark gray; wing feathers more or less edged with white; *throat black,* rest of under parts white; flanks washed with brownish buff in fall, paler in spring. Bill and feet black.

Dist. — Oregon Chickadee. *P. a. occidentalis.*

Cal. R. in extreme north central portion of state, Siskiyou Co.

Ore. } *Wash.* } Common R. along streams and in more open woodland west.

Long-tailed Chickadee. *P. a. septentrionalis.*

Ore. } *Wash.* } Common R. of open woodland east.

Nest, of fur, hair, etc., in holes in stubs. *Eggs,* 5–8, white, spotted larger end with reddish brown.

Mountain Chickadee. *Penthestes gambeli* subsp.

A visitor from the East misses the familiar Black-capped Chickadee from the rich bird life in the lowlands of southern California. Let him, however, climb a few thousand feet up any of the mountain ranges, among the yellow pines, and there will be, if not his eastern friend, at any rate a close relative. The Mountain Chickadee is so close to the eastern bird, so like in voice, habits and appearance, that it will take a few moments to discover the difference. The bird clings head downward to an outer twig, hammers a seed open on a limb, lisps *tsee-dee-dee* to its fellows and is apparently the same active, cheery mite. The sweet whistled call is more often made up of three (sometimes four) notes than that of the Eastern bird. Sometimes the three notes come down the scale to the tune of 'Three Blind Mice.' At other times the last two are the same pitch *tee dee dee.* Occasionally the bird either leaves off the third note or adds a fourth. As the Chickadee gleans from twigs, it utters a hoarse *tsick tsick dee dee* or a husky *tsee dee,* and other little gurgling or lisping calls, and a sharp *tsik-a* when startled or excited. Except in the breeding season Chickadees rove in bands, often associated with other small birds. The chief difference in plumage between the Mountain and the Black-capped Chickadees is the *white line which runs into the black cap over the eye.*

MOUNTAIN CHICKADEE

5–5½

Cap black, broken by a narrow white line from the bill over and behind the eye; throat black; cheeks white; back and tail gray; under parts grayish white (brownish gray on the sides). Bill and feet black.

Dist. — Bailey Mountain Chickadee. *P. g. baileyæ.*

Cal. R. in conifers on higher mountains from San Diego Co. north to Ventura Co., and in Monterey Co.; wanders in winter to lower levels, occasionally to the coast.

Short-tailed Mountain Chickadee. [*P. g. abbreviatus.*]

Cal. R. in conifers in the Sierras and in northwestern Cal., but not on the coast belt.

Ore. *Wash.* } Common R. in conifers along the Cascades as far north as Mt. Rainier, and eastward in winter to the valleys; casual in winter west.

Inyo Mountain Chickadee. [*P. g. inyoensis.*]

Cal. R. in the higher mountains east of the Sierras.

Mountain Chickadee. *P. g. gambeli.*

Wash. Casual near Canadian boundary, one record.

Nest, of fur, etc., in holes in stumps. *Eggs,* 5–8, usually plain white, sometimes faintly spotted with reddish brown.

Hudsonian Chickadee. *Penthestes hudsonicus* [*columbianus*]

The northwestern representative of the Hudsonian Chickadee has been found in heavy timber in northwest Okanagan Co., Wash., close to the Canadian boundary. Its entire upper parts are ashy brown, lacking the white on the nape and reddish brown back of the Chestnut-backed Chickadee.

Chestnut-backed Chickadee. *Penthestes rufescens* subsp.

In the evergreen forests of western Oregon and Washington and in the coast belt of northern California when a band of Chickadees come lisping through the trees, an observer notes their rich *chestnut backs* and when one appears for a moment in strong light, the *dark brown cap.* The notes and habits of the Chestnut-backed Chickadee are very like those of the Black-capped and Mountain Chickadees. It clings to the under side of a twig, or flies to a limb to hammer open a seed or nut. After some practice a student notices that the *zee-zee* notes of the Chestnut-backed Chickadee are hoarser, more rasping than those of the Black-capped (Oregon) Chickadee, and that it frequently utters a *check check* unlike any note of the other Chickadees. Its *tsic tsic tsic tyee* ends in a more drawling, huskier note than its relatives' corresponding call. It is found in Oregon and Washington, particularly in Washington, in stands of conifers chiefly in dry and elevated situations, not in the deciduous growth along streams which the Oregon Chickadee prefers. On the mountain slopes it flocks after the breeding season with the Mountain Chickadee, and everywhere in fall and winter it forms alliances with Kinglets, Nuthatches, Hutton Vireos and other small tree-haunting species.

$4\frac{1}{2}$–5

Ad. — Top of head dark brown; sides of head white, reaching to nape; *back dark chestnut;* throat sooty black; flanks with more or less chestnut; rest of under parts whitish. Bill blackish; feet lead-blue (B.). **Im.** — Black replaced by sooty brown; chestnut duller.

Dist. — Santa Cruz Chickadee. *P. r. barlowi.*
Cal. Common R. in the coast belt from northern San Luis Obispo Co. to the Golden Gate.
Marin Chickadee. *P. r. neglectus.*
Cal. Common R. in the coast belt in Marin Co.
Chestnut-backed Chickadee. *P. r. rufescens.*
Cal. Common R. in conifers in the northern coast belt from Sonoma Co. north to the Oregon line, west to Mt. Helena and the Siskiyou Mts.
Ore. } *Wash.* } Common R. in conifers west.

Nest, of fur, hair, etc., with a heavy base of moss in holes in stubs. *Eggs,* 5–9, white, sparingly spotted chiefly about the larger end with reddish brown.

VERDINS: *Subfamily Remizinæ*

VERDIN. *Auriparus flaviceps flaviceps*

One cannot walk five minutes in the mesquite thickets of the desert or along a wash bordered by palo verde without hearing the sharp, insistent *zee* of the Verdin, or the rapidly repeated *tschik, tschik-tschik,* which is given when the bird is excited or flies with jerky flight to the next bush. After a moment the little gray body and *yellow head* appear as the bird gleans actively among the bushes or clings chickadee-like from the tip of a twig. There is a small *chestnut patch on the bend of the wing,* which shows only when the bird is near and particularly when it opens its wings. The Verdin's nest is a common sight in the mesquite branches, a ball of sticks and fibrous material, oblong in shape with an opening on the side. The Verdin's song consists of three notes, the last two often lower than the first, *tsee, tee tee*. There is no bird with which the Verdin with its yellow head and gray under parts can be confused.

VERDIN

4–4½

Ad. — *Whole head* (except black line from eye to bill) *yellow*, brightest on throat, sometimes extending to upper breast; back, wings and tail ashy gray; *chestnut patch on bend of wing;* under parts, below the yellow throat, ashy gray. Bill black; feet dark gray. **Im.** — Yellow of head replaced by gray; no chestnut on bend of wing.

Dist.—*Cal.* Common R. of mesquite thickets on the deserts of southern Cal., north to Victorville on the Mohave, and to Palm Springs.

Nest, a bulky structure of twigs and grasses, with an entrance hole on the side close to the top, in bushes or low trees. *Eggs*, 3–5, bluish green, speckled chiefly about larger end with reddish brown.

BUSH–TITS: *Subfamily Psaltriparinæ*

Bush-Tit. *Psaltriparus minimus* subsp.

From a live oak a cloud of little gray birds with long tails hurriedly and in twos and threes cross the open space to the next shelter. Twenty or thirty have crossed the open, and still one or two keep crossing and when the observer is sure that the last has crossed, still another flies out and hurries to join the rest. All the time the flock utter gentle high-pitched twittering notes, which become sharper and more prolonged if the birds are startled or alarmed. When feeding, the single birds scatter to the outer twigs, where they often hang like Chickadees. Only during the short breeding season are the birds seen in pairs, busily building the long pendent nest or feeding the numerous young that so strangely manage all to occupy in comfort the bottom of the pouch. As soon as the young can fly, one family group joins the next, and the little bands continue for another winter their busy gleaning from tree to tree.

BUSH-TIT

4–4½

Top of head brownish; rest of upper parts gray or brownish gray; tail half the length of the bird; under parts dull whitish. Bill and feet black.

Dist. — Coast Bush-Tit. *P. m. minimus.*
Cal. Common R. in valleys, foothills and lower mountain slopes in the coastal belt.
Ore. Common R. along the coast.
Wash. R. in the lowlands of the Sound region.
California Bush-Tit. *P. m. californicus.*
Cal. Common R. of the San Joaquin and Sacramento Valleys, northeastward to Modoc Co. and on the eastern slope of the Sierras in Inyo Co.
Ore. R. in the valleys of southern Ore. west of the Cascades.

Nest, a bulky pouch, 8 or 9 in. long, of moss, with an opening at the side near the top, hung in trees at moderate elevations, often in oaks. *Eggs*, 5–9, white.

Lead-colored Bush-Tit. *Psaltriparus plumbeus*

In the desert ranges of southeastern California, a flock of small brown birds with long tails glean among the twigs of juniper or piñon pine, clinging to the twigs like Chickadees, or fly hurriedly one after another across the open space to the next bush or tree. They keep up a constant chorus of slight lisping notes.

4–4½

Upper parts gray; *top of head same color as back;* sides of head brownish; tail long; under parts pale gray, washed with brownish on the flanks and belly. Bill and feet black.

Dist. — *Cal.* Common R. in the desert ranges of southeastern Cal.
Ore. R. in the Steens Mts. of southeastern Ore.

Nest and *Eggs* as in preceding species.

NUTHATCHES: *Family Sittidæ*

Slender-billed Nuthatch. *Sitta carolinensis aculeata*

A sharp nasal *keer, keer* from the yellow pines of mountain slopes or the oaks of the higher foothills calls our attention to a *bluish gray bird* with *black cap* and white breast, working busily over and under the large limbs of trees. The Slender-billed Nuthatch seldom works up the bole of the tree in a perpendicular position; it often comes down the trunk and peers at an observer with head pointing downward and slightly uplifted. More often it works along the large limbs, sometimes peering over the sides or working entirely around to reappear on the

SLENDER-BILLED NUTHATCH

other side. When two birds are working near together, they utter a low *quit quit.* A high *querr* is the alarm note about the nest. In early spring and summer the male repeats a mellow *too too too,* like the blowing of a little trumpet; this song is generally given from a twig, an unusual perch at any other time. Occasionally a Nuthatch forages on the ground at base of trees or on fallen logs.

The black cap and much greater size distinguish the Slender-billed from the Pygmy Nuthatch; the breast and belly are always pure white, never reddish brown as in the Red-breasted Nuthatch, though there is a small reddish brown area far back under the base of the tail. The Red-breasted Nuthatch is sometimes very pale below, but never pure white and can always be distinguished by the black line through the eye bordered above by a white line. The sharp *keer* of the Slender-billed Nuthatch is readily distinguished from the musical twitter of the Pygmy Nuthatch; it is lower than the common call of the Red-breasted Nuthatch, and not so nasal or insistent.

5–6

Ad. ♂. — *Top of head and nape black; back* and middle tail feathers bluish gray; tail short, outer feathers black, with large white spots; sides of head and under parts white; area under base of tail pale reddish brown. Bill long, slender, blackish above, pale at base below; feet dark brown. **Ad.** ♀. — Similar but black of head less clear and more restricted.

Dist. — *Cal.* Common R. of the conifers in the mountains, except in the humid coast belt, also more sparingly in oaks in the foothills of the coast ranges, wanders to lower levels in winter.
Ore. Common R., wandering after breeding.
Wash. Of irregular occurrence, probably R. throughout; more common east; wanders after breeding.

Nest, in holes in trees lined with leaves, hair or fur. *Eggs,* 5–7, creamy white, dotted chiefly about the larger end with reddish brown and lilac.

Rocky Mountain Nuthatch. *S. c. nelsoni.*
Ore. (Baker Co.).

Red-breasted Nuthatch. *Sitta canadensis*

From the firs of western Washington or Oregon or in the higher mountains of California a little horn is steadily blown in spring or early summer, *ank, ank, ank,* in a high-pitched nasal tone. At other times a single note or two calls attention to a small short-tailed bird working along the larger limbs of trees, close to the bark, over and under or even downward head first. Sometimes when the Red-breasted Nuthatch is alarmed either near its nest or on discovering some owl in its hiding place, a different note is endlessly repeated on a higher pitch, *kit, kit, kit.* The Red-breasted Nuthatch is often one of the mixed band of birds that forage in fall and winter through the woods, associating with Kinglets, Creepers, Chickadees and the smaller woodpeckers. At irregular intervals Red-breasted Nuthatches wander in winter far from their breeding range, reaching the coast of southern California in numbers; in other years they remain the whole year in the deep forests of fir. In fall and winter the under parts are rich rusty brown but fade toward spring; the color of the under parts and the *black line through the eye, bordered above by a white line,* readily distinguish the Red-breasted Nuthatch from the Slender-billed Nuthatch; the *black cap* distinguishes it from the Pygmy Nuthatch.

$4\frac{1}{2}$

Ad. ♂. — *Top of head and stripe through eye black;* line over eye white; back and central tail feathers bluish gray; under parts reddish brown or brownish white; outer tail feathers with white spots. Bill dark; feet dark brown. **Ad. ♀ and Im.** — Top of head bluish gray, stripe through eye blackish; usually paler below.

Dist. — *Cal.* R. in conifers of the higher mountains; occasionally common in winter at lower levels.

Ore., *Wash.* } Common R. in conifers, wandering to lower levels in winter.

Nest, of grasses, feathers, etc., in a hole in a stub; pitch is smeared around the entrance. *Eggs*, 4–6, white, spotted with reddish brown.

PYGMY NUTHATCH. *Sitta pygmæa* subsp.

In the open groves of yellow pines along the mountains or in the Monterey pines of the Monterey peninsula, an observer suddenly becomes aware of a band of busy, noisy little birds flying to the thick clusters of pine needles, peering under and over the larger limbs, or flying with jerky, bob-tailed flight to the next tree. They call to one another incessantly with a high staccato *tĭ-dĭ, tĭ-dĭ, tĭ-dĭ,* which becomes a rapid series of high cheeping notes when a number are together, and in spring is combined with a vigorous trill. As they fly they utter a soft *kit, kit, kit.* The size of the Pygmy Nuthatch and the *brown* or *brownish gray head* distinguish it from either the Slender-billed or the Red-breasted Nuthatch, both of which have black crowns. The short tail and habit of working along the large limbs, often head downward, distinguish it from any other small tree-haunting bird.

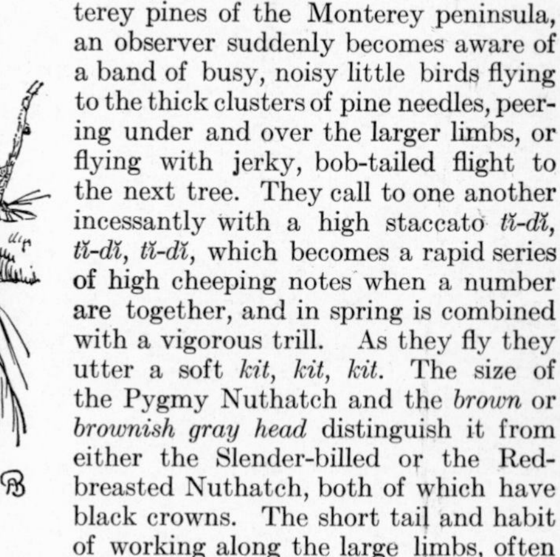

PYGMY NUTHATCH

$3\frac{3}{4}$–$4\frac{1}{2}$

Ad. — Top of head grayish brown, blackish line from bill through eye; *white or gray patch on nape;* tail when spread showing black and white on outer feathers; rest of upper parts bluish gray; under parts white, often dingy on the belly; *tail very short.* Bill chiefly black, light gray at base of lower mandible; feet black.

Dist. — White-naped Nuthatch. *S. p. leuconucha.*

Cal. Common R. of yellow pines in the higher mountains of southern Cal.

Pygmy Nuthatch. *S. p. pygmæa.*

Cal. Common R. locally in pines in the Sierras from Kern Co. north, and along the coast from Monterey to Mendocino Co.

Ore. } Common R. in the yellow pines east.
Wash. }

Nest, of feathers, wool and grass, in a hole in a stub. *Eggs*, 6–9, spotted with reddish brown.

CREEPERS: *Family Certhiidæ*

Creeper. *Certhia familiaris* subsp.

One must have an ear attuned to the faintest lisping notes to become aware of a Creeper. A thin high *screep* sounds from somewhere in the massive trunks of redwood, pine or fir, and if we watch intently, we become aware of a slender brown bird creeping close against the bark of some large limb or fluttering down to the base of a neighboring tree. The tail is pressed close against the rough bark and the head and slender curved bill peer and pry into the crevices for insects or their eggs. The Creeper is pressed so close to the bark that it usually hides its white under parts, except the white throat, which is very evident as the bird looks up from time to time. The Creeper's song begins with the same high sibilant note that constitutes its ordinary call, followed by a more rapid phrase; the whole might be written *tsēē, tsēē, tseé-tsi-tsi-tsēē*. When it flies, it often utters a slight *tsĭ tsĭ*.

CREEPER

If the Creeper is seen, there can be no doubt as to its identity, but both its song and its call notes are easily confused with those of the Golden-crowned Kinglet, with which it is associated in much of its range. The Creeper's call note is more prolonged; the Kinglet's is always two or three short notes rapidly repeated. The Kinglet's song starts upward, then tumbles down in a little run; the Creeper's has distinctly less range.

$5\frac{1}{2}$

Upper parts brown, streaked with white; white or tawny spots in wing; under parts white. Bill slender, curved, black, paler below; feet pallid brownish white (B.).

Dist. — Sierra Creeper. *C. f. zelotes*.

Cal. Common R. in heavy timber from San Diego north on the higher mountains east of the humid coast belt, wandering to lower levels in winter.

Ore. } R. in heavy timber in the Cascades, wandering to
Wash. } lower levels in winter.

California Creeper. *C. f. occidentalis*.

Cal. Fairly common R. in heavy timber in the coast belt from Monterey Co. north.

Ore. Common R. in conifers west.
Wash. Not common R. west.

Rocky Mountain Creeper. *C. f. montana.*

Ore. *Wash.* } Probably the breeding form in the mountains of extreme eastern Ore. (Baker and Wallowa Cos.) and in the Okanagan Hds. and Blue Mts. of eastern Wash.

Nest, of twigs, strips of bark, feathers, etc., behind a strip of loosened bark. *Eggs*, 5–8, white, spotted chiefly about the larger end with reddish brown.

WREN-TITS: *Family Chamæidæ*

Wren-Tit. *Chamœa fasciata* subsp.

Even those who ordinarily have no ear for bird songs often comment on a loud, ringing voice from the chaparral-covered hillsides in the foothills that repeats the same staccato note, finally running the series rapidly together. This is the Wren-Tit, heard a hundred times before it is once seen. If one sits down near some tangle along the trail, a curious *prr, prr* may often be heard, and a bird made out moving about in the depths of some brush, rarely coming into full view. Occasionally one gets a glimpse of a small gray bird with a glaring white eye, and a long ragged-looking broad-tipped tail held at a slight angle above the body. There are different types of the ringing call, varying in the manner with which the last notes are either run together or kept separate. Occasionally the final notes are slightly lower than the opening ones, but never in a descending scale, such as those of the Canyon Wren or the Black-chinned Sparrow. The Wren-Tit also utters a series of similar notes without the ringing quality, and with no increase of speed.

WREN-TIT

The notes of the Wren-Tit are unmistakable, and the bird itself, with its white iris and long tail, often showing the separate graduated feathers at the tip, should be readily recognized. The Bush-Tit has a long tail but the bird is much smaller, has a black eye, and appears often on the tips of outer twigs, instead of skulking in hiding like the Wren-Tit. The Wren-Tit generally keeps close to the ground in low bushes, but occasionally feeds twenty or thirty feet from the ground in dense live oaks. In the interior valleys it is absent in the open country but common on the thickly grown banks of streams; along the humid coast from northern California to northern Oregon it is absent in deep woods but common on the brush-covered bluffs along the coast.

6½

Head and neck grayish brown; rest of upper parts lighter; *tail long* (more than half the length of the bird), the feathers graduated, the central pair much longer than the outer; under parts cinnamon-brown (paler in the southern form); throat and breast streaked with dusky. Bill and feet brown; iris white.

Dist. — Intermediate Wren-Tit. *C. f. fasciata.*
Cal. Common R. of the coast region from San Francisco Bay south to southern Monterey Co.
Pallid Wren-Tit. *C. f. henshawi.*
Cal. Common R. west of the Sierras north to San Luis Obispo and San Benito Cos. along the coast, and in the interior to Shasta Co.
Ore. Probably the form in Jackson and Klamath Cos.
Ruddy Wren-Tit. *C. f. rufula.*
Common R. of the coast belt in Marin, Sonoma and Mendocino Cos.
Northern Wren-Tit. *C. f. phæa.*
Cal. *Ore.* Fairly common R. in a narrow strip along the coast from Humboldt and Del Norte Cos., Cal., north at least to Tillamook Co., Ore.

Nest, neat compact cup of plant fibers in low bushes. *Eggs*, 3–5, pale greenish blue.

DIPPERS: *Family Cinclidæ*

Dipper; Ouzel. *Cinclus mexicanus unicolor*

It is an astonishing sight to see a bird that appears to be a close relative of the thrush and bluebird dive headlong into a foaming mountain stream and disappear in its waters. Without webbed feet or any of the special adaptations of water birds, the Dipper has adopted the water as its element and lives its whole life over and in the pools and waterfalls of brooks and rivers. Its plump dark gray body is usually first seen on some flat stone in the middle of the stream, where it bobs nervously until with a little chattering cry it flies rapidly up and down, close over the water, always following the windings of the stream. Its mossy nest is sometimes placed directly behind a waterfall so that in its passage to and from the nest the bird must dash through the spray. The Dipper's song is strong and sweet, made up of a great variety of trills and flute-like passages, delivered with great spirit and brilliance. All through the year even in the midst of winter storms, the song reëchoes from the canyon walls above the splash of falling water. The uniform *slaty gray* of its plumage, its *stout chunky body*, and its habit of bobbing or curtseying distinguish the Dipper from any other bird; at close range the whitish upper eyelid is frequently seen drawn across the eye. A Dipper feeds either among the rocks in the shallow portions of a stream or along a shore, or by walking under water on the bottom, using its wings to assist its progress. Its common call note is a sharp *bzeet*, or *tsit*, which is rapidly repeated in flight.

7–8.50

Ad. in breeding plumage. — *Entire plumage dark slaty gray;* small white spot on upper eyelid; tail short. Bill black; feet yellowish. **Ad. in winter and Im.** — Paler below; bill yellowish at base.

Dist. — *Cal.* / *Ore.* / *Wash.* } Common R. on mountain streams.

Nest, bulky, of moss, with opening on the side on rocks near water. *Eggs*, 3–5, white.

WRENS: *Family Troglodytidæ*

Cactus Wren. *Heleodytes brunneicapillus couesi*

The dreaded cholla cactus, whose gray spines cling with such persistence to the unwary, has no terror for the birds that nest in the desert. Nearly every sizable clump holds in the upper branches a long rounded mass of grass stalks, with an opening at the side, through which one can see the lining of feathers and often the young of the Cactus Wren safely guarded by the prickly barrier. From a distant clump of cactus the penetrating call of the Cactus Wren is repeated, and answered from another farther off. The rapidly uttered *choo-choo-choo-choo* is one of the most characteristic sounds of the desert. The Cactus Wren, like all its tribe, can slip and slink out of sight in spite of its unwrenlike size. But if one drives through the winding desert roads, its brown body is a frequent sight flying off with a pitching flight, showing the white tips of the outspread tail. The bird feeds much on the ground, hopping about at the base of sheltering clumps of cactus, from which issue its scolding notes when disturbed, *chut-chut-chut*, or when more excited a hoarse *chair chair chair*. Often a Cactus Wren perches on the top of a tree yucca or cactus, and shows the dark streaks that unite to form a band across the breast, the white line over the eye and, when it turns, the dark brown top of the head. When perched it frequently jerks its tail.

CACTUS WREN

$8–8\frac{3}{4}$

Top of head and nape rich brown, unstreaked; *stripe of white from bill over eye;* back grayish brown, streaked with white; wings dusky barred with white; tail long, slightly rounded, all but the central feathers blackish barred with white; throat and upper breast with large black spots forming almost a band;

rest of under parts with smaller spots; lower belly reddish brown. Bill slightly curved, dark gray, paler below; feet light gray.

Dist. — *Cal.* Common R. in the deserts of southern Cal. and about San Diego, north in dry washes along the coast to Los Angeles Co. and east of the mountains to Owens Valley.

Nest, bulky, of sticks, grasses, etc., conspicuously placed horizontally in cactus or thorny bushes with opening at one end. *Eggs*, 4–7, whitish or buffy, spotted, often very heavily, with reddish brown.

Rock Wren. *Salpinctes obsoletus* subsp.

Wherever rocks have disintegrated and left scattered boulders on hillsides, or long talus slopes on mountain-sides, often far from any stream, a small gray bird bobs energetically on some solitary rock, or if undisturbed pours out of its long slender bill trills and sweet notes that suggest the perfect technique and joyous vigor of a Mockingbird. The volume is much less and there is much less variety, *tí-ou, tí-ou, tí-ou, tí-ou,* is a common strain, then perhaps *flee flee flee*, or *cheep-oo cheep-oo cheep-oo*, each strain definite, and succeeded by another quite distinct with a change of pitch. The call note, often given with an energetic bob, sounds like *tick-ear*. When the bird spreads its tail just before it alights on a projecting rock, it displays a black band near the ends of the outer feathers, which are deeply edged with whitish or buff. There is no difficulty in identifying this active little creature, which plays hide and seek with the observer in and out of the rocks. The Cañon Wren rarely strays far from water, and is at once recognized by the *pure* white throat and upper breast and the deep chestnut of the belly. In the Rock Wren the breast is *dull* white finely speckled, and there is no reddish brown on the belly.

ROCK WREN

5–6

Top of head, upper back, wings and tail grayish brown (speckled in strong light with dusky and white); whitish line over eye; lower back reddish brown; the outer tail feathers black near tips and broadly tipped with tawny; under parts dingy white, tinged on the flanks and lower belly with tawny. Bill slender, dusky above, light brown below; feet dusky.

Dist. — Rock Wren. *S. o. obsoletus.*
- *Cal.* Fairly common R. in any rocky region; more widespread in winter.
- *Ore.* Not common R. east of the Cascades, casual west.
- *Wash.* Common S.V. (Mar.–Nov.) east of the Cascades.

San Nicolas Rock Wren. *S. o. pulverius.*
Common R. on San Nicolas I., Cal.

Nest, usually in crevices of rocks, of grasses, rootlets, etc., always with a collection of pebbles or chips of rock leading to the nest opening. *Eggs*, 5–8, white, finely and sparsely spotted with reddish brown.

CAÑON WREN. *Catherpes mexicanus* subsp.

Where rocks are piled loosely along the steep sides of a canyon, a small bird slips in and out of the crevices, its brown head and white breast appearing for an instant over the edge of the rock, or perched for a moment on a boulder, bobbing vigorously. When the Cañon Wren shows its whole body, the deep *chestnut of the belly* shows in *marked contrast to the white breast*. This deep chestnut belly distinguishes the Cañon Wren at once from the Rock Wren, which occasionally inhabits the same pile of rocks or talus slopes. From the bare grim walls of rock the Cañon Wren pours out a cascade of sweet liquid notes, like the spray of a waterfall in sunshine. The opening notes are single staccato notes followed by long-drawn double notes, *tsee-i, tsee-i,* slower and descending in pitch, ending with still lower *tóo-ee tóo-ee tóo-ee.* When slipping in and out of crevices, the Cañon Wren almost always makes its presence known by a constant series of sharp little protesting notes, *tschee tschee.* If in its journeyings up and down the mountain stream the Cañon Wren finds human habitations or woodpiles, it enjoys like other wrens climbing along the eaves and ridgepoles or slipping in and out of logs and brush.

CAÑON WREN

$5\frac{1}{2}$–$5\frac{3}{4}$

Ad. — Top of head, back and wings brown, lightly speckled with black and white; lower back and tail rich reddish brown, tail crossed by four or five narrow black bars; sides of head, *throat and upper breast white, rest of under parts abruptly passing into dark reddish brown.* Bill long, slender, slightly curved, dark above, paler below, especially toward the base; feet dusky.

Dist. — Nevada Cañon Wren. *C. m. conspersus.*

Cal. Fairly common R. on the desert ranges east of the Sierras; occurs widely over southern deserts in winter.

Ore. R. in the Steens Mts. in Harney Co.

Wash. Possibly the form resident in the Grande Ronde region.

Dotted Cañon Wren. *C. m. punctulatus.*

Cal. Fairly common R. locally in the mountains of southern Cal. north to Shasta Co., and sparingly in west central Cal.

Ore. Rare R. in southern and central eastern Ore.

Wash. Probably R. in eastern Wash.

Nest, of twigs and moss, in crevices in rocks or about buildings near streams. *Eggs*, 3–6, white, spotted with reddish brown and lilac.

BEWICK WREN. *Thryomanes bewicki* subsp.

From any chaparral-covered slope where the Wren-Tit's ringing note is heard, from thickets along streams or in the broken country among desert hills, from late winter on, a clear high song is heard which somewhat resembles a Song Sparrow's. When the song is analyzed it is found generally to consist of three distinct parts, a high quick opening of two or more notes, then lower notes rather *burry* in quality, and in closing a very delicate fine trill. There are endless variations, but the three distinct parts can almost always be distinguished in the full song; occasionally the first or last are left off. If the singer is found, perched on some high twig with tail depressed, a white line over the eye and a fairly long, slender, slightly curved bill mark him as one of the many subspecies of the Bewick Wren.

BEWICK WREN

In the fall many Bewick Wrens move down from the chaparral slopes and inhabit shrubbery near habitations, though some stay in the canyons all winter. In and out of the vines or flower beds about the house or from twig to twig in the lower trees, the Wrens slip actively, rarely giving one an opportunity to observe the *white line over the eye* and the *long tail broader at the tip than at the base*. They are talkative at all times. The commonest note, either single or repeated, is a high-pitched energetic *chick, chick*, or *whit, whit.* This may be varied to a throaty *kut, kut, kut.* Another characteristic note is a harsh *spee* or *chee*, like a Shrike's in miniature.

The Bewick Wren in winter frequents the same places in the lowland which the House Wren occupies in summer; occasionally both are present at the same time. For a beginner the line over the eye is the unfailing mark of a Bewick Wren. After long acquaintance the longer, more expressive rounded tail, the lighter throat and breast and the grayer, less brown upper parts of the Bewick distinguish it from the House Wren (see following species). Both birds have a harsh call-note but the House Wren has no note like the *chick, chick, chick* of the Bewick. In summer the House Wren rarely invades the chaparral or brush in which the Bewick is at home.

$5\frac{1}{2}$

Upper parts brown; *long whitish line over and back of eye;* tail comparatively long, rounded, all but central *tail feathers black, tipped with white*, showing when tail is spread; throat whitish; rest of under parts light gray. Bill long, slender, slightly curved, blackish above, lighter below; feet brownish.

Dist. — Desert Bewick Wren. *T. b.* [*eremophilus*] = *T. b. bairdi.*

Cal. Fairly common in the desert ranges of southeastern Cal.

San Diego Wren. *T. b. charienturus.*

Cal. Common R. in the chaparral of southern Cal. west of the desert divides, north to Santa Barbara and Mt. Pinos, Ventura Co.

Catalina Island Wren. [*T. b. catalinæ.*]
Catalina I.
San Clemente Wren. *T.* [*b.*] *leucophrys.*
San Clemente I.
Santa Cruz Wren. [*T. b. nesophilus.*]
Santa Cruz and Santa Rosa Is.
San Joaquin Wren. [*T. b. drymæcus.*]
Common R. of chaparral, and along banks of streams in the lowland throughout the San Joaquin and Sacramento basin, and north to Modoc Co.
Vigors Wren. *T. b. spilurus.*
Common R. from northern Monterey Co. to the Golden Gate and around south arm of San Francisco Bay at least to Berkeley.
Nicasio Wren. [*T. b. marinensis.*]
Fairly common R. along the coast from San Francisco Bay north to Humboldt Co.
Seattle Wren. *T. b. calophonus.*
Ore. / *Wash.* } Common R. in brushy places west.

Nest, bulky, of sticks and feathers, in holes in trees or in buildings, or in crevices or crannies. *Eggs*, 5–7, white or pinkish speckled with reddish brown and lilac.

Western House Wren. *Troglodytes aëdon parkmani*

Few birds so well express the abounding vitality so characteristic of birds as the House Wren. In and out of brush and tangled thickets, expressing its moods with a variety of scolding and chattering notes, cocking its tail from the ridgepole, or on the dead limb in which it is nesting, or bubbling over with its energetic and tuneful song, in any situation and at any time the Wren is vigorous and alive. When feeding, the Wren threads its way through the foliage of low bushes, or in and out of brush heaps like a mouse, protesting against intrusion with a rapid *churr, churr, churr* or a harsh scolding note like the syllable *chee.*

WESTERN HOUSE WREN

The various subspecies of the Bewick Wren are often found either in the same region as the House Wren, or near by. The former breeds generally on wilder chaparral-covered slopes, while the House Wren prefers either forest country, or gardens and buildings. In winter most of the House Wrens migrate; only a few remain even in southern California. At this season Bewick Wrens move down from the chaparral and occupy the gardens. The House Wren has a shorter tail, a darker throat and breast and no white line over the eye. The song of the House Wren has a greater uniformity of character, not being readily separated into distinct parts like the Bewick's. The scolding call of the House Wren is harsher and more guttural than the Bewick's.

5

Upper parts brown, wings and tail waved with dusky; *tail short;* under parts gray, lightly waved with dusky. Bill short, slender, dusky above, lighter below; feet brown.

Dist. — *Cal.* Common S.V. (Mar.–Oct.) nearly throughout; a few winter north to central Cal.

Ore. / *Wash.* Common S.V. (Apr.–Sept.) throughout, probably casual W.V. west.

Nest, bulky, of twigs, lined with feathers, in holes in trees or in buildings. *Eggs*, 5–8, pinkish white, thickly spotted with reddish brown or purplish brown.

Western Winter Wren. *Nannus hiemalis pacificus*

In May and June in the deep forests of the northwest coast the tinkling song of the Winter Wren is a constant and delightful sound. At the edge of a clearing, or where a stream has made an opening in the tall ranks of Douglas firs, the tiny brown birds slip in and out of the tangled roots of some fallen giant or perch on a stub and pour out their runlets of melody. The song is easily recognized; it is wren-like in the rapidity with which the notes are shaken out, but it is thin and high, and goes on and on with one set of quavering notes after another as if it could never stop. When the Wren is seen, it suggests the House Wren, but is darker, smaller and has an extremely short tail. The alarm note is an emphatic *chick*, a little like a Song Sparrow's, often rapidly repeated. When excited, the bird bobs like a Rock Wren. It occurs in migration and in winter in dense thickets, skulking in brush heaps and tangled vegetation. Its call note and habit of bobbing distinguish it from the occasional House Wren which winters in the same region.

WESTERN WINTER WREN

4

Upper parts dark brown, a faint line over the eye; wings and tail barred with blackish; *tail very short,* under parts brownish, paler on belly. Bill slender, short, dark above, paler below; feet brown.

Dist. — *Cal.* Common R. in the northern high Sierra region, from the Yosemite north and in deep forests along the coast from Monterey Co. northward; in winter occurs more widely through northern and central Cal. and in small numbers as far south as Los Angeles Co.

Ore. / *Wash.* Common R. in thick forests throughout; more widely distributed in migration.

Nest, chiefly of moss and twigs, in crevices in roots or stumps of trees. *Eggs*, 5–7, white, sparingly dotted with reddish brown.

MARSH WREN. *Telmatodytes palustris* subsp.

From the tules that border marshes or irrigation ditches comes an emphatic scolding *tuk, tuk, tuk*, followed by a burst of rapid bubbling notes, then another preliminary *tuk, tuk,* and a second explosion, like the rapid vibration of a stringed instrument. Another bird answers and another. Then one singer appears almost at the top of the tule, and clinging to the edge of the stalk, his tail cocked backward toward his head, he splutters out all the tunes in his music box. It is hard to get a good view of a Tule Wren. The bird climbs in and out of the reeds and slips along the ground under them, scolding with a harsh *churr, churr, churr*. When he comes into view, the general color is brown above, gray below; a close inspection shows an area of black in the middle of the back and a *faint white line over the eye.*

TULE WREN

$4\frac{1}{2}$–$5\frac{1}{2}$

Top of head and back brown; *a white line over eye;* a patch of black in the middle of the back, usually striped with white; tail brown, barred with dusky; under parts white, tinged with brown on the sides. Bill blackish above, pale below; feet brown.

Dist. — Tule Marsh Wren. *T. p. paludicola.*

Cal. R. in marshy tracts along the coast from Los Angeles Co. to San Francisco Bay region.

Ore. / *Wash.* } Not uncommon R. in marshes west.

Suisun Marsh Wren. [*T. p. æstuarinus.*]

Cal. R. in the marshes around San Francisco and from Merced Co. in the San Joaquin Valley, northward at least to Colusa and Sutter Cos.; occasional in winter south to Los Angeles Co.

Western Marsh Wren. *T. p. plesius.*

Cal. S.V. in northeastern Cal. (Modoc Co.); abundant W.V. in southern Cal. from the Colorado and Mohave Deserts to the coast.

Ore. } Common S.V. in marshes east, common in winter in
Wash. } eastern Ore. and rarely in eastern Wash. southerly.

Nest, a ball of tule stems or stems of aquatic plants and supported by living tules. *Eggs*, 5–7, brown, heavily speckled with darker brown.

THRASHERS, MOCKINGBIRDS, etc.: *Family Mimidæ*

Sage Thrasher. *Oreoscoptes montanus*

The sage-brush plains of eastern Oregon often cover the landscape with a gray mantle as far as the eye can reach. This country is the home of the Sage Thrasher. Here it lives and moves and has its being, showing its *white-spotted tail* as it flies across the road, or its *streaked breast* and

SAGE THRASHER

straight slender bill as it perches on the top of a sage bush. When the bird is perched, the tail is jerked upward at infrequent intervals; the straight bill gives the head a pointed look in flight. When on the ground, the Sage Thrasher runs and stands much like a Robin. When alarmed it often runs on the ground concealed by intervening bushes, instead of flying. In April and May when the birds are mating, the male Thrasher gives vent to its ardor, not by mounting in the air like many ground birds, but by flying in a somewhat clownish zigzag low over the sage. At the end of this flight the bird lights with wings upraised and flutters them for an instant. Its song, given from the top of the sage or from a fence post along the road, is a long succession of warbling phrases with very little range of pitch and with constant repetition of one accented note. The bird's alarm note is a *chuck*, *chuck* suggesting a blackbird, and a sweet high *wheurr*.

In fall and winter and early spring Sage Thrashers are common on the deserts on the east side of southern California, feeding on the ground among the desert bushes or flying off when startled. The general brown color, straight pointed bill and above all the white spots on the outer tail feathers are sure recognition marks, in all the country north of Tehachapi; in southern California the Cactus Wren also shows white-tipped tail feathers. (See p. 240.)

8–9

Ad. — Upper parts grayish brown; wing with two narrow white bars; *outer tail feathers edged and tipped with white;* the others (except the central pair) tipped with white; throat white, bordered by narrow brown lines; *under parts* whitish, tinged with buffy brown and *streaked*, especially on the breast, with lines of small dusky spots. Bill straight, shorter than head, blackish, paler at base; iris yellow; feet black in front, light brown behind.

Dist. — *Cal.* Common W.V. on the deserts of southeastern Cal. and in small numbers west of the mountains; S.V. in sage-brush plains and high valleys from Ventura Co. north chiefly east of the Sierras.

Ore. *Wash.* } More or less common S.V. (Apr.–Oct.) in sage-brush east.

Nest, bulky, of stems and leaves of sage, in a sage-bush. *Eggs*, 3–5, greenish blue, spotted with brown.

Western Mockingbird. *Mimus polyglottos leucopterus*

It is one of the surprises of a bird student on his first visit to the Coast to see Mockingbirds singing from the chimneys of a hotel, flirting their long tails on the curbing of city streets or pursuing one another in and out of city traffic. All they ask are yards about the houses, a bit of lawn to feed on and vines or thick bushes in which to nest. The Mockingbird is an extremely trim and elegant figure with a very expressive tail. When the bird is on the ground or on a post, the tail is generally held at an upward angle. In southern California Mockingbirds begin to practice their varied repertoire at any time after the first rains and in March they go mad with ecstasy. A Mockingbird in the height of the breeding

WESTERN MOCKINGBIRD

season pours forth one brilliant phrase after another, modulating skillfully from one to the next, and when song alone fails to express his ardor, he flies up a few feet from his perch and flutters down again with wings and tail spread. Mockingbirds sing much at night, especially on moonlight nights. Individual Mockingbirds differ greatly in their repertoire. Many sing chiefly their own songs, made up of high clear notes repeated rapidly a number of times; these are clearer and more rapidly repeated than the phrases of the California Thrasher. Occasionally a bird adds to his own song remarkable imitations of the sounds he hears about him, chiefly the notes of other birds. These imitations are generally harsh sounds, like the notes of California Woodpeckers, Shrikes, Kingbirds or the Ash-throated Flycatchers, or rapidly repeated phrases like those of the Plain Tit or Cactus Wren. Besides the song, the commonest notes of the Mockingbird are a loud smack or kissing sound, and a harsh, grating *chair*.

Beginners often have difficulty in distinguishing a Mockingbird from a Shrike. The Mockingbird is much more slender with a head not heavy in comparison with the body, and a slender bill. The Shrike is chunkier, has a large head and powerful bill. (See p. 271.) The Mockingbird gives the general effect of a gray bird, with a large white patch across each wing and white outer tail feathers; the Shrike shows much more black contrasted with white. The Mockingbird has an easy level flight; the Shrike uses rapid wing-beats till he can reach his perch by an upward pitch.

$10\frac{1}{2}$

Upper parts dark gray; a *large white patch across blackish wing; outer tail feathers white their whole length,* next two pairs with much white; throat and belly whitish; breast light gray. Bill black; iris light grayish yellow (Ridgway); feet blackish. **Im.** — Upper parts brownish gray; under parts spotted.

Dist. — *Cal.* Common R. of the southern deserts, along the coast north to Santa Barbara, and in the interior to the Sacramento Valley.

Nest, bulky, of sticks, lined with finer materials, in thick bushes, thorny trees or vines. *Eggs,* 4, pale bluish or greenish, boldly marked with reddish brown.

CATBIRD. *Dumetella carolinensis*

The *slim gray form, blackish cap* and *chestnut under tail-coverts* leave no doubt as to the Catbird's identity. The bird slips into the tangle of bushes along a stream, snatches now and then a little fruit from the garden, and, half hidden in a bush, sings a mixture of fine phrases and harsh notes. Besides the mewing call that has given the bird its name, it has a mellow *chuck* and occasionally a grating chatter, *kak, kak, kak.* When it hops along on the ground or on a fence, the tail is either cocked at an angle or thrown jauntily from side to side, with an alert, saucy air.

8–9

Entire body *slaty gray,* except the head and tail, which are *black;* feathers under base of tail chestnut. Bill and feet black.

Dist. — *Cal.* Accidental.
Ore. Locally common S.V. (May–Sept.) east.

Wash. Fairly common S.V. (May–Sept.) in brushy regions along streams and draws east; accidental west.

Nest, of twigs and strips of bark, in bushes. *Eggs*, 3–5, dark glossy greenish blue.

Bendire Thrasher. *Toxostoma bendirei*

Probably not a dozen readers of this book will ever see a Bendire Thrasher in California. The bird has been found breeding on the Mojave Desert and east of Palm Springs, but in such limited numbers that a search through those arid wastes would be almost a hopeless task. The Bendire may be told from Le Conte and Crissal Thrashers by the *short, straight bill* and by the pale grayish brown spots on the breast. The song of the Bendire Thrasher is a continuous very sweet warble, quite different in form from the succession of short phrases which make up the usual Thrasher song.

$9\frac{1}{2}$–$10\frac{1}{2}$

Upper parts pale grayish brown; under parts brownish white; tail feathers with faint whitish tips; breast faintly spotted with grayish brown. Bill and legs black.

Dist. — Extremely rare and local in southeastern Cal.

California Thrasher. *Toxostoma redivivum*

Near brushy foothills, when everything is quiet, a large brown bird will often come out from the bushes and begin to hack in the ground vig-

CALIFORNIA THRASHER

orously with a long, curved bill. At the least alarm it runs rapidly into cover, the long tail held up at an angle behind. As it runs, a small patch of rusty brown under the tail is evident. In almost any month of the year, and regularly and freely after the winter rains, the California Thrasher's song rings out from all the chaparral-covered slopes, or from the thickets along streams. The singer is perched on some high twig, the long tail depressed, and the curve of the long bill evident in silhouette. When seen near to, the white throat shows plainly. The song is made up of separate phrases, some of them sweet and musical, others rather harsh; there is a tendency to repeat each phrase. Singers vary in excellence; occasionally one is strikingly good and might be confused with a Mockingbird, but as a rule the Thrasher lacks the brilliance and the rapid utterance of the Mocker. Thrashers occasionally mock but to a very limited extent. The common call is a sharp *hreek*.

$11\frac{1}{2}$–13

Upper parts dark brown; sides of head darker; wings short; *throat whitish;* breast grayish brown, darker than upper belly; lower belly and area under tail rusty brown. *Bill long, strongly decurved,* black; feet dusky.

Dist. — *Cal.* Common R. in foothills and brushy valleys west of the desert divides north to Shasta Co.

Nest, bulky, of sticks in bushes. *Eggs,* 3–4, greenish blue, speckled with brown.

Le Conte Thrasher. *Toxostoma lecontei lecontei*

As one drives over the deserts of southeastern California a dark green sea of creosote-bush extends on every side as far as the distant horizon. Each bush is separated from the rest by an open space of gravelly soil and the bushes themselves are made up of loosely spreading branches that hardly hide the ground beneath. But try to follow the *slim, ashy gray bird with long, curved bill* that runs off among the bushes and get a lesson in the game of hide and seek. With *blackish tail* cocked up the bird runs almost as fast as a horse, always keeping the thickest cover between himself and the observer. Only occasionally when a motor car comes suddenly upon him does he fly a short distance before he dives down among the bushes. In spring the silence of the desert is broken by a loud musical outburst from the top of a cactus or mesquite, the bird sitting thrasher-fashion with his tail depressed and long, curved bill wide open. Throughout the northern part of its range in California, the Le Conte Thrasher is the only Thrasher present, but from Palm Springs south and east, the Crissal Thrasher must be reckoned with; the Le Conte Thrasher generally keeps to the level wastes covered with low bushes, while the Crissal Thrasher prefers the thick clumps of mesquite. The light gray of the Le Conte distinguishes it from the much darker brown of the Crissal. The common call is a low whistled *hew-eep*.

$10\frac{1}{2}$–11

Upper parts light grayish brown, except the dusky tail; stripe of whitish, narrowly bordered by dusky, along side of throat; under parts pale buffy white, darker on breast; area under tail yellowish buff. Bill blackish; iris reddish brown; feet dark brown.

Dist. — *Cal.* Fairly common R. of the deserts from the Colorado R. west to Palm Springs, north to Walker Pass, and in the southern end of the San Joaquin Valley, north to Wasco.

Nest, bulky, of twigs, grasses, etc., lined with plant wool, in cactus, mesquite or low bushes. *Eggs,* 3–4, pale bluish green, sparsely speckled with reddish brown or lavender.

CRISSAL THRASHER. *Toxostoma crissale*

Each clump of mesquite in the loose sand of the Coachella Valley is finally raised on a mound of sand and forms a dense haven of refuge for Cactus Wrens, Plumbeous Gnatcatchers and Crissal Thrashers. From somewhere in the thicket the Thrasher, if undisturbed, pours forth after the winter rains a succession of spirited phrases, very like those of the California Thrasher but somewhat more musical, sweeter and less vigorous. At the least hint of intrusion the bird slips down into the thicket. Here its long slim form shows now and again as it slips from one bough to another, or picks briskly on the ground with its long, curved bill. Occasionally the right pose will reveal the dark reddish brown area under the base of the tail, the crissum from which it gets its name. The common call note of the Crissal Thrasher suggests the syllables *chi-déary.*

The ranges of the California and Crissal Thrashers barely overlap; south of Palm Springs there are no California Thrashers, north of the Gorgonio Pass no Crissal Thrashers. The Le Conte's Thrasher is a bird of more open country than the Crissal, with paler upper parts and a much paler crissum.

$11\frac{1}{2}$–$12\frac{1}{2}$

Upper parts brownish gray; throat white with a dusky bordering stripe; breast and belly light brownish gray; *area under base of tail dark reddish brown.* Bill black; iris yellow; feet dusky.

Dist. — *Cal.* Common R. of the low ground in the desert from the Colorado R. west to Palm Springs, and as far north as Needles.

Nest, bulky, of twigs, in mesquite or other desert bushes. *Eggs,* usually 3, pale green.

THRUSHES, SOLITAIRES and BLUEBIRDS: *Family Turdidæ*

TOWNSEND SOLITAIRE. *Myadestes townsendi*

On steep, rocky, fir-covered slopes above a tumbling mountain stream, a long, slim, gray bird flies from a low dead stub to the ground, picks up an insect and flies back to another perch. In flight it shows *white outer tail feathers,* and a row of narrow *buffy spots in the wing,* giving it somewhat the appearance of a dwarfed and duller-colored Mockingbird. The Townsend Solitaire feeds much like a Bluebird, except that its point of vantage is more often in the shade than in the open. Occasionally it flutters to the side of a tree trunk, skillfully picking off an insect, or lights on logs and rocks. It sings usually from a bare stub on the top of a tall tree, often a hundred feet above the ground. The song consists of high, clear warbled phrases, with the quality of the Black-headed Grosbeak's song and a tempo between that of the Warbling Vireo and the Purple Finch. The song is continued on an average for about twenty seconds. In the height of the mating season the Solitaire leaves its lofty perch and flies upward in a series of spirals and then, high above the canyon walls or wooded mountain slopes, flies about with wings and tail spread uttering its clear notes; finally it plunges downward 'in a succession of steeply pitched zigzags' (Whittle) and returns to the dead stub or joins its mate near the nest. The alarm note is a single, metallic *eek*, like the creak of a rusty wheel.

TOWNSEND SOLITAIRE

$7\frac{3}{4}$–$9\frac{1}{2}$

Ad. — General coloration gray, paler below; *a narrow white ring around eye;* whitish edging of feathers showing on closed wing; narrow buffy bar across blackish wing showing when wing is spread; *outer tail feathers edged and broadly tipped with white.* Bill and feet black. **Im.** — Spotted with buff.

Dist. — *Cal.* Common R. of high mountains; in winter descends to lower levels.

Ore. / *Wash.* Fairly common R. on the higher mountains, descending in winter to lower levels.

Nest, of twigs and moss, on the ground, at the base of a tree, or in a crevice of a bank, often on rocky slopes above a stream. *Eggs*, 3–5, whitish, spotted with reddish brown.

Willow Thrush. *Hylocichla fuscescens salicicola*

From the willow thickets that border the streams in eastern Oregon and Washington there issues in summer a song which in quality of tone surpasses any but that of the Hermit Thrush. The song is made up of three or four phrases, which suggest the syllables *vée-ury,* each lower in pitch than the preceding, followed by notes which vibrate like those of a stringed instrument. The whole performance, coming from the depths of a thicket, especially in late evening when only a few other species are still singing, has a mysterious charm, suggesting gypsy music. The singer often precedes the song with a call note, *phew* or *phee-oo,* which may be either low and sweet, or uttered more sharply and in a higher pitch. The Willow Thrush is seldom seen. A bird occasionally flies low and rapidly from one thicket to another, and if an observer waits quietly in the covert which is its home, he may at last see the bird's *tawny brown back* and the buffy wash across the breast, which is indistinctly spotted with yellowish brown, not sharply with black as in the other thrushes. The Olive-backed Thrush is often found in the same willow thickets, but may be distinguished by the buffy eye-ring, the grayer tone of the brown upper parts and the blackish spots on the white breast.

7–7¾

Ad. — Entire upper parts uniform brown, tinged in strong light with tawny; breast and sides of throat washed with buff, lightly spotted with tawny brown. Bill dusky above, pale below at base; feet pale brown.

Dist. — *Ore. Wash.* Not common S.V. (May–Aug.) near water, in *Wash.* from the eastern base of the Cascades to the eastern border; in *Ore.* in the eastern tier of counties.

Nest, of leaves, on or near ground. *Eggs*, usually 4–5, greenish blue, occasionally speckled with reddish brown.

Russet-backed Thrush. *Hylocichla ustulata ustulata*

One soon learns to recognize the song of a thrush by the quality of the tone, even though the form of the song varies greatly in the different species. From the dense thickets of willow along stream beds in the lowlands of southern California, or from any damp shaded coverts west of the Sierras and Cascades farther north, one hears in spring and summer a succession of phrases ascending in pitch and charged with the unmistakable vibrant timbre of a thrush. The Russet-backed Thrush, owing to the nature of its haunts, is even more difficult to see than the Hermit Thrush. It feeds, like the Hermit, on the ground, running over the damp shaded earth, drawing its form up when it halts, and showing as it faces the observer a buffy breast, spotted with brown. Its *upper parts* are of *uniform color*, lacking the contrast of reddish tail and brown back which characterizes the Hermit, nor does it raise its tail when excited as the Hermit does. Often its presence in its leafy retreat is announced by a variety of call or alarm notes which vary in pitch and intensity. The commonest are a sharp but mellow *whit*, a *whee* which often changes in

RUSSET-BACKED THRUSH

pitch and a harsh grating *cherrr*. The Russet-backed Thrush is the only thrush that one hears in the lowlands of California. Here and there it ranges well into the Hermit's country, but even then keeps to the thickets along the streams, and does not frequent the open coniferous groves where the latter is found. In northeastern California and in eastern Oregon and Washington the Russet-backed Thrush is replaced by its eastern form, the Olive-backed, from which it cannot be distinguished in the field. (See below.)

7–7½

Upper parts russet brown; eye-ring buffy; sides of head tinged with buff; upper breast pale buffy, marked with dark brown spots; belly whitish. Bill dark above, pale below; feet pale brown.

Dist. — *Cal.* Common S.V. (Apr.–Aug.) in the vicinity of streams, west of the desert divides; common M. throughout.

Ore. / *Wash.* Common S.V. (Apr.–Sept.) near water west.

Nest, of twigs, moss and grasses, in bushes or small trees. *Eggs*, usually 3–5, light greenish blue, spotted with brown.

Olive-backed Thrush. *H. u. swainsoni*

In appearance, habits and notes the Olive-back is practically identical with the Russet-back. The two can be distinguished in the field only by their respective choice of breeding places, the Russet-backed in willows west of the Sierras and Cascades, the Olive-backed chiefly in firs eastward.

Dist. — *Cal.* Fairly common S.V. from the vicinity of the Warner Mts. (Modoc Co.) south along the eastern slope of the Sierras to the region about Mammoth, Mono Co.

Ore. / *Wash.* Not uncommon S.V. (May–Aug.) in timber from eastern slope of Cascades eastward.

Nest and *Eggs* as in Russet-backed Thrush.

Hermit Thrush. *Hylocichla guttata* subsp.

In winter in southern California a small trim brown bird runs a few steps on the lawn, picks something from the ground and then draws itself up, showing, when it faces about, a white breast heavily spotted with black. When startled it flies to the nearest bush or tree, and as it perches on a twig it slowly raises its reddish brown tail, often at the same time nervously opening and closing its wings. Its alarm note, often uttered at the same time, is a low *chuck*, frequently given two or three times rapidly. Another note given from its hiding place is a harsh nasal *pee*, or a clear *chee* without the nasal quality. At no time in its winter home do we hear the full, beautiful cadences of its breeding song, though a wintering bird occasionally utters in late spring a few whispered phrases of its song.

In cool canyons and on the chaparral-covered hillsides, especially where the Christmas-berry flourishes, Hermit Thrushes often call from some bushy shelter or fly silently from one thick bush to the next. In such places Fox Sparrows also are common in winter. The Hermit Thrush and the Fox Sparrow resemble each other closely in general coloring, but the thrush has a slender bill, and stands high on slender legs, the Fox Sparrow has a short thick bill, and its body is nearer the ground. The Thrush never scratches for food; the Sparrow scratches vigorously, jumping forward and bringing both feet backward over the dry leaves or loose earth. (See p. 322.)

DWARF HERMIT THRUSH

Hermit Thrushes belonging to subspecies different from the wintering Hermits, but identical in habits and in general appearance, nest in high or cool forests. On the breeding ground it is the song rather than the sight of the bird that attracts our attention and identifies the singer. There is no other song with which any one with a good ear will confuse it; it includes three or four passages, separated by considerable intervals and at higher or lower pitch, but each opens with a flute-like note that is held a moment. It is this opening note that gives the performance the effect of a chant of sacred music. None of the other fine performers among the mountain birds, the Fox Sparrow, the Green-tailed Towhee or the Solitaire, has the same spiritual quality of tone, or gives the effect of religious ecstasy.

The territory which the breeding Thrushes occupy is also the home of breeding Fox Sparrows, but the former are rarely seen except in groves of trees, whereas the Fox Sparrow occupies open tracts covered with thick bushes. The slow raising of the reddish tail is the sure mark of the Thrush.

$6\frac{1}{2}$–$7\frac{3}{4}$

Head, back and wings brown (of various degrees of warmth in the different forms listed below, darker in the winter visitants, grayer in the breeding birds); *tail reddish brown*, in marked contrast to the back; under parts white, throat and breast spotted with black. Bill dusky above, paler beneath; feet light brown.

Dist. — Alaska Hermit Thrush. *H. g. guttata*.

Cal. Common W.V. (Oct.–early Apr.) in valleys and foothills throughout. Birds apparently of this form found breeding near the coast of Humboldt Co.

Ore. Common W.V.

Wash. Principally migrant (Feb.–May; Sept.–Dec.) west of the Cascades, less common east. A few doubtless winter.

Dwarf Hermit Thrush. *H. g. nana*.

Cal. Common W.V. (Oct.–early Apr.) along the coast, common in the San Francisco Bay region, less common south.

Ore. } M. west.
Wash. }

White Mountains Hermit Thrush. [*H. g. polionota.*]

Cal. S.V. on the White Mts., Inyo Co.

Sierra Hermit Thrush. *H. g. sequoiensis.*

Cal. Fairly common S.V. (Apr.–Sept.) in the higher mountains.

Ore. } Common S.V. (Apr.–Sept.) in the Cascades, and in
Wash. } Wash. west to the Olympics.

Monterey Hermit Thrush. *H. g. slevini.*

Cal. Fairly common S.V. along the northwest coast from Monterey Co. north to Humboldt Co.; migrant in southern Cal.

Audubon Hermit Thrush. *H. g. auduboni.*

Ore. } S.V. in northeastern Ore. and in the Blue Mts. of south-
Wash. } eastern Wash.

Nest, of twigs, bark strips, rootlets, etc., generally in low trees. *Eggs*, 3–4, pale green.

Varied Thrush; Oregon Robin. *Ixoreus nævius* subsp.

In deep forests of fir in western Washington and Oregon where the sun barely struggles through to fleck the lower branches, out of the silence comes a long-drawn quavering note with something of the quality of escaping steam; after a short interval the note is repeated in a higher pitch, again in a lower, *ee-ee-ee-ee.* The notes have a meditative quality due to their deliberation and above all a strangeness due partly to their quality and partly to the complete invisibility of the singer. By patient waiting an observer finally discovers on one of the limbs of the tree (rarely on the topmost spray) a stout Robin-like bird, with a conspicuous *black collar across a deep orange breast.* In winter Varied Thrushes move southward to the lower levels and to the mountains of California; in some years they are common in cool canyons even to the coast. They feed on frozen apples and madrone berries and in southern California are often found on the ground under live oaks, flying up at the least alarm and uttering a low *tsch* or *ŏŏk.* They are at all times shy and secretive birds. In flight they

VARIED THRUSH

show buffy spots in the outstretched wing and white tips on the outer tail feathers; the rich coloring of the throat and the dark collar readily identify them. When perched, the head and neck are generally more in line with the body than a Robin's.

9–10

Ad. ♂. — Upper parts slate-color, a stripe of orange behind eye; two bars across wing and a patch in the wing orange-brown; outer tail feathers tipped with white; under parts orange-brown, changing to white on lower belly; *black collar across breast.* Bill black; feet dull yellowish. **Ad.** ♀. — Paler; upper parts and collar grayish brown. **Im.** — Similar to ♀, but with only an imperfect collar, or collar absent; breast speckled with dusky brown.

Dist. — Varied Thrush. *I. n. nævius.*

Cal. Common W.V. in the northern coast belt north of Monterey Co.; breeds sparingly in Humboldt Co.

Ore. / *Wash.* } Common R. in heavy forests.

Northern Varied Thrush. *I. n. meruloides.*

Cal. Irregularly common W.V. (Oct.–Mar.) in the interior and southern parts of the State west of the desert divide.

Ore. / *Wash.* } M. and W.V. (Sept.–Apr.) throughout.

Nest, bulky, of twigs, grasses and moss, in saplings or trees at a moderate height. *Eggs*, 3–4, pale greenish blue, sparingly spotted with brown.

WESTERN ROBIN. *Planesticus migratorius propinquus*

Happy the community where Robins wake a lover of rural sounds with their early morning chorus. This chant is heard only where the soil remains moist enough to breed angle-worms for a Robin to tug at and carry squirming to his brood. Washington and Oregon have Robins in the dooryards, in the blossoming (and ripening!) cherry trees, but in southern California school-children know the Robin chiefly from literature or from a summer camping trip in the mountains. In the fall Robins appear in California lowlands, particularly in olive orchards and pepper trees; here toward spring they practice somewhat half-heartedly their cheerful song. The song is a series of rising and falling phrases, four often constituting a series, which is then repeated or varied. In summer Robins sing most vigorously before it is light, and after continuing for about an hour, disperse to feed. Then there is desultory singing from individuals through the morning,

WESTERN ROBIN (♂)

and at dusk another general but not quite so vigorous chorus. The Robin's common call note, given when perched, is a single low *pip, pip*, often followed by a low *tut, tut*, which becomes a shrill *pip, pip, pip*, when the bird gives vent to excitement. Another common call note often given in flight is a shrill *tsee, tsee*. The Robin's strangest note is a high, thin *hiss*, often given from the ground, and inaudible except within a few feet of the bird. When a Robin flies over an observer, the white feathers under the tail offer a striking contrast to the darker breast. Just after alighting, a Robin pumps its tail vigorously once or twice.

10–11

Ad. ♂ in breeding season. — *Top and sides of head black*, eyelids and spot before eye white; back gray; wings brown; tail black (outer feathers occasionally with small white tips); throat white, streaked with black; area under base of tail white; *rest of under parts reddish brown. Bill yellow*, upper mandible tipped with black; feet blackish. **Ad. ♀.** — Head and tail the same color as the back; breast paler than in ♂; throat whiter; bill less yellow. **Ad. in winter.** — Upper parts browner; reddish brown of breast veiled with the white edgings of the feathers. **Im. in summer.** — Back speckled with whitish; breast spotted with black; indistinct wing-bars.

Dist. — *Cal.* Common S.V. on the mountains and in the foothills of the Sierras, also in parks and gardens around San Francisco Bay; winters abundantly but irregularly elsewhere, even on the deserts.

Ore. } *Wash.* } Common S.V. throughout, many wintering west of the Cascades, and less commonly east.

Eastern Robin. *P. m. migratorius.*

Wash. One record.

Nest, bulky, of twigs and grasses, usually with a core of mud, in trees or against buildings. *Eggs*, 3–6, greenish blue.

Western Bluebird. *Sialia mexicana occidentalis*

When the tops of the mountains reflect the first rays of the winter sun, small bands of Western Bluebirds fly overhead, their chestnut breasts showing dark in the sunlight, calling to each other with a staccato *pew, pew*. All through the foothills pairs or groups perch on the telephone wires or on fence posts, the head and neck bent slightly forward, giving the bird a round-shouldered look. They visit the edges of grain and bean fields, or feed in company with Audubon Warblers and Linnets on the ground in walnut orchards. They are very fond of mistletoe berries and frequent the huge clusters of this plant in the trees along the rivers that flow from the Sierras to the interior valleys. In March the small flocks break up into pairs and go chiefly to the high wooded hills or lower mountain slopes, among the oaks and yellow pines, but a few breed even in the low country where the mountains come close to the sea. In the breeding season the male utters a low *chu, chu, chu*, apparently his only song, but before dawn a camper among the pines hears a chorus of the rich call notes repeated from all sides as if from birds flying about in the darkness.

The *deep chestnut breast* of the male and the rich blue of his outspread wings and tail are unmistakable. A beginner might take a Lazuli Bunting for a Bluebird, if he did not see the two white bars on the Bunting's wing. The chestnut breast distinguishes the Western from the Mountain Bluebird. Females of the two species resemble each other closely. Both are chiefly brownish, except in flight, when they show blue on the outspread wings and tail. The female Western Bluebird has a *wash* of *reddish brown* on the *sides* of the *breast* which the female Mountain Bluebird lacks.

$6\frac{1}{2}$–7

Ad. ♂. — *Head and upper parts deep blue*, except a chestnut patch in the back (sometimes divided by blue into two patches, or absent); throat blue; rest of *under parts chestnut*, fading to gray on the belly. Bill and feet black. **Ad.** ♀. — Brownish above and below, except the bluish upper surface of wings, rump and tail; a wash of light reddish brown on sides of breast; eye-ring whitish. **Im.** — Similar to ♀, but rump gray, and breast more or less streaked with whitish.

Dist. — *Cal.* Common R. in the foothills and the yellow pine belt of the mountains; common at lower levels in winter.
Ore. Common R. west; common S.V. locally east.
Wash. S.V. (Feb.–Nov.) both east and west; a few winter.

Nest, in deserted woodpecker holes, or in other cavities in trees, occasionally, and in Wash. commonly, in bird boxes. *Eggs*, 4–6, pale bluish green.

Mountain Bluebird. *Sialia currucoides*

When a male Mountain Bluebird flies from a fence post and spreads his azure wings and tail, the beauty of the color brings an exclamation of delight even from a casual observer. In winter any extensive open country, such as the wheat fields of interior California, is visited by flocks of Mountain Bluebirds. The females are brownish below, but here and there are males with the *entire plumage pale turquoise blue.* Over the open fields individuals may be seen flying a few feet above the ground, then suddenly mounting a short distance, and hovering with rapid wingbeats, tail spread and feet dangling. If an insect is espied, a graceful flight to the ground secures the prey; if nothing is discovered, another short flight ends in another moment of hovering. The Mountain Bluebird at all times is singularly silent. An occasional low *terr* is its commonest note, uttered by a flock in flight. The only song which the writer has heard is the repetition of a few short notes, like the syllables *kĕ kŭ* or *kŭ, kŭ, kŭ.* When concerned about their young, the parents utter a vigorous *tschuk, tschuk.* In March Mountain Bluebirds return to their breeding grounds in the high mountains. They breed chiefly on the higher, more barren ranges and particularly east of the main divides. Here they occupy holes in trees, chiefly in open groves, burns or clearings, but in the plains of eastern Oregon and Washington they nest commonly in buildings in settlements.

The *absence of any chestnut on the breast* distinguishes the male Mountain Bluebird from the commoner and more widely distributed Western Bluebird. The female Mountain Bluebird lacks the dull wash of reddish brown on the sides of the breast which characterizes the female Western Bluebird. As a rule the Mountain Bluebird sits straighter on a perch, with head up, less round-shouldered than the Western Bluebird.

7–7¾

Ad. ♂. — *Entire plumage*, except the whitish belly, *turquoise or rich cerulean blue.* Bill and feet black. **Ad.** ♀. — Brownish except blue rump and tail, and wings, which are tinged with blue; belly whitish. **Im.** — Like ♀, but rump ashy gray; breast and sides streaked with whitish.

Dist. — *Cal.* Locally common S.V. chiefly on the eastern slopes of the high mountains; wanders irregularly in winter (Oct.–Mar.) to open country even to the coast.

Ore. Common S.V. (Feb.–Nov.) east; less common in winter.

Wash. Common S.V. (Feb.–Nov.), mainly east but also on Mt. Rainier; casual in migration to the coast.

Nest, in deserted woodpecker holes, and in eastern Ore. and Wash. in bird-boxes or about dwellings. *Eggs*, usually 5, pale greenish blue.

KINGLETS and GNATCATCHERS: *Family Sylviidæ*

GNATCATCHERS: *Subfamily Polioptilinæ*

Western Gnatcatcher. *Polioptila cærulea obscura*

A petulant little note, like the syllable *pee*, sounds from the thickets of chaparral on the foothills, or in winter from almost any cover of bushes

WESTERN GNATCATCHER

and low trees. If we follow the sound, we find a dainty *bluish gray* bird, flitting actively among the twigs, constantly cocking its long, slender *black tail* or flipping it from side to side, or when opening it in flight showing conspicuous white outer feathers. In the breeding season a close inspection of the head of the male shows black across the forehead and in front of the eye, but the *top* of the head is *bluish gray*.

The song, generally heard only at the height of the mating season, is a squeaky performance, like the syllables *chee cheer chee che*, followed by two or three little warbled phrases.

The Western Gnatcatcher can readily be distinguished from both its Black-tailed and Plumbeous congeners if the tail is spread and shows the *outer tail feathers white for their full length*. The gray of the upper parts is lighter in the Western Gnatcatcher and the call note is not so whining or so cat-like, but sharp and emphatic though slight. North of Ventura County, California, the Western Gnatcatcher is the only species to be expected, south of that the Black-tailed and the Western occur together in canyon washes, and south and east of Palm Springs the Western and the Plumbeous occur together in the desert in winter.

$4\frac{1}{2}$–5

Ad. ♂ in breeding plumage. — Most of head and all of *back bluish gray;* eye-ring white; forehead and line in front of eye black; tail black, the *two outer feathers on each side white* for much of their length; under parts white. Bill and feet black. **Ad. ♂ in winter.** — Lacks the black on forehead. **Ad. ♀.** — Lacks the black on forehead; color of head and back duller, more brownish.

Dist. — *Cal.* Common R. in chaparral-covered slopes from San Diego northward, locally to Shasta and Mt. St. Helena; in winter common on the deserts to the Colorado R.

Nest, a compact cup of plant fibers in shrubs or trees, ornamented with lichen. *Eggs*, 4–5, white, spotted with reddish brown.

PLUMBEOUS GNATCATCHER. *Polioptila plumbea*

In the thorny mesquite thickets in the Colorado Desert south of Palm Springs, or in the rank growth of salt-bush on the desert floor, a male Gnatcatcher in spring and summer shows a glossy black cap which at once distinguishes it from the Western Gnatcatcher of the chaparral-covered foothills further north. In winter, however, both species are common on the desert east to the Colorado River, and as the Plumbeous Gnatcatcher loses its black cap at that season, it is difficult to distinguish the two species. The darker gray of the Plumbeous Gnatcatcher and the small amount of white in the tail when spread are helps to

PLUMBEOUS GNATCATCHER (♂)

identification, but the call notes are often the only sure distinctions. The call of the Plumbeous Gnatcatcher is a series of two or three short notes, *chee chee chee*, unlike the single emphatic *pee* of the Western. The song of the Plumbeous Gnatcatcher is a slight *tsee-dee-dee-dee-dee*, suggesting a chickadee. The Plumbeous and Black-tailed Gnatcatchers are still more difficult to distinguish in appearance, but fortunately their ranges are practically distinct. The actions of the Plumbeous Gnatcatcher are very similar to those of the two other species; it hunts actively through bushes and low trees, constantly flipping its slender tail to one side or the other.

$4\frac{1}{2}$

Ad. ♂ in spring and summer. — Top of head glossy black; back bluish gray (duller than in the Western Gnatcatcher); *outer web of outer tail feather white*, inner web tipped with white, the next tipped with white; under parts white. Bill and feet black. **Ad. ♂ in early winter.** — Head same color as back. **Ad. ♀.** — No black on head; upper parts duller. **Im.** — Upper parts brownish.

Dist. — *Cal.* Common R. of the desert north to Palm Springs, and along the Colorado R. to Needles, less common in the Mohave.

Nest and *eggs* as in preceding species, but nest not decorated.

Black-tailed Gnatcatcher. *Polioptila californica*

Few birds are so restricted either in the nature of their haunts or in the extent of the country they inhabit as the Black-tailed Gnatcatcher. It is found only in Southern and Lower California, in the stony plains along the western slopes of the foothills, over which the mountain streams in flood have spread their load of rock and gravel. These plains are overgrown with sumach, cactus and sage, and in these bushes the little Gnatcatcher spends its days, slipping from one bush into the next, flipping its black tail from side to side, and calling to its mate with a drawling *pee-e-ee*, very similar in tone to that of the Western Gnatcatcher but prolonged and with a downward inflection, suggesting the mew of a little kitten. The tail is nearly black; the outer feather is only narrowly edged with white, so that when the tail is spread in flight, there

BLACK-TAILED GNATCATCHER (♂)

is no such display of white as in the Western Gnatcatcher. The Western Gnatcatcher, especially in winter, is common in the same out-wash plains and dry canyon-sides that the Black-tailed inhabits, but it is possible after a little practice to distinguish the two by appearance as well as by note. The coloring of both upper and under parts is darker in the Black-tailed than in the Western Gnatcatcher; the latter, when seen breast on, looks white compared with the dull gray of its Black-tailed cousin. The male Black-tailed Gnatcatcher in spring and summer has the whole top of the head glossy black, and is easily distinguished by this mark from the Western at that season, but not from the Plumbeous Gnatcatcher. The two black-capped species, however, do not overlap. (See preceding species.)

4½

Ad. ♂ in spring. — Top of head black; eye-ring white; *back dark gray; tail blackish* with merely a white edge to the outer feather; under parts dull gray, *tinged with brownish on belly.* Bill black; legs dusky. **Ad. ♂ in winter.** — Lacks the black cap. **Ad. ♀.** — Head dull gray, otherwise like ♂.

Dist. — *Cal.* Summer R. in out-wash plains along the slopes of the foothills west of the mountains from San Diego Co. through Los Angeles Co.

Nest and *eggs* as in the Western Gnatcatcher.

KINGLETS: *Subfamily Regulinæ*

Western Golden-crowned Kinglet. *Regulus satrapa olivaceus*

In the deep forests from the Sierras north through Oregon and Washington a slight, lisping note is a characteristic sound from the thick branches of the firs. A close examination discloses a small gray bird, which shows now and then a *yellow or orange crown, bordered by black lines.* In winter the Golden-crowned Kinglet is common along the coast as far south as Monterey, associating with Chickadees, Creepers and Nuthatches, as they glean among the branches. It is difficult for a beginner to distinguish the thin notes of the Kinglet, *zee, zee, zee,* from the wiry *scree* of the Creeper, which is found in summer and winter in the same forests. The Kinglet's call is broken into separate syllables; the Creeper's is usually given as one prolonged note. The song of the Golden-crowned Kinglet sounds as if the bird were mounting a tiny stairway of lisping notes and then tumbling down at the end. The Kinglet feeds in the thick clusters at the tips of the twigs, and often flutters for an instant in front of the spray to pick off small insects. It is very active, constantly opening and shutting its wings even when perched. It may be distinguished from the Ruby-crowned Kinglet by its notes, quite unlike the harsh *kerr* of the latter, and by the fact that the crown-patch of the adult bird is always visible and always bordered by black lines. The female's crown-patch is yellow, the male's orange.

4

Ad. ♂. — Upper parts gray, with a greenish tinge in strong light; wing-bars whitish; *crown orange, bordered by yellow and black;* line over eye white; under parts dull whitish. Bill and feet black. **Ad. ♀.** — Crown-patch entirely yellow, bordered by black. **Im.** — Lacks yellow crown-patch; black border very indistinct.

Dist. — *Cal.* Not common R. in the higher mountains and along the coast from Marin Co. north. Common W.V. along the coast north of Monterey, more sparingly elsewhere south to Los Angeles Co.

Ore. / *Wash.* } Common R. in heavy conifers, M. elsewhere.

Nest, a mass of moss, hung in a dense spray of a conifer. *Eggs*, 5–11, white or buffy, speckled usually with reddish brown.

Ruby-crowned Kinglet. *Regulus calendula* subsp.

From October to April every bush or tree in the gardens and parks and on the wooded hillsides of southern California is visited sooner or later by the active gray form of a Ruby-crowned Kinglet. If an observer follows up the little grating *kerr* of the bird, he finds a tiny creature, olive gray above and paler beneath, with a prominent black *eye encircled by a whitish ring*, and with two dull whitish bars across the wing. There are often two birds in different parts of the same tree, but for the most part the birds are widely scattered and only single birds are met. The bird moves restlessly from one twig to the next, picking off an insect here and there and constantly half opening and closing its wings, even when perched. Toward spring when two males are pursuing each other or in courtship when a male is showing off, the whole head blazes into a scarlet patch as the head feathers are erected and their red bases revealed. For the most part there is only a narrow line of scarlet visible well back on the head, not bordered by black as in the Golden-crowned Kinglet.

In March, and occasionally earlier the wintering males begin to sing. The song varies greatly in different individuals but at its best is extremely musical and astonishingly loud for so tiny a performer. It begins with two or three high notes which are uttered at increasing speed, then a soft *kew, kew, kew*, followed by a phrase of three syllables *teé-di-di*, which is repeated two or three times. This charming song is heard constantly in the high mountains from the firs in which the Kinglet breeds. Besides the common harsh *kerr*, the Ruby-crown has an alarm note *chüp, chüp*, and a rapidly repeated *whil, whil, whil*, when excited.

In winter the Hutton Vireo, which is almost an exact larger edition of the Ruby-crowned Kinglet, is frequent in the live oaks of the lowlands. To distinguish the two, note the brisk active ways of the Kinglet, and its nervous habit of flitting its wings. The Vireo is a stockier bird and much more deliberate in its movements. It drops lazily from one twig to the next, and often stays for some seconds motionless or with only a slight movement of the head. The Vireo at close range shows a heavier bill and a more prominent eye.

$4–4\frac{1}{2}$

Ad. ♂. — Upper parts gray, with a greenish tinge in strong light, rump olive; crown with a partially concealed patch of scarlet feathers; eye-ring white; two whitish wing-bars. Bill and feet black. **Ad.** ♀. — Lacks the scarlet crown-patch.

Dist. — Western Ruby-crowned Kinglet. *R. c. cineraceus.*
Cal. S.V. in the higher mountains; winters (Oct.–Apr.) abundantly in the lowland.
Ore. } Common M. throughout and S.V. (Apr.–Oct.) to coni-
Wash. } fers in the mountains, chiefly east.
Sitka Kinglet. *R. c. grinnelli.*
Cal. }
Ore. } Common W.V. along the coast from Monterey Co.,
Wash. } Cal., northward.

Nest, a bulky structure of bark, feathers and moss, hung in a branch of a conifer. *Eggs*, 5–9, whitish or buffy, finely spotted with reddish brown, chiefly about the larger end.

PIPITS: *Family Motacillidæ*

Pipit; Titlark. *Anthus rubescens*

As one walks through low open fields in winter or along the beach, brown birds rise with a sharp *tsip-tsi-tsip*, and fly off with a rather jerky flight. When they settle again on the ground, the tail is oscillated. The general color of the upper parts is brown, the bill is slender and the breast streaked; the *outer tail feathers show white* as the bird rises. The bird walks with an easy tripping gait or runs rapidly after an insect. When a number of birds fly over, the flock is not compact; they alight and feed in the same loose formation. Pipits occasionally light on fence wires and low posts, even on telephone wires. When not startled, the call consists of single or double notes like the syllable *tseep*, rather sharp and high. Horned Larks often feed in the same country as the Pipits, and have very similar notes. The Pipit's notes are lighter, more musical and often made up of more syllables than the Horned Lark's. The Horned Lark has a double note, one syllable higher than the other which is characteristic, but often gives only a single *tseep*, which is more sustained than the short quick call of the Titlark. There should be no difficulty in distinguishing the two birds when they are on the ground. The Pipit is a slender bird, not stocky like the Horned Lark, and it lacks the black and yellow markings of the Lark's throat and head; in flight the Pipit shows more white in the outer tail feathers and no blackish central tail feathers. The Pipit moves its tail up and down constantly; the Horned Lark never.

PIPIT

6–7

Ad. — Upper parts grayish brown; *outer tail feathers white;* line over eye whitish or buffy; under parts varying from dingy white to buffy; breast and sides streaked with dusky. Bill slender, blackish, base of lower mandible paler; feet brown.

Dist. — *Cal.* Common W.V. (Sept.–May) to lowlands throughout.
Ore. Common migrant and W.V. west (Sept.–May); S.V. in the Wallowa Mts.
Wash. Common migrant (Feb.–May; Aug.–Nov.); S.V. to the high mountains in the Cascades; perhaps occurs in winter west.

Nest, bulky, of moss and grasses on the ground. *Eggs*, 4–6, heavily spotted with grayish brown.

WAXWINGS: *Family Bombycillidæ*

Bohemian Waxwing. *Bombycilla garrula*

Flocks of silky-plumaged birds occasionally descend in winter on the berry-bearing trees and shrubs of northern villages and even cities. Bohemian Waxwings settle in close array on a tree and sit motionless and almost silent with elevated crests, or wheel off when startled in a compact flock. The note of the Bohemian Waxwing given when the birds wheel off in flight is a low rough *scree*, with more body than the sibilant call of the Cedar Waxwing. The flight is rapid; the bird alternates two or three strokes of its long, pointed wings with an instant's sailing. When both Waxwings are together in a flock, the larger size of the Bohemian is clearly evident; when the Bohemian Waxwings are alone, as often in midwinter, the lack of yellow on the belly, the *white spots on the wings* and the *chestnut patch under the base of the tail* distinguish them.

$7\frac{1}{2}$–$8\frac{3}{4}$

Plumage silky; upper parts shading from reddish brown on head to clear ashy gray on rump and tail; wings blackish; crest long, either elevated or depressed; chin and streak through eye black; *spots on wing white*, shorter wing feathers often tipped with red appendages; tail deeply tipped with yellow, *belly gray;* area under *tail chestnut*. Bill blackish; feet black.

Dist. — *Cal.* Irregular W.V., rarely south of northern Cal.
Ore. Irregular W.V. (Nov.–Apr.); commoner east.
Wash. Regular W.V. (Sept.–late Apr.), principally east, less regular west, sometimes in flocks of thousands; probably casual S.V. and breeding northeast.

Nest, bulky, of grasses, moss, etc., in trees. *Eggs*, 3–5, bluish white spotted with black.

Cedar Waxwing. *Bombycilla cedrorum*

A compact flock of medium-sized birds fly overhead in spring and fall, showing light under parts, and perch close together in the upper branches of some tree. If they fly close to the observer, he hears very thin notes like the syllable *zee*. When they alight, their snuff-brown heads show crests, and their bellies are pale yellow. All their plumage is sleek, as if freshly preened. On warm quiet days when insects are flying, Cedar Waxwings fly out and up from a perch, catch an insect and then drop gracefully back; the yellow edging of the tail is then conspicuous. At other times they feed on pepper and mistletoe berries or on small fruit, reaching far over to pluck a berry from a twig too slender to support their weight. The red wax-like tips of the flight feathers of the wing are present on some birds, absent on others. At no time has the Cedar Waxwing any other note than the sibilant described above, though when a flock all flies off together the notes become a little higher and sharper.

CEDAR WAXWING

Only the Bohemian Waxwing can be confused with the Cedar Waxwing. The other birds that have a crest of brown feathers are the Plain Titmouse, much smaller and never in flocks that perch motionless and silent, and the female Phainopepla, which is generally accompanied by black males. To distinguish the Bohemian Waxwing from the Cedar Waxwing takes careful observation. The latter has no white spots on the wing, the cinnamon color of the breast fades to yellowish not grayish on the belly, and the area under the base of the tail is whitish.

$6\frac{1}{2}$–$7\frac{1}{2}$

Ad. — Plumage silky; upper parts shading from rich cinnamon on top and sides of head to ashy gray on tail; long crest elevated or depressed; some of the shorter wing feathers often tipped with red appendages; tail tipped with yellow; line through eye and across forehead black; chin black; breast cinnamon, shading to *yellowish on belly*. Bill blackish; feet black. **Im. in late summer.** — Brownish gray, paler below; everywhere streaked with whitish.

Dist. — *Cal.* Irregular M. and W.V.; S.V. to northwestern Cal.
Ore. Common S.V. (May–Oct.); a few may winter.
Wash. Common S.V. (late Mar.–early Nov.), wandering irregularly in the fall; a few winter.

Nest, a bulky structure of twigs, grasses, moss, etc., in trees. *Eggs*, 4–5, bluish, spotted with black.

SILKY FLYCATCHERS: *Family Ptilogonatidæ*

Phainopepla. *Phainopepla nitens*

South of Palm Springs where the mistletoe forms conspicuous brown clumps in the mesquite and palo verde, slender black birds show here and there against the sky line. As one walks through the thicket, a muffled *whŭp* comes from the distant birds and a harsh *cherr* from those whose privacy is disturbed. The male is a striking and elegant creature, a trim *glossy black* figure with a conspicuous crest, showing in flight *pure white wing-patches*. The flight is easy, with slow wing-strokes and with a rather jerky effect; after the bird alights, the tail is jerked.

PHAINOPEPLA
♂ and ♀

When the birds are paired, a slim brown female shares the bush with the male. She lacks the white wing-patch, but shows in flight a pale area in the brown wing. In the nesting season the males sing constantly but not with great enthusiasm; *chee tit cherr-a-wee* or *chee werr* suggest the rather harsh notes of their somewhat formless and listless song. The male is often more active than the female in building the nest, and shares with her the task of incubating the eggs and feeding the young. Long after the birds in the mesquite of the Colorado Desert region have hatched their young, Phainopeplas invade the foothills of the hot country as far north as the Sacramento Valley. They breed there on oak-covered hillsides or in washes of canyon streams. At all seasons the Phainopepla is an expert flycatcher, flying up or out from its elevated perch and dropping back after the capture of its prey. Besides the mistletoe, pepper-trees and other small fruit furnish food in winter.

7–7¾

Ad. ♂. — Entire plumage *glossy black*, except a *broad white patch in the wing; crest* of long, loose feathers, either elevated or depressed. Bill and feet black; iris red. **Ad.** ♀. — Entire plumage dark gray, browner below; a light gray area in the dark wings, showing in flight; crest as in male. **Im.** — Similar to ♀ but white edgings conspicuous on feathers of wings and tail.

Dist. — *Cal.* Common R. in the deserts in southeastern Cal.; common S.V. locally in foothills and valleys north to southern Shasta Co. Winters irregularly in the interior valleys north of Tehachapi and regularly in the deserts southward.

Nest, rather shallow, of twigs, plant fibers, etc., on a limb at a moderate elevation. *Eggs*, 2–3, grayish or greenish white, well speckled with brown or blackish.

SHRIKES: *Family Laniidæ*

Northern Shrike; Northwestern Shrike. *Lanius borealis* [*invictus*]

One occasionally sees in winter in Washington or Oregon a black and white bird about the size of a Robin flying with a series of quick wing-strokes followed by a long upward slide to the top of a bush, small tree or post, or hears the bird from its perch utter a succession of harsh calls, mews and screams, interspersed with a few sweet notes. Sometimes a wanderer over the winter fields finds a small bird or a mouse which a Shrike has wedged into a fork or impaled on thorns. The marked contrast of black and white, and the characteristic flight, two or three rapid strokes, followed by a scaling pitch on set wings, distinguishes the Shrike from all other birds of the open fields, except the closely allied White-rumped and California Shrikes. The latter are rare or absent in winter north of northern California, but an absolute determination of the Northern Shrike depends on the absence of black over the base of the bill. (See next species.)

$9\frac{1}{4}$–$10\frac{3}{4}$

Ad. — Upper parts ash-gray, becoming whitish on forehead, over the eye and on the rump; a blackish stripe back of the eye, extending to the base of the bill, *not over the bill;* wing black with white bar; tail black, outer feathers tipped with white; under parts grayish white, crossed with dark wavy lines which show only at close range. Bill and feet blackish. **Im.** — Upper parts grayish brown; wings and tail duller than in adult, under parts much more distinctly crossed with dark gray wavy lines.

Dist. — *Cal.* Irregular W.V. in northern Cal.
Ore. Not common W.V. (Oct.–Mar.), commoner east.
Wash. Fairly common W.V. (Oct.–Mar.), less common west.

California Shrike / White-rumped Shrike } *Lanius ludovicianus* subsp.

At intervals on the telephone wires along highways are perched stoutly-built birds with whitish under parts that show much black and white in the wings and tail in flight. They are commonly near open fields, to which they descend from time to time to seize a grasshopper in the bill. When they fly off, they fly low with a pitching flight and, just before they reach a landing station, two or three rapid beats of the short wings are followed by a long upward sail to the tip of a bush or to a telephone pole. The broad black bar through the eye, the stout bill and heavy head are conspicuous marks. The ordinary notes of the Shrike, when excited, are extremely harsh; a hoarse *tee* is the commonest cry. As the mating season approaches and occasionally even in fall, the Shrike repeats without much animation more musical notes, *chil-lip*, *che-urr* and *klo*.

CALIFORNIA SHRIKE

The Shrike is sometimes confused by beginners with the Mockingbird. The Shrike is generally found where single trees or low bushes are separated by open spaces and the Mockingbird in yards and plantations, though in the desert and near ranch buildings the two species are often found together. The Shrike is plump and stocky with a heavy head and bill; the Mockingbird is slender with a head and neck narrower than the body. The Shrike when perched shows a marked contrast of black and light gray; the Mockingbird is nearly uniform gray with a small white bar on the wing. In flight each bird shows white in the extended wing, but the Shrike shows this contrasted with black. The Shrike's tail shows white tips as well as white margins, in sharp contrast with black.

8–10

Ad. ♂. — Top of head and back dark bluish gray; broad line of black from bill through eye, meeting its fellow on forehead; *wings black with white bars;* rump white or whitish; inner tail feathers black, the *outer chiefly white*, the next tipped with white; under parts white. Bill and feet black. **Ad.** ♀. — Similar but duller; under parts less white. **Im.** — Black and white less clear; under parts clouded or waved with dusky.

Dist. — White-rumped Shrike. *L. l. excubitorides.*
Cal. Common R. of the desert regions east of the Sierran divide.
Ore. } *Wash.* } Fairly common S.V. (Mar.–Sept.) east.
California Shrike. *L. l. gambeli.*
Cal. Common R. west of the Sierran divide, chiefly in the open inland plains and valleys.
Ore. Not common R. west.
Wash. Apparently casual M. and S.V. (Apr.–Nov.) southerly.
Island Shrike. *L. l. anthonyi.*
Cal. Fairly common R. on some of the Channel Is.

Nest, a bulky structure of twigs in thick bushes or low trees. *Eggs*, 4–7, gray or greenish gray, spotted with brown.

VIREOS: *Family Vireonidæ*

Red-eyed Vireo. *Vireosylva olivacea*

From the cottonwoods along certain streams of eastern Washington and northern Oregon, there issues all through the summer day a song which suggests the Robin's but with less volume and energy, and with a greater variety of phrase. The phrases are made up of from two to four notes, with either a rising or falling inflection, as if the bird were carrying on a conversation. There is a longer pause after each phrase than in a Robin's song. The Red-eyed Vireo often sings for a long time from the same twig and is so plainly colored that it is often hard to discern in its leafy cover. When seen near to, the *blackish line bordering the gray cap,* and the *dusky line through the eye* distinguish the Red-eyed from the Warbling Vireo; the latter has a light line over the eye but no dark lines above or below the light line. The song is by far the best mark of distinction in the two species — a series of broken phrases constantly varied from the Red-eye, a leisurely continuous warble with a definite beginning and end from the Warbling Vireo. The call of the Red-eyed Vireo is a querulous *quee,* which though similar to the mewing call of the Warbling Vireo is distinctive when learned.

RED-EYED VIREO

$5\frac{1}{2}$–$6\frac{1}{2}$

Ad. — Top of head ashy gray, with a narrow black border; a white line from bill over and beyond eye; a *dusky stripe through eye;* rest of upper parts brownish gray (tinged with olive in strong light); under parts white. Bill dusky above, paler below; iris red; feet dark gray.

Dist. — *Cal.* A single record.
Ore. Not common S.V. locally (May–Sept.) from northeastern Ore. west to Portland.
Wash. Not common S.V. (May–Aug.) locally along streams both east and west.

Nest, a cup made of strips of bark, *hung* from a forked twig. *Eggs,* 3–4, white, speckled with reddish brown.

Western Warbling Vireo. *Vireosylva gilva swainsoni*

From the leafy tops of willows and cottonwoods along the banks of streams there sounds continually in early summer a sweet warbling song. The song of the Warbling Vireo is not broken into phrases as is that of the Cassin Vireo, nor is it marked by the rising and falling inflection of the Least. In the height of the nesting season it is characterized by endless repetition; a bird in full song repeats the same warbled phrases over and over several thousand times a day. Besides the song, the Warbling Vireo utters a low *chut chut,* a scolding chatter and a querulous mewing *twee* similar

WESTERN WARBLING VIREO

to that used by the hungry young, and uttered with rasping insistence when the bird's nest or young is considered in danger. Warbling Vireos are found with Least Vireos in the lowland willows, and with Cassin Vireos in the mountain groves. Their habit of feeding in higher branches, and the absence of an eye-ring distinguish them from the Least Vireo. The slightly heavier bill and more deliberate movements distinguish the Warbling Vireo from any other whitish-breasted Warblers, and the absence of the eye-ring from the Cassin and Hutton Vireos.

5–5½

Ad. — Upper parts brownish gray (olivaceous in strong light); a dull white line over the eye; under parts whitish gray (tinged with yellow on the sides). Bill dusky above, light below; feet gray. **Im.** — Top of head and hind-neck paler; two buffy bars on wing.

Dist. — *Cal.* Common S.V. (late Mar.–Sept.) along streams.
Ore. / *Wash.* } Common S.V. (Apr.–Sept.) in deciduous trees throughout.

Nest, a compact cup of bank and moss *hung* from a twig often at a considerable elevation. *Eggs*, 4–5, white, spotted with reddish brown or lilac.

Cassin Solitary Vireo. *Lanivireo solitarius cassini*

A leisurely succession of short cheery phrases, some of great sweetness, with a marked upward or downward inflection, from a bit of open woodland in spring announces the arrival of the Cassin Vireo. The leisurely, almost indolent habit of the bird makes it possible to follow up the song and examine the singer, as he hops from one twig to another, pausing to sing a phrase or two or to secure an insect. A squeaking sound, such as bird students use to attract birds, will generally bring the bird still closer, so that his *conspicuous white eye-ring and white line from eye to bill* are easily observed. The song varies considerably, but some phrases usually heard are *che wee whee ee which oo chee wi* and sooner or later a double phrase *chi wee chee wee,* without the interval usual between each pair of notes. In summer the Cassin Vireo swings a beautiful cup-shaped nest from the forked twig of some low tree, either in the cool canyons of the lower mountain slopes or, farther north, in the mixed growth of woodland streams. When the bird has eggs or young, it vies with the Junco in scolding an intruder. The white eye-ring and greenish yellow on the flanks distinguish the Cassin from the Warbling Vireo, its whiter breast and the line from eye to bill from the Hutton.

CASSIN VIREO

5–5½

Top and sides of head dark gray (olivaceous in strong light); white eye-ring and line from eye to bill; two white wing-bars; white under parts; yellowish on sides. Bill dusky; feet gray.

Dist. — *Cal.* / *Ore.* / *Wash.* } Common M. and S.V. (Apr.–Sept.) on the lower mountain slopes or in forested lowlands throughout.

Nest, a cup of strips of bark and fibers, *hung* from a twig. *Eggs*, 4–5, white, spotted with reddish brown, chiefly around the larger end.

HUTTON VIREO. *Vireo huttoni huttoni*

In the live oaks west of the Sierras and in young firs west of the Cascades, at any season of the year, a small but stocky gray bird hops indolently from one twig to another, calling persistently in spring and summer in a peevish tone. The head is large and round, the eye prominent and outlined with an incomplete *white eye-ring*, and there are faint white wing-bars. The Hutton Vireo's common note is either a single *cheep*, like a chicken separated from its mother, or a *chee-dee* or *kee-wi* which in spring it repeats over and over for long periods; the latter suggests the common call note of the California Purple Finch. It has besides a *tschuk tschuk* uttered in a low inquiring tone, and a low *whit whit*. The Hutton Vireo may easily be confused with the Ruby-crowned Kinglet, which is common in winter in the oaks and is an almost exact reproduction on a smaller scale of the Vireo. The Vireo's comparatively stout bill and much more phlegmatic behavior should distinguish it from the Kinglet. The Hutton Vireo might be confused with the Cassin Vireo, but should be distinguished by the absence of the white line from the bill to the eye and the lack of the yellow wash on the flanks.

HUTTON VIREO

$4\frac{1}{4}$–$4\frac{3}{4}$

Upper parts gray (olivaceous in strong light); a *whitish eye-ring* (incomplete above); two white wing-bars; under parts dingy yellowish. Bill horn-color; legs dusky.

Dist. — *Cal.* Common R., particularly in live oaks west of the Sierras.
Ore., *Wash.* } Locally R. in coniferous and deciduous thickets and low trees along the coast and about Puget Sd.

Nest, a cup, chiefly of moss, *hung* from a twig of a tree. *Eggs*, 3–4, white, dotted with brown about the larger end.

LEAST VIREO. *Vireo belli* subsp.

If a student stands for a moment at the edge of a thicket of willows and low bushes along any stream in southern California, he will hear from April to August a series of low husky warbled notes ending with a rising inflection, like an anxious query; an instant later the song is repeated with a downward phrase at the close as if the question were answered, *cheedle, cheedle chee ee; cheedle, cheedle chee.* By careful watching we may catch sight of a small bird, light gray and whitish below, hopping or flying from one twig to another, but always low down in the densest part of the tangle. The Least Vireo is less phlegmatic in its movements than the other Vireos, but more deliberate than a Warbler. There is no distinctive field character by which to identify a Least Vireo. Hutton and Cassin Vireos, besides their more arboreal habits, both have conspicuous white eye-rings. The Warbling

LEAST VIREO

Vireo perhaps comes closest to the Least Vireo. The latter may be distinguished by its distinctive song, by its preference for thickets of low trees and by its faint wing-bars.

$4\frac{1}{4}$–5

Upper parts gray, ashy on head; eyelids, especially the upper, whitish; back tinged in strong light with greenish; an indistinct whitish line from bill over eye; wings and tail dusky; indistinct whitish wing-bars; throat and belly whitish; sides tinged with yellow. Bill dark above, light gray on sides and below; feet dark gray.

Dist. — California Least Vireo. *V. b. pusillus.*

Cal. Common S.V. to the thickets and willows along streams, north along the coast to Monterey Co., in the interior valleys north to Marysville.

Arizona Least Vireo. *V. b. arizonæ.*

Cal. Common S.V. along the valley of the lower Colorado R. from Yuma to Needles.

Nest, a cup of plant fibers, *hung* from a branch of low bushes. *Eggs*, 3–4, white, spotted with reddish brown.

GRAY VIREO. *Vireo vicinior*

In extreme southern California on mountain slopes where chamise (*Adenostoma*) is the prevailing cover, the loud, musical song of the Gray Vireo is repeated by rival males. If a student knows the song of the Cassin Solitary Vireo, he will at once see the resemblance. The song is divided into three or four separate phrases which follow each other in a regular sequence; these are repeated over and over with untiring persistence. An attempt to reduce the song to syllables is as follows: *chee wi, chee wi, choo* or *che weet, chee; che churr weet.* The birds keep in the midst of the bush in which they are feeding, flying from the heart of one to the middle of another, so that a good view of one is rare, but no other Vireo inhabits these extensive scrubby thickets, and only the Cassin has a song that resembles the Gray Vireo's.

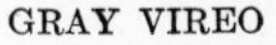

GRAY VIREO

$5\frac{3}{4}$

Upper parts dark gray; eye-ring white; under parts grayish white. Bill blackish; feet dusky.

Dist. — *Cal.* Local S.V. in the chaparral belt of southern Cal. north to Cajon Pass, and locally to Walker Pass, Kern Co.

Nest, of plant fibers, etc., in bushes. *Eggs*, 3–4, white, sparingly dotted with reddish brown.

WOOD WARBLERS: *Family Mniotiltidæ*

BLACK AND WHITE WARBLER. *Mniotilta varia*

The Black and White Warbler is a rare straggler to the coast; it has been noted in California at least eight times. Great care must be taken not to mistake the Black-throated Warbler for the Black and White Warbler. The latter has a *white line through the crown*, and the *whole body* except the white belly is *streaked with black and white*. Its song is a wiry *wée-see wée-see wée-*

see, wees, much sharper in tone than the Black-throated Gray's. The bird feeds by 'creeping' over the trunks and large limbs of trees, and perches on the twigs only occasionally.

Lucy Warbler. *Vermivora luciæ*

A small active bird, gray above and white below, hunts busily in summer through the tender green of the mesquite along the Colorado River and its tributaries. The male sings constantly in April and May a clear, lively song, beginning with half a dozen rapidly repeated *chits*, then changing to a lower or occasionally to a higher pitch and ending with a *zwee*. The song suggests that of the Lutescent Warbler but is more vigorous and more distinctly divided into parts. The call note is a faint *tsip*. When the male pursues the female and spreads his wings before her, the *chestnut rump* shows clearly, and in very favorable circumstances the slight amount of chestnut on the crown can be seen.

4

Ad. — Upper parts ashy gray; eye-ring and line from bill to eye white; crown-patch (generally concealed or wanting in ♀) and *rump chestnut;* two outer tail feathers with dull white spots at tip of inner edge; under parts white or buffy white. Bill dusky above, lead-color on sides and below; feet blackish. **Im.** — Lack the crown-patch; under parts pure white.

Dist. — Common S.V. (Mar.–Aug.) in the mesquite belt along the lower Colorado R.; casual west to Mecca.

Nest, of grasses, etc., in a hole or crevice in a stump or tree. *Eggs*, 3–5, white or creamy, speckled with reddish brown chiefly about the larger end.

Calaveras Warbler. *Vermivora ruficapilla gutturalis*

From the oaks on mountain slopes one hears in summer a song with a marked division into two parts, the first a succession of sharp notes on the same pitch, followed by a second series lower and more rapid; it may be written *tsee tsee tsee tsee tsit tsit tsit*, or *wee-tse, wee-tse, wee-tse, chiddle, chiddle, chiddle*. The call and alarm note is a sharp *tsip*. The singer generally forages well up in the trees, and it may be only after a long chase that the student will discover a small bird, *yellow below, with ashy gray top and sides of its head*, showing at close range a whitish eye-ring. The song may be confused with that of the Yellow Warbler, which is sharper and more varied, and that of the Pileolated, which is a series of staccato *chips* increasing in intensity. The Calaveras Warbler is distinguished from the other Warblers with yellow under parts — the Yellow, the Lutescent and the Pileolated — by the ashy gray sides and top of the head and by the whitish eye-ring.

4–4¾

Ad. ♂. — *Top and sides of head ashy gray* (with a chestnut crown-patch showing only at close range); eye-ring white; upper parts olive-green, brightest on rump; under parts yellow, except white lower belly. Bill blackish; feet brown. **Ad.** ♀. — Ashy of head less pure; crown-patch more concealed; yellow duller. **Im.** — Colors still duller, but eye-ring evident in any plumage.

LUTESCENT WARBLER
CALAVERAS WARBLER
AUDUBON WARBLER ♂
AUDUBON WARBLER IN WINTER
WESTERN YELLOW-THROAT

CALIFORNIA YELLOW WARBLER
TOWNSEND WARBLER
HERMIT WARBLER
PILEOLATED WARBLER
TOLMIE WARBLER

Dist. — *Cal.* Common S.V. (Apr.–Aug.) in the mountains from Kern and Lake Cos. northward; common M.
Ore. Fairly common S.V. (Apr.–Aug.) east, casual M. west.
Wash. Fairly common S.V. (Apr.–Aug.) west, scarce east except as M. along base of the Cascades.

Nest, on or near the ground, of bark strips, weed stems, grasses, etc. *Eggs*, 3–5, creamy white, spotted with reddish brown, chiefly about the larger end.

ORANGE-CROWNED WARBLER, LUTESCENT WARBLER, DUSKY WARBLER — *Vermivora celata* subsp.

Four forms of the Orange-crowned Warbler are found in the Coast States, but only two, the Lutescent and the Dusky Warblers occupy a well-defined place in the bird life of the average observer. The song of the Lutescent Warbler, drifting down from a brush-covered mountain slope is one of the first indications in southern California of the return of the migrants. It is a faint rapid trill, rising a little in pitch, then falling and lessening in energy toward the end. The singer is perhaps best recognized by the absence of any distinctive marks, a small active bird, showing for a moment in the foliage, with *greenish yellow under parts*. The ordinary call note of the Lutescent is a *tsip*, fairly emphatic for so small a bird, suggesting a faint or distant *chip* of the Brown Towhee. In the same trees and shrubs both in migration and in breeding season there are generally Pileolated Warblers with much brighter yellow under parts, and a black or brown cap. The Lutescent Warbler is less active and nervous than the Pileolated, but also less apt to come out in good view. (See p. 284.)

Another form of the Orange-crowned Warbler with dusky greenish under parts breeds on several of the Channel Is. and locally on the mainland. In winter when the Lutescent Warblers have gone south, many Dusky Warblers cross the channel and are found on the mainland, chiefly from Santa Barbara south. A beginner could not distinguish between the two races, but it is safe to assume that a dull-colored Warbler seen in December or January, dark olive-gray above and showing a trace of yellowish below, moving rather sluggishly among the twigs of live oaks not far from the coast, is a Dusky Warbler. The common note in winter is a single *tschick* uttered at intervals as the bird is feeding. No one should attempt to name the Dusky Warbler until he is thoroughly familiar with the Hutton Vireo and Ruby-crowned Kinglet, both of which are found in the same trees at the same season.

$4\frac{1}{4}$–$4\frac{3}{4}$

Top of head with an orange patch (usually concealed); faint yellowish line from above eye to bill; upper parts with a greenish tinge, brightest on rump; under parts dull yellow, greenish yellow or grayish white. Bill and feet dusky.

Dist. — Eastern Orange-crowned Warbler. *V. c. celata.*
Cal. Not uncommon W.V. in southern Cal.; M. elsewhere.
Ore., *Wash.* Probably casual M. in the Cascades and west.

Rocky Mountain Orange-crowned Warbler. *V. c. orestera.*

Cal. S.V. in eastern Cal. west to Mono L.
Ore. } *Wash.* } M. and W.V. in the Cascades and west.
Lutescent Warbler. *V. c. lutescens.*
Cal. } *Ore.* } *Wash.* } Common S.V. (Mar. or Apr.–Sept.) west of the Sierras and Cascades.
Dusky Warbler. *V. c. sordida.*
Cal. S.V. on most of the Channel Is., and on a few points of the mainland; winters on the mainland, chiefly from Santa Barbara south.

Nest, on the ground in a depression or under a plant or tree. *Eggs*, 3–5, white, speckled with reddish brown.

Yellow Warbler. *Dendroica æstiva* subsp.

The clear, incisive *tsee, tsee, tsee, tsitsi wee see* of the Yellow Warbler sounds from April to August from the willows and cottonwoods of nearly every stream from the coast well up into the mountains. The singer shows clear yellow above and duller yellow below, one of the few Warblers that it is easy to identify. The Yellow Warbler is less nervous than the Pileolated, and keeps chiefly in trees or higher bushes. The call note is *tschick.*

4–5

Ad. ♂. — *Top of head yellow*, rest of upper parts greenish yellow, brightest on rump; wings dusky; *tail* dusky *with yellow spots* toward the tips of the outer feathers; under parts yellow, streaked with chestnut on breast and sides. Bill dark; feet pale brown. **Ad.** ♀. — Upper parts dull greenish yellow; under parts pale yellow, streaks indistinct or wanting.

Dist. — Eastern Yellow Warbler. *D. a. æstiva.*
Wash. Probably casual M.
Sonora Yellow Warbler. *D. a. sonorana.*
Cal. Abundant S.V. in the valley of the lower Colorado R.
California Yellow Warbler. *D. a. brewsteri.*
Cal. Common M. nearly throughout; common S.V. (late Mar.–Aug.) in most of the territory west of the Sierran divides and from the Modoc region south to Lake Tahoe.
Ore. } *Wash.* } Common S.V. (late Apr.–Sept.) in deciduous growth in the lowlands west.
Alaska Yellow Warbler. *D. a. rubiginosa.*
Cal. } *Ore.* } *Wash.* } M. (May; Aug.–Sept.).

Nest, a compact cup of plant fibers in bushes and low trees. *Eggs*, 4–5, white, spotted with brown, black or lilac.

Alaska Myrtle Warbler. *Dendroica coronata hooveri*

Only after a student has become thoroughly familiar with the sharp *chip* of the Audubon Warbler and has observed that the female and young often show the yellow on the throat only at just the right angle or not at all, may he try to identify the rarer Myrtle Warbler. Its habits are similar to those of its near relative, the Audubon Warbler, with which it often associates. Not more than three outer tail feathers on each side show spots of white, but the only sure method of field identification is the combination of an absolutely white throat with a softer call note, *tsup* instead of *chip*.

$4\frac{3}{4}$–$5\frac{1}{2}$

Similar to the Audubon Warbler (see next species), but only three outer tail feathers on each side with spots of white and *throat white*.

Dist. — *Cal.* A not uncommon spring M. along the coast, and an uncommon W.V. from central California southward.
Ore. Not common M. and possibly W.V.
Wash. Irregular spring M. (Mar.–May) both east and west, commoner west; occasional in the fall.

Audubon Warbler. *Dendroica auduboni auduboni*

An observer with even the slightest interest in birds, cannot fail to notice in winter small birds flying out from the trees and bushes of dooryards, from tall groves of eucalyptus or from the scattered sumach bushes of dry hillsides, with a sharp *tsip*, showing as they fly a *bright yellow rump* and a pattern of white spots in the outspread tail. There is probably no one bird so widespread in winter in southern California as this trim Warbler, though Linnets and Nuttall and Gambel Sparrows occur in far larger flocks. Even along the beach Audubon Warblers hunt flies in the piles of decaying kelp. The Audubon Warbler on warm still days flies straight up for a few yards from a bush or tree, and after catching some insect in the air, drops daintily down again to the perch. When perched, the tail is constantly twitched. Adult birds when facing the observer show a yellow throat clearly set off from the head and breast, but young birds often have so little yellow that the throat appears white. In early spring the male begins to assume the breeding plumage; yellow appears in the crown, black and yellow on the sides of the breast and a white bar on the wing. The Audubon Warbler's song, heard in forests of pine or fir, is a rather characterless succession of notes, beginning *tsit, tsit, tsit,* followed by a loose, less energetic trill on a lower pitch. If the yellow rump is seen there is no bird with which even a brownish female or young Audubon Warbler can be confused, except the Myrtle Warbler (see preceding species), which is a rare winter visitant and migrant.

$4\frac{3}{4}$–$5\frac{1}{3}$

Ad. ♂ in breeding plumage. — Upper parts bluish gray, streaked with black; eyelids narrowly white; crown-patch and *rump bright yellow;* wings with a broad white patch; four or five tail feathers on each side blotched with white near tip; *throat yellow;* breast black; a patch of yellow on the upper flanks; rest of under parts white, streaked with black on the sides. Bill black, feet dark brown. **Ad. ♀ in breeding plumage.** — Similar to ♂, but duller, the black of the breast obscured with white; wings only barred with white. **Ad. and Im. in winter.** — Upper parts brown; yellow crown-patch obscured; yellow of throat and flanks paler, under parts (except yellow throat) chiefly white, washed and streaked with brownish; rump and tail as in summer. **Im. in summer.** — Under parts streaked with dusky.

Dist. — *Cal.* Common S.V. in coniferous forests on the mountains throughout except along the northern coast belt; common M. throughout and abundant W.V. (Sept.–May) almost throughout.

Ore. } Common S.V. (Apr.–Nov.) in coniferous forests through-
Wash. } out, not so common in dense woods west; common M. throughout. A few winter east, commoner west.

Nest, bulky, of bark and needles, heavily lined with feathers, usually in conifers. *Eggs*, 3–5, olive or greenish white, spotted with black, brown or lilac.

Black-throated Gray Warbler. *Dendroica nigrescens*

A trained ear can generally identify a Warbler's song almost as far as it can be heard, but even an expert gives a very cautious verdict in western Washington, where Hermit, Townsend and Black-throated Gray Warblers are all found breeding. Under the tall Douglas firs an observer must often crane his neck till it aches before the singer comes to the end of a spray and shows some characteristic mark. The Townsend Warbler does not breed south of Oregon and the Hermit breeds regularly only along the Sierras from Mt. Whitney to Shasta, so that in southern California, in the oaks or pines of the dry mountain slopes, a wheezy, drawling song in the breeding season may safely be attributed to the Black-throated Gray. The following transcriptions will give the general character of the song, but individuals vary almost indefinitely: *zee ee, zee ee, zee ee, zee, zip; wees-a, wees-a, wees-a, wee zee; wee-di, wee-di, wee-di, dee dee.* The first three phrases generally have a lazy quality and a marked swing. In migration the Black-throated Gray gleans actively among the twigs of oaks or pines almost anywhere in California, except in the humid northwest coast belt. The black and white markings on the head are unmistakable.

BLACK-THROATED GRAY WARBLER (♂)

5

Ad. ♂. — Top of head black, separated from black cheek-bar by a white stripe behind eye; another white stripe separates cheek-bar from black throat; a near view shows a yellowish spot in front of eye; back bluish gray; wings dusky, crossed by two white bars; three outer tail feathers chiefly white; under parts white, streaked with black on the sides. Bill and feet black. **Ad.** ♀. — Similar but duller. Top of head streaked with gray; throat white, bordered below by a black collar; bill paler. **Im.** — Top of head like back; less black on throat; less white in tail.

Dist. — *Cal.* Common S.V. (Apr.–Sept.) on lower mountain slopes throughout, except in the humid northwest; common M. throughout.

Ore. } Common S.V. (Apr.–Oct.) in deciduous growth, borders
Wash. } of clearings and prairies.

Nest, a compact cup of plant fibers lined with feathers in low bushes or in trees. *Eggs*, 3–5, creamy white, spotted with reddish brown and lilac.

Townsend Warbler. *Dendroica townsendi*

One hears in the breeding season in the red firs of western Washington a short wheezy song from tall tree-tops, and if one is fortunate catches a glimpse of the *black throat and rich yellow cheeks* of the Townsend Warbler. In winter along the coast of California from Monterey to San Diego, the bird gleans in leisurely fashion among the Monterey pines or the moss-hung live oaks. The song of the Townsend Warbler is difficult to distinguish from that of the Black-throated Gray, but except in migration the two are heard together only in western Oregon and Washington. The Townsend Warbler's song has less of the drawling inflection in the opening notes than the Black-throated Gray's and often ends with a prolonged *ee-zee*. A song noted by the writer in the Olympics in western Washington was transcribed as a hoarse *swee swee swee zee.* There is no other bird with which a Townsend Warbler, if seen to good advantage, can be confused; the Audubon Warbler has a yellow throat and blue-gray cheeks, the Hermit has yellow cheeks with no black above the throat.

$4\frac{1}{4}$–5

Ad. ♂ in summer. — Top of head black; *cheek-patch black bordered by a yellow line above and a broader one below;* back greenish in strong light, streaked with black; wings and tail blackish, the wings with two white bars; two or three outer tail feathers blotched near tips with white; *throat black;* breast bright yellow; sides streaked with black; belly white. Bill blackish; feet brown. **Ad. ♂ in winter and Ad. ♀.** — Black on head obscured by greenish; black of throat partly concealed by yellow. **Im.** — Upper parts not streaked with black; cheek-patch greenish; throat chiefly yellow.

Dist. — *Cal.* Common M.; W.V. (Oct.–Apr.) from central Cal. south along the coast.
Ore. S.V. west; M. east.
Wash. Common S.V. (Apr. or May–Sept. or Oct.) in conifers; common spring M. on the plains east; a few winter west.

Nest, of twigs, grasses, etc., at various heights up to 60 ft. in trees. *Eggs*, white or creamy white, speckled, blotched or lined with chestnut and lavender.

Hermit Warbler. *Dendroica occidentalis*

A Warbler singing in tall firs from the Sierras north awakens our suspicions by a more rapid tempo than the Black-throated Gray's, but keeps with tantalizing indifference to the thick sprays far up in the tree. If by some lucky chance, it pursues an insect that it has dislodged down to the lower branches, it needs only a glimpse of the yellow head with no black cheek-patches to identify it as the Hermit Warbler. When an unusually heavy migration of Warblers comes through California, Hermit Warblers feed with Lutescent and Tolmie Warblers on the bush-covered hillsides, and show off their *yellow cheeks*, *white wing-bars* and *white outer tail* feathers even on the ground. The song varies greatly in different individuals; two common forms may be written *wees-a wees-a wees-a wees* and *tsip tsip tsip dee dee*. The opening notes are always brisk, with less of the wheezy quality of the Black-throated Gray and more sure and spirited than the song of the Audubon Warbler. The ordinary call note is a sharp *tsik*. The yellow sides and top of the head easily distinguish the Hermit Warbler from the Townsend with its black cheek-patch.

$4\frac{1}{2}$

Ad. ♂. — *Whole head* except black throat *rich yellow;* back gray, streaked with black; wing-bars white; *outer tail feathers largely white;* under parts white, unstreaked. Bill blackish; feet brown. **Ad.** ♀. — Head dull yellowish; top of head mottled with blackish; throat whitish, spotted with dusky. **Im.** — Less yellow on top of head; throat white.

Dist. — *Cal.* Common S.V. (Apr.–Aug.) along the Sierras from Mt. Whitney to Shasta; irregularly common M. in southern Cal., and occasional in winter in west central Cal.
Ore. A not uncommon M. and S.V. locally west.
Wash. S.V. in small numbers locally (Apr.–Aug.) west, also in the Okanagan Hds.

Nest, of weed stems, twigs, mosses and needles in conifers. *Eggs*, 4–5, dull white, spotted or blotched with brown and lilac.

Grinnell Water-Thrush. *Seiurus noveboracensis notabilis*

The Water-Thrush has been recorded from the Coast only half a dozen times. The streaked under parts, its ground-haunting habits and the tilting of the tail distinguish it from all but the Titlark. The latter is a bird of the open, the Water-Thrush a bird of moist but shaded ground. The call or alarm note is a clear metallic *chip*.

5–6

Upper parts dark brown; line over the eye whitish (buffy in strong light); under parts buffy, everywhere streaked with dark brown. Bill and feet dark.
Dist. — Rare or casual M.

Tolmie Warbler; Macgillivray Warbler. *Oporornis tolmiei*

From thick bushes in forest clearings or on wet mountain slopes a very characteristic song is repeated in summer over and over from the same spot. The song varies considerably in different individuals but generally consists of four or five hoarse phrases hurriedly repeated, followed by two or three single notes in a lower (sometimes a higher) pitch. It may be suggested by the syllables *tswee, tswee, tswee, tswee wit wit* or *churr churr swee swee tí-di*. The singer is often concealed in the thicket, but occasionally shows his *ashy head and throat* and *yellow lower belly*. When singing or flitting about in the bushes a Tolmie Warbler jerks its tail nervously to one side. It is a shy bird, concealing itself in the tangled bushes at the first alarm. Its alarm note is a sharp *tik* or *pit*.

$4\frac{3}{4}$–$5\frac{1}{2}$

Ad. ♂. — *Head, neck and upper breast ashy gray*, deepening to black before eye and blackish on breast; *eyelids white;* upper parts greenish gray; *belly bright yellow;* bill blackish above, under mandible flesh-color; feet light brown. **Ad.** ♀. — Top of head brown, breast pale gray.

Dist. — *Cal.* Common S.V. (Apr.–Sept.) in the Sierras from the Yosemite northward, and on the coast ranges from San Francisco Bay region north. Common M. (Apr. and May; Sept. and Oct.).

Ore. / *Wash.* } Common S.V. (end of Apr.–Oct.) in brush throughout.

Nest, of grasses near ground in weeds or bushes. *Eggs*, 3–5, white, spotted with dark brown and lavender.

Yellow-throat. *Geothlypis trichas* subsp.

From the tules bordering a pond or from the bushes at the edge of low wet ground comes a *tschek* of protest. A small olive-backed bird is fidgeting about and shows as it turns toward us for a moment a *yellow throat* and breast. If we make a squeaking noise to attract its attention, it may finally appear at the top of one of the stalks, and, if it is a male, turn toward us a *broad black mask through the eyes and forehead*, edged above with light ashy gray. The song of the Yellow-throat is a short vigorous strain usually made up of a phrase of three notes, one of which is strongly accented, *weé-chee-chee, weé-chee-chee, weech*, or *wi-chi-cheé, wi-chi-cheé, wi-chi-cheé*. Both sexes also utter a rapid wren-like scolding note.

The Tule Wren inhabits the same jungles of reeds and tules in which the Yellow-throat lives. It takes a practiced ear to distinguish the calls and scolding notes of the two birds, though the songs are quite distinct. The Yellow-throat's calls are higher and lighter than the Wren's. No bird can be confused with the male Yellow-throat, if the black mask through the eye is seen. The female is much duller yellow below, and might be confused with a female Yellow Warbler or a Lutescent Warbler, which during migration occasionally frequent the same bushy borders. The Yellow-throat is stockier than either of the other Warblers and has more of a brownish wash on the under parts.

$4\frac{1}{2}$–5

Ad. ♂. — Upper parts yellowish brown; forehead and *broad stripe through eye black*, bordered above by ashy gray; *throat and breast bright yellow*, belly paling to whitish. Bill black; feet flesh-color. **Ad.** ♀. — Without the black and ashy on head; throat yellowish; breast buffy; belly whitish. **Im.** — Upper parts with a brownish tinge; under parts buffy.

Dist. — Western Yellow-throat. *G. t. occidentalis.*

Cal. Common M. throughout; S.V. to fresh-water marshes from west central Cal. north to Oregon line and from Owens Valley to the Nev. line.

Ore. / *Wash.* } S.V. (late Apr.–Sept.) in marshes and willow thickets east.

Tule Yellow-throat. *G. t. scirpicola.*

Cal. Common R. on fresh-water marshes in southern Cal. north to Santa Barbara and Kern Co.

Salt Marsh Yellow-throat. *G. t. sinuosa.*

Cal. Common R. locally on salt- and fresh-water marshes about San Francisco Bay.

Pacific Yellow-throat. *G. t. arizela.*

Ore. / *Wash.* } Common S.V. (Apr.–Sept.) in wet thickets and marshes west, migrant east.

Nest, a deep cup of grass or leaves, on or near the ground. *Eggs*, 3–4, white, marked with black, lavender and brown.

Long-tailed Chat. *Icteria virens longicauda*

It takes a beginner some time to realize that many of the varied notes he hears from the dense willow thickets along a lowland stream come from one bird, the Long-tailed Chat. The commonest and most characteristic note is a high-pitched *tu-tu-tu-tu-tu* but this may be followed by a low hoarse *chă*, then by a squeaky *keet* or a rather musical *whoit.* By patient watching one may at last catch sight of the performer, a dark brown medium-sized bird with deep yellow under parts and a white line over the eye. At each variation in its song the bird turns and faces in a different direction, stretching its head upward; it frequently mounts singing into the air and then sinks slowly with wings raised over its back and feet dangling.

LONG-TAILED CHAT

At this season, particularly when the moon is bright, the song of the Chat may be heard at any hour of the night from the willows or brush-covered canyon sides.

$6\frac{1}{2}$–$7\frac{1}{4}$

Upper parts grayish brown, tinged with greenish; eyelids and *line over eye to bill white; throat and breast rich yellow;* belly white. Bill black; legs dark.

Dist. — *Cal.* Common M. and S.V. (Apr.–Sept.) in willows along streams and up brushy canyons locally throughout.
Ore. Not uncommon S.V. (May–Sept.).
Wash. Irregular S.V. (May–Sept.) east, casual west.

Nest, bulky, of leaves, bark-strips and grasses, in bushes and low trees. *Eggs*, 3–5, white, spotted with reddish brown and lilac.

Pileolated Warbler. *Wilsonia pusilla* subsp.

A flash of clear yellow from a bird searching restlessly in the thick bushes at the edge of a mountain stream or lake may indicate either a Yellow or a Pileolated Warbler. If the bird is exceedingly active and is constantly flipping its tail with a sidewise movement, the observer will sooner or later catch sight of the small area of velvety black on the crown which characterizes the Pileolated Warbler. All Warblers are active compared to Vireos, but the Pileolated is the most restless of our species; it frequently flies up from a branch to catch a passing insect. Beginners find it difficult to distinguish the song of the Pileolated from that of the Lutescent, with which it is often associated. The distinction lies in the sharpness and staccato quality of the Pileolated's notes, and the final crescendo. There is of course much individual variation, but the typical song may be written: *chit-chi, chit-chi, chit-chi, chit-chi, chit-chi CHIT CHIT CHIT;* the song of the Lutescent is softer, more trilled and generally trails off at the close into weaker notes in a lower pitch. The call note of the Pileolated is diagnostic, a husky *tsik* or *tschek*, suggesting a Yellow-throat's but not so heavy. The Pileolated Warbler is one of the commonest birds in migration; at times every oak tree or tangle of low bushes seems alive with their bright and active forms.

$4\frac{1}{4}$–$4\frac{1}{2}$

Ad. ♂. — *Top of head velvety black,* bordered over the forehead by golden yellow; upper parts yellowish green; *under parts bright yellow.* Bill dark above, light below; feet brown. **Ad.** ♀ **and Im.** — Crown-patch restricted or wanting.

Dist. — Golden Pileolated Warbler. *W. p. chryseola.*

Cal. Common S.V. along streams and lake borders in the Sierras and in the Coast Ranges locally from San Diego northward; common M. throughout.

Ore., *Wash.* Common S.V. (May–Sept.).

Pileolated Warbler. *W. p. pileolata.*

Cal., *Ore.*, *Wash.* Fairly common M., generally passing through later than the preceding. May breed from northeastern Cal. (Modoc Co.) through eastern Ore. and Wash.

Nest, in low bushes or on the ground, a bulky ball of grasses and moss. *Eggs,* 3–4, white, spotted with reddish brown and lilac.

Redstart. *Setophaga ruticilla*

Here and there in eastern Oregon and Washington in open woodland along streams the *coal-black head* and *flame-colored shoulders* of a Redstart show in the foliage as he utters his sharp *wee-see-see.* The Redstart's song is very difficult to distinguish from that of the Yellow Warbler, which frequents the same streams; it is sharper, more insistent and less complicated, and the phrases are generally on the same pitch, not ending as in that of the Yellow Warbler with a second phrase at a different pitch. A male in its first spring season resembles a female in coloration, so that one hears the song uttered apparently by a female. Both sexes have a habit of keeping the tail spread, showing the yellow or salmon band.

$4\frac{1}{2}$–5

Ad. ♂. — *Head, throat and back black* (lustrous in strong light); *sides of breast* and flanks *reddish orange;* large bar across wings and tail light salmon; belly white. Bill and feet black. **Ad.** ♀. — Head gray; throat grayish white, orange and salmon replaced by yellow. Young ♂ resembles the ♀ till the second spring.

Dist. — *Cal.* Casual visitant.
Ore. S.V. (May–Aug.) locally east.
Wash. Not common S.V. (May–Aug.) in deciduous growth east.

Nest, of plant fibers, bark strips, etc., in trees. *Eggs*, 3–4, white, spotted with reddish brown or lilac.

BLACKBIRDS, ORIOLES, etc.: *Family Icteridæ*

Bobolink. *Dolichonyx oryzivorus*

Only along the northeastern border of the Coast States can one hear the rollicking song of the Bobolink, or see the black and white figure of the male slide down on quivering wings over the grass in which the demure brown female is brooding. In some of the valleys of eastern Oregon colonies of Bobolinks occupy the meadows of wild hay that border the streams and lakes. The male in breeding plumage is unmistakable; no other bird is wholly black below and white and black above, and no other bird pours out such an ecstasy of bubbling syllables on the wing. The female and young are harder to recognize; the general buffy color of their plumage distinguishes them from the much darker female Red-winged Blackbirds which occupy the same meadows.

BOBOLINK (♂, breeding)

$6\text{–}7\frac{1}{4}$

Ad. ♂ in breeding plumage. — Nape buffy white; shoulders and lower back white; otherwise black. Bill blackish; feet brown. **Ad.** ♀. — Upper parts buffy brown, streaked with black; under parts yellowish brown, unstreaked except on flanks; bill and feet brown. **Ad. ♂ in fall.** — Similar to ♀ but streaking blacker. **Im.** — Similar to ♀ but no streaking on flanks.

Dist. — *Cal.* Rare S.V. in northeastern Modoc Co.; accidental in the rest of the State.
Ore. Local S.V. (May–Sept.) in the meadows and valleys east.
Wash. Local S.V. near Spokane.

Nest, in a depression in the ground, of dried grasses and weed stalks. *Eggs*, 5–7, from gray reddish brown, irregularly spotted and blotched with brown and purple.

Cowbird. *Molothrus ater* subsp.

In March and April in southern California, small bands of glossy black and grayish brown birds perch in the tops of the willows along streams, the males posturing before the females, swelling out their feathers, spreading their wings, stretching their necks upward and gurgling out a liquid note, *gloo-gloo-glook;* a moment later with a rolling chatter the little band is off through the tree-tops. As soon as the smaller birds begin to lay, female Cowbirds slink through the willows, looking for the nests of their intended victims, in which to deposit their eggs, which are hatched and reared by the dupes at the expense of their own broods. The young Cowbird follows its foster parents till it is full-grown and then joins its own kind. Besides the liquid gurgle, given generally from a perch, the male utters a whistled *whee-éet,* often given when taking flight; both sexes have a chattering call, usually given on the wing. Cowbirds come with other blackbirds to stock-pens and corrals, in the neighborhood of streams, or walk about grazing cattle. The males may be distinguished from blackbirds by their smaller size, their *chestnut-brown heads* and their short conical bills; females and young are smaller and lighter brown than the females of either the Brewer or the Red-winged Blackbird, both of which look blackish in comparison.

COWBIRD (♂)

Ad. ♂. — Head and neck dark chestnut-brown, sharply defined from the glossy black body (iridescent in good light). Bill short, conical, black; feet black. **Ad.** ♀. — Smaller than the male, grayish brown, very faintly streaked. Bill and feet blackish brown. **Im.** — Like female but paler, and more heavily streaked with dusky.

Dist. — Dwarf Cowbird. *M. a. obscurus.*

$5\frac{3}{4}$–7

Cal. R. from the Mexican line to Death Valley and Independence, Inyo Co., on the east, to southern Santa Barbara Co. on the west, and north to Alameda Co.

California Cowbird. [*M. a. californicus.*]

R. in the San Joaquin Valley from the southern end to northern Merced Co.

Nevada Cowbird. [*M. a. artemisiæ*]

$7\frac{1}{2}$

Cal. S.V. from Death Valley, Panamint Mts., and Owens Valley east of the Sierras and in Modoc Co.

Ore. / *Wash.* } S.V. (May–Aug.) on the plains east, rarely west.

Nest, lays in the nests of other birds. *Eggs,* whitish, spotted and blotched with brown, chiefly at the larger end.

Yellow-headed Blackbird. *Xanthocephalus xanthocephalus*

A marsh east of the Sierras and Cascades in the breeding season is a medley of bird voices. Above the scolding of Yellow-throats and Tule

Wrens rise the uncouth cries of Yellow-headed Blackbirds, suggesting often the drawl of a discontented hen. The males are unmistakable; the *whole head, neck and chest* are *bright yellow,* often deepening to orange, and in flight a *broad patch of white shows in the wing.* When the birds perch on the tops of the tules the white often shows in the closed wing.

YELLOW-HEADED BLACKBIRD (♂)

The females are dark above but show dingy yellow on the throat and upper breast, and lines of yellowish above the eyes. The common call note is a low-pitched *kuck, kuck* or higher *cack,* accompanied when the bird is perched by a jerk of the tail; the song suggests the syllables *ca-cá-ow* or *chick, clook, clook, käh, käh.* Even when their nesting ground is invaded, the birds seem rather indifferent, perching near by and calling *cruck, cruck,* but showing little of the agitation and aggressiveness of Red-winged Blackbirds. When the young are calling for food, their shrill *turree* rises everywhere from the depths of the tules. In migration Yellow-headed Blackbirds frequent tule-bordered ponds or visit corrals and stock-pens in company with other blackbirds. In the Imperial Valley in winter they form part of the huge flocks of blackbirds that fly over the alfalfa fields or gather about the feeding troughs of stock.

$7\frac{1}{2}$–10

Ad. ♂. — *Head, neck and chest yellow,* sometimes deepening to orange; line from eye to bill black, rest of plumage black, except a *large white patch in the wing.* Bill and legs black. **Ad.** ♀. — General plumage dark brown, line over eye, throat and upper chest yellowish; no white wing-patch. Bill dark brown; feet blackish.

Dist. — *Cal.* Common S.V. in the interior valleys and east and northeast, locally south; common M. except northwest. W.V. north to Los Angeles Co.

Ore. } Common S.V. east.
Wash. }

Nest, of tules and grasses, fastened to tules 1–3 ft. above the water. *Eggs*, 3–5, grayish to greenish white, blotched and speckled with brown and gray.

RED-WINGED BLACKBIRD. *Agelaius phœniceus* subsp.

In spring in every marsh male Red-winged Blackbirds cling to the tules, spreading their black wings till the scarlet epaulets blaze out, and gurgling a musical *ook-a-lee.* If the brown female comes from her nest in the tangle, the male is off in hot chase. No hawk or heron can fly over the reeds without suffering a spirited and noisy attack from the watchful males. When quietly guarding the nest, the male utters at regular inter-

RED-WINGED BLACKBIRD
(♂ and ♀)

vals a musical, long-drawn *teé-urr.* When the nest is approached both birds utter various alarm notes, a low *cut cut* and a high *kee kee.* In winter immense clouds of Red-wings come into the reeds toward evening, dropping as they fly a sharp *tschi* or a metallic *kink;* there is a prodigious noise from the reeds as the birds settle for the night. A Redwing's flight is in long shallow undulations, so that when a flock passes by, some birds are rising while others are falling. When walking or when perched, the tail is oonstantly jerked.

When the wing is closed, the buffy or orange edge of the scarlet patch shows in all but the Bicolored Red-wing (see below). If a Red-wing shows a clear white edge to the red patch it is a different species, the Tricolored Red-wing (see next species). The female Red-wing shows sharp streaking on the under parts which distinguishes her from the female Brewer Blackbirds and female Cowbirds.

$6\frac{3}{4}$–$9\frac{1}{4}$

Ad. ♂ in breeding season. — Entire plumage black, a scarlet patch on the bend of the wing, bordered in all but one subspecies by orange or buff. Bill and feet black. **Ad. ♂ in winter.** — Feathers of middle back edged with rusty. **Im. ♂.** — Epaulets lightly spotted with black; feathers heavily edged with rusty. **Ad. ♀ in breeding season.** — Top of head dark brown, with buffy stripes through the crown and over the eye; back dark brown; under parts whitish, heavily streaked with dark brown; throat tinged with buff or pinkish. **Ad. ♀ in winter.** — Under parts tinged with buff.

Dist. — Sonoran Red-wing. *A. p. sonoriensis.*
Cal. R. along the Colorado R. from Yuma to Needles, north and west through the Imperial Valley to the northern end of Salton Sea.
San Diego Red-wing. *A. p. neutralis.*
Cal. R. in southern Cal. west of the desert, from San Diego to Monterey Co., and in the southern part of the San Joaquin Valley.
Kern Red-wing. *A. p. aciculatus.*
Cal. R. in Walker Basin and along the south fork of Kern River.
Bicolored Red-wing. *A. gubernator californicus.*
Note. Treated in the A.O.U. check-list of 1910 as a species.
Cal. R. about San Francisco Bay and in the Sacramento and San Joaquin Valleys. This subspecies lacks the orange or buff edging of the scarlet *shoulder-patch, showing red only.*
Nevada Red-wing. *A. p. nevadensis.*
Cal. *Ore.* *Wash.* } From northeastern Cal. through eastern Ore. and Wash. In Wash. chiefly S.V. (Feb.–Nov.).
Northwestern Red-wing. *A. p. caurinus.*
Cal. *Ore.* *Wash.* } R. from northwestern Cal. (where rare) through western Ore. and Wash.

Nest, of dried grasses in bushes near water or fastened to tules. *Eggs*, 3–5, pale bluish or olive, lined, blotched or scrawled with black, brown or purplish gray.

TRICOLORED RED-WING. *Agelaius tricolor*

In the San Joaquin and Sacramento Valleys there are many small irrigation reservoirs fringed with a dense growth of tules. From these in spring and early summer issues a medley of droning and braying sounds, and lines of blackbirds fly out in all directions to the neighboring fields or fly back with food for the young. The males show a clear white edging along the red shoulder patch. The song of the Tricolored Red-wing lacks the liquid quality of the preceding species. The song may be written *oh-kee-quáy-a,* with a braying quality. The common call note is a nasal *kape.* In winter a fence enclosing a stock-pen is often bordered with rows of blackbirds; those that show no orange or buff in the closed wing, but a line of white contrasting with the black wing are Tricolored Red-wings. The flight of the Tricolored Red-wing is similar to that of the preceding species. The bill is more slender and the male in good light shows a bluish gloss. The female is darker below than the female Red-wing, but can be distinguished in the field only after considerable practice.

$7\frac{1}{4}$–9

Ad. ♂. — Entire plumage black, with bluish gloss in strong light; epaulet dark red with white edge. Bill slender, black; legs black. **Ad.** ♀. — Upper parts dark brown; throat pale; breast white, streaked with dusky; belly dusky. Bill and feet dusky.

Dist. — R. in central and southern Cal.

Nest and *eggs* similar to those of preceding species.

Western Meadowlark. *Sturnella neglecta*

There are about a dozen birds whose removal from the landscape would be noticed even by the average person, and one of the first to be missed would be the Meadowlark. There is so much unforested country along the coast, so many rolling brown hills or cultivated fields that would be suddenly silent if the rich, throaty chuckle of the Meadowlark were no longer heard. Even above the noise of the motor car it explodes on one's ear from the long uplifted bill of the bird on a post by the roadside. Its bright yellow breast with the V-shaped mark of black upon it is turned toward us if the bird is unconcerned, but note how rarely one sees this spot of color, if walking. The bird constantly turns toward an intruder the brown back, as it crouches low or steals off in the grass. If pressed too close, the Meadowlark flies off, taking several rapid strokes of its short broad wings, and then sailing a short distance. When it lights it often stretches up to its full height, rapidly opening and shutting the tail so that the white outer feathers are apparent. It utters a low-pitched *tschuk* when alarmed, and in flight a soft *peet*. A third common note is a roll or chatter.

WESTERN MEADOWLARK

Who would attempt to describe the song of the Western Meadowlark? Any one, however, can hear it on almost any day of the year except at the climax of the dry season in late summer and early fall, when the birds are for the most part silent. But even at this season flocks gather in the stubble fields or in some low tree, and indulge in a chorus of subdued notes, high and low, but often including a suggestion of the full song; sometimes a single bird indulges in this 'whisper' song. Let the first winter rains come, and the full series of descending phrases bursts forth again. To any one familiar only with the plaintive whistled song of the Meadowlark in the East, the throaty quality, the vigor and joyousness of the loud sudden outburst is so unexpected that one must see the bird utter the sound to connect it with a Meadowlark. At the height of the mating season when the male is pursuing the female, he utters a breathless succession of cheeping notes without the mellow quality of the ordinary song.

There is no bird with which the Meadowlark can be confused, if the yellow breast with its black V or the brown upper parts showing in flight the white outer tail feathers are clearly seen. The Horned Lark has a yellow throat edged with black, is much smaller and shows only an outer edging of white in the tail.

$7\frac{3}{4}$–10

Ad. in breeding plumage. — Upper parts brown, streaked with black; line through crown buffy; line from bill to eye yellow; tail feathers short, outer ones mainly white; *under parts bright yellow with black crescent across breast.* Bill, upper surface and tip dusky, sides and under surface light colored; feet stout, light brown. **Ad. in winter.** — Black and yellow of under parts veiled with the light edgings of the feathers. **Im.** — Yellow of breast much paler, black crescent replaced by dark streaks.

Dist. — *Cal.* Abundant R. throughout, except in the heavily forested areas.
Ore. Common R. on the plains east and in cultivated country west.
Wash. S.V. and irregular R. on plains east, and in prairies and clearings west.

Nest, on the ground, of dried grasses, often arched over. *Eggs*, 3–7, white, spotted with brown and purple.

Scott Oriole. *Icterus parisorum*

No one can pass through a forest of Joshua trees in the Mojave Desert without being struck by their grotesque and varied shapes. In May the black and yellow figure of the male Scott Oriole flashes through their misshapen forms or sings from the tip of a spiny branch. It is an active bird, constantly taking long flights from one tree or bush to a distant clump. The song is high and clear, made up of whistled phrases which suggest the Western Meadowlark, but lack the wide range and throaty quality of the latter. In the mating season the female also utters a phrase or two of real song, similar to the male's but not so strong nor so prolonged. The cup-shaped nest is generally placed on the under side of a branch of the yucca, fastened to the stiff leaves which project down-

BULLOCK ORIOLE ♂
SCOTT ORIOLE ♀
ARIZONA HOODED ORIOLE ♂

BULLOCK ORIOLE ♀
SCOTT ORIOLE ♂
ARIZONA HOODED ORIOLE ♀

ward. The bird often ranges among the junipers and pinyon pines that mingle with the tree yucca in the stony canyons along the edge of the desert, and in the Washington palms along the western edge of the Colorado Desert. The male may readily be distinguished from both the Bullock and the Arizona Hooded Orioles by the fact that the entire head and neck is black.

$7\frac{1}{4}$–$8\frac{1}{3}$

Ad. ♂. — *Head, throat, upper breast and upper back black; lower back yellow;* tail two thirds black at tip, yellow at base; *belly bright lemon yellow;* wings chiefly black, with yellow and white wing-bars. Bill and feet dark gray. **Ad.** ♀. — Upper parts brown, brightening to yellowish on rump and tail; throat often dull black; under parts brownish yellow, brightening on belly and under tail. Bill and feet dark gray. **Im.** ♂. — Black and yellow of **ad.** shaded with gray.

Dist. — *Cal.* S.V. (May–Aug.) among tree yuccas, agaves or juniper in southeastern Cal. from Jacumba, San Diego Co., to Walker Pass, Kern Co. Casual west of the desert divides.

Nest, of fibers fastened to limbs of yucca. *Eggs*, 2–4, pale blue, blotched with brown and gray.

Arizona Hooded Oriole. *Icterus cucullatus nelsoni*

Early in April a sharp *eek* is heard from some tall Washington palm in the streets or yards of southern California, and a slender bird in yellow and black appears perched on the top of a frond. In spite of its bright colors the Arizona Hooded Oriole keeps so closely to the clustered fronds in the tops of tall palms that its high, thin *eek*, or its chattering *chek, chek, chek* is often the only indication of its presence. The song is very seldom heard even in the height of the breeding season; it is a rapid series of throaty notes, more warbled and less whistled than the songs of the other two species. Besides the notes described above, the bird has a scolding wren-like *kerrk*, sometimes rolled out into a chatter. For the markings distinguishing the Arizona Hooded and the Bullock Orioles see the following species.

7–$7\frac{3}{4}$

Ad. ♂. — *Top of head, lower back and rump yellow*, deepening on the sides of the neck to orange; wings black with a narrow bar of white; *upper back and tail black;* sides of head (below the eye) and throat black, black extending to upper breast, but cut off by yellow from black of back; rest of under parts yellow. Bill (curved to a slender point) and feet dark gray. **Ad.** ♀. — Head and tail dull yellowish; back grayish olive; wing with two dull white bars; under parts dull yellow.

Dist. — Common S.V. (Mar.–Aug.) locally at lower levels in southern Cal., from San Diego to Santa Barbara, and in the Colorado Desert.

Nest, a basket of palm fibers hung from twigs or the fronds of palms. *Eggs*, 4–6, bluish white, blotched and scrawled with brown and purple.

Bullock Oriole. *Icterus bullocki*

In late March or early April a flash of orange or black in the delicate green of cottonwoods, a characteristic chatter, or the *kip, kit-tick, kit-tick, whew, wheet* of the song announce the arrival in southern California of the Bullock Oriole. The bird is a lover of trees and swings its cup-shaped nest of felt from every clump of cottonwoods or other deciduous trees along the irrigation ditches or about ranches in the cattle country east of the mountains. From the latitude of Santa Barbara and Fresno northward, the Bullock is the only oriole, but south of this line the Arizona Hooded Oriole also occurs. The *black top of the head* of the Bullock and the *broad bar of white in the wing* distinguish it; the white bar is particularly conspicuous in flight. The female Bullock is yellower on the breast than the female Arizona Hooded.

$6\frac{3}{4}$–$7\frac{1}{2}$

Ad. ♂. — *Top of head and upper back black;* line over forehead and over eye orange; narrower line of black from bill through eye to back; *wing with broad patch of white;* tail chiefly yellow, central feathers black, others tipped with more or less black; a narrow stripe of black down throat; *rest of under parts orange.* Bill grayish black; feet dusky gray. **Ad.** ♀. — Upper parts gray, washed with yellow on head; tail yellowish brown, showing most yellow when spread; wings dusky with two white bars; sides of throat and breast yellowish; rest of under parts grayish white. Bill blackish above, bluish gray below and on sides; feet dull bluish gray.

Dist. — *Cal.* Abundant S.V. (Mar.–Sept.) along streams, about settlements and on lake borders throughout, except along the coast southerly and in the northwest; common M. everywhere.

Ore. / *Wash.* Common S.V. (May–late Aug.) in deciduous trees on the plains east, and along streams in western Ore. and in the Puget Sound region; common M. everywhere.

Nest, a cup of vegetable fibers, hung to branches from 6 to 40 ft. in trees, generally cottonwoods or willows. *Eggs*, 3–6, bluish white or pale buffy, lined and scrawled with blackish.

Brewer Blackbird. *Euphagus cyanocephalus*

About the corrals and yards of every large ranch, flocks of Brewer Blackbirds are a characteristic sight, walking in and out among the stock, or perching in long rows along the fences, the iridescent colors and yellow eye of the males contrasting with the sober brown of the females. In cities and towns the birds frequent parks or light on the piles of lumber on the wharves, and line the telephone wires. They breed in colonies, choosing some thick tree such as the Monterey cypress or pepper tree. Toward dusk Brewer Blackbirds fly in small companies from different directions into some thick clump of trees, where they roost for the night. Their hoarse squeaking notes suggest unoiled machinery. In the height of the mating fervor the males stretch their necks and heads up when they utter their wheezy song, or bend forward spreading out the feathers of the neck and breast. At all seasons Brewer Blackbirds commonly walk with their wings slightly drooping. Red-winged Blackbirds and in southern California Cowbirds frequent the stock-pens and corrals along with Brewer Blackbirds. The unstreaked breasts distinguish the Brewer Blackbirds from female Redwings, and the greater size, darker plumage and long, sharp-pointed bills distinguish them from the female Cowbirds. The yellow (apparently white) eye and long sharp-pointed bill distinguish the male Brewer from the male Cowbird.

BREWER BLACKBIRD (♂)

$7\frac{3}{4}$–$9\frac{3}{4}$

Ad. ♂. — Wholly black, browner on head and neck, purplish in strong light, body greenish in strong light; tail long and slightly rounded; iris apparently white. Bill sharp-pointed, black; feet black. **Ad.** ♀. — Head and neck brownish gray (with a faint tinge of violet in strong light); rest of upper parts dark brown (tinged with bluish green in strong light); under parts brownish gray; eye brown.

Dist. — *Cal.* Abundant R. throughout in open country; rare in the northwest coast belt.
Ore. Common R. in open country throughout.
Wash. Common S.V. east; a few winter, especially southerly; common R. west, fewer in winter.

Nest, of sticks, grass, etc., in thick trees or bushes, or on the ground, generally in colonies. *Eggs,* 4–8, grayish or greenish, variously marked with brown and lavender, or almost entirely brown.

TANAGERS: *Family Thraupidæ*

Western Tanager. *Piranga ludoviciana*

When a male Western Tanager swings off through the dark aisles of evergreens even the unobservant exclaim at the *bright yellow and black* of its plumage, and when the bird sings from the tip of a spray and shows its *crimson head,* we feel that Nature has been generous indeed. A Tanager is always deliberate and often sits for a long period on one perch singing short phrases at longish intervals. The song sounds much like a Robin's; it is made up of short phrases with rising and falling inflections *pir-ri pir-ri pee-wi pir-ri pee-wi.* It is hoarser than a Robin's, lower in pitch and rarely continued for more than four or five phrases; it lacks the joyous ringing quality of the Robin's. The Tanager's call note is one of the most characteristic sounds of the mountains of California and the evergreen forests in the lowlands of Oregon and Washington. It may be written *prit-it* or *pri-ti-tick*, followed often by a lower *chert-it*. The adult when feeding young utters a low purring note, and the young a *chi-wee*, suggesting the note of the young Willow Goldfinch or the call of the Purple Finch. In migration the Western Tanager visits the willows in lowland stream beds, the oaks along the foothills, brushy borders, where it feeds greedily on cascara (*Rhamnus*) berries, gardens and orchards. A female Tanager might be mistaken for a female Bullock Oriole; the Tanager's upper parts are darker, and the sides of the head much less yellow.

WESTERN TANAGER (♂)

$6\frac{1}{3}$–7

Ad. ♂. — *Head crimson;* middle of back, wings and tail black; other parts and bars on wing yellow. Bill gray; feet dark gray. **Ad.** ♀. — Top of head and rump dull greenish yellow; wings dusky, with white or yellowish bars; under parts dull yellow.

Dist. — *Cal.* Common M. (late Apr. and May; Aug. and early Sept.) throughout; common S.V. (May–Aug.) in the mountains.
Ore. } Common S.V. (late Apr.–Sept.) in deciduous and coniferous forests throughout.
Wash. }

Nest, of twigs on a horizontal limb. *Eggs*, 3–5, pale bluish green, lightly spotted with brown and lilac.

Cooper Summer Tanager. *Piranga rubra cooperi*

The Summer Tanager has chosen the hottest part of California for its summer home, the dense growth of willow along the Colorado River, from Yuma to Needles. These thickets are filled in May and June with a medley of bird voices — the hoarse cooing of White-winged Doves, the bickering of Abert Towhees and the clownish calls of the Chat. A sharp ear will detect among these sounds a call note *ki-yup* or *pit-ic*, suggesting the Western Tanager's but not so emphatic. Then apparently from far off will come a sweet pensive song, suggesting a distant Robin. The singer though shy and often hidden in some leafy cottonwood will eventually come into view and show the dull red of the Summer Tanager.

$6\frac{3}{4}$–$7\frac{3}{4}$

Ad. ♂. — Entire plumage rose-red, except the wings, which are brown, tinged except at tip with red. Bill dusky above, paler below; feet dark brown. **Ad.** ♀. — Upper parts yellowish brown, brightest on head and rump; under parts brownish yellow. Bill and feet brown. **Im.** ♂ **in spring.** — Red and yellow in patches.

Dist. — *Cal.* Common S.V. (May–Sept.) in the willows and cottonwoods of the Colorado R. from Yuma to Needles.

Nest and *eggs* like those of the preceding species.

FINCHES, SPARROWS, etc.: *Family Fringillidæ*

GROSBEAKS, etc.: *Subfamily Richmondeninæ*

Black-headed Grosbeak. *Zamelodia melanocephala*

The return in April of the Black-headed Grosbeak at once fills great spaces that have been silent with sweet and penetrating melody. The eager males, each singing from a high perch on its own breeding ground, broadcast their powerful song in all directions so that a listener standing in orchard or woodland is never out of range of two or three performers. The song is mellow though powerful, made up of rising or falling passages generally including a rolling note, and in the height of the bird's ecstasy trails off at the close in broken exclamations. When his ardor cannot be expressed from a perch, the male pours out his most passionate phrases from the wing. Grosbeaks feed much on the ground, and about public camps often become very tame, hopping close to tents or buildings in search of bits of food. The young have a low sweet note *whee, whée-you,* which they utter both from the nest and when following the parents to be fed.

BLACK-HEADED GROSBEAK (♂)

The male is easily recognized by his black head and cinnamon-brown breast and the chestnut or creamy buff of his nape. When he flies much white shows in wings and tail, and the rump is cinnamon-brown. The female may be known by her heavy light-colored bill, buffy white collar and bar of white on the wing. The call note, given by both sexes, is a sharp *peek.*

$6\frac{1}{4}$–$7\frac{3}{4}$

Ad. ♂. — *Head black,* often with a streak of chestnut through the crown, broad collar across nape chestnut-brown; back streaked with black, white and cinnamon; wings and tail black; *broad white patch in wings* and two white wing-bars; rump chestnut; several outer tail feathers with large white spots near the tips; *under parts rich orange-brown*, becoming yellow on belly. Bill large, dark gray above, light gray below; feet dark gray. **Ad.** ♀. — Head blackish with white or light brownish lines over eye and through crown; nape varying from pale chestnut to light gray; back brown; two white wing-bars; breast light orange-brown, belly yellow. Bill dark above, light below; feet light gray.

Dist. — Pacific Black-headed Grosbeak. [*Z. m. capitalis.*]

Cal. Common S.V. (Apr.–Sept.) throughout in deciduous growth, chiefly along streams.

Ore. Common S.V. (May–Sept.) west, rare east.

Wash. Fairly common S.V. (May–Sept.) throughout in deciduous growth.

Rocky Mountain Black-headed Grosbeak. *Z. m. melanocephala.*

Cal. Migrant along lower Colorado R.

Nest, a loose structure of twigs in small trees and bushes. *Eggs*, 3–4, bluish white, spotted with light brown.

Blue Grosbeak. *Guiraca cærulea* subsp.

A Blue Grosbeak perched on a tuft of weeds near a willow thicket is a beautiful spot of color, almost *wholly rich deep blue* with a *bar of chestnut across the wing*. Its habitat, however, is almost entirely restricted to the low ground along streams, lakes and irrigation ditches, so that dwellers in cities and in foothill country rarely see it. Its song is a very pleasing warble, not vigorous enough to carry very far, suggesting in its form and quality an indolent House Finch. The male when singing often occupies the same perch for a long period. No other bird in lowland country is rich blue over the entire under parts. The Lazuli Bunting and the Western Bluebird both have some brown or chestnut on the breast. The female Blue Grosbeak might easily be confused with the female Lazuli Bunting. Both jerk their brown bodies nervously among low weeds, but the Grosbeak is not only larger and paler, with a swollen bill, but has *two light brown bands across the wing*.

BLUE GROSBEAK

6–7

Ad. ♂. — *Head, rump and under parts dark blue;* back blackish, feathers often edged with chestnut; *wings with two chestnut bars*. Bill large, upper mandible dusky, lower light gray; feet blackish. **Ad.** ♀. — General color brown, lighter below; rump tinged with bluish; two dull cinnamon-brown wing-bars. Bill and feet brown. **Im.** ♂ **in spring.** — Blue and brown in patches.

Dist. — California Blue Grosbeak. [*G. c. salicaria*]
Cal. Locally common S.V. (Apr.–Sept.) to southern and central Cal. chiefly in willows along streams.
Arizona Blue Grosbeak. *G. c. lazula.*
Cal. Along the lower Colorado R.
Nest, of rootlets in bushes and small trees. *Eggs*, 3–4, bluish white.

Lazuli Bunting. *Passerina amœna*

On dry brushy hillsides and canyon slopes in May and June a small bird singing from a high twig, a telephone wire or even from a low bush shows an exquisite *blue head and back* and a *broad white bar in the wing.* The song is best distinguished by its marked division into short phrases which vary distinctly in pitch, generally beginning high, falling to successively lower levels and then rising again. The following syllables may give an idea of its character but the variations are endless — *tsip tsip tsip zwee tsit tsit tsit tsit.* In the height of the mating season the male sometimes indulges in a flight song, and when courting he elevates his tail, spreads his wings and stretches up his head and neck. Both sexes have a *tsip* of alarm, and when excited jerk the tail nervously to one side.

LAZULI BUNTING

Even a beginner should have no difficulty in distinguishing the male Lazuli Bunting from the Western Bluebird; the Bunting has only a narrow band of chestnut on the upper breast and a white belly below, while the Bluebird's entire breast is chestnut. The broad bar of white, moreover, on the wing is an unfailing mark. The much rarer male Blue Grosbeak lacks the chestnut breast and the white wing-bar. The female Lazuli Bunting is a difficult bird to place; she is dull brown, unstreaked, with the conical bill of a sparrow. The nervous flip of the tail often helps to identify her. The female Blue Grosbeak and the female Lazuli Bunting are very similar; the smaller bill of the Bunting is a distinguishing mark.

5–5½

Ad. ♂. — *Head, neck and back rich azure blue* (black before eye) washed with brown on the back; wings and tail dusky, tail tinged with blue; *white bar on wing; breast chestnut;* rest of under parts white. Bill black above, paler below; feet black. **Ad.** ♀. — Upper parts grayish brown; under parts pale brown, fading to dingy white on belly; two light buffy wing-bars. **Im. in summer.** — Streaked below.

Dist. — *Cal.* Common S.V. (Apr.–Sept.) in the foothills and drier valleys throughout.
Ore. Common S.V. (Apr.–Sept.) west, common southeast, rarer northeast.
Wash. Common S.V. (Apr.–Sept.) east and west; apparently absent along the coast.

Nest, of weed stalks and plant fibers, loosely constructed, in low bushes. *Eggs*, 3–4, bluish white, generally unmarked.

OLD-WORLD SPARROWS: *Subfamily Passerinæ*

ENGLISH SPARROW. [*Passer domesticus*]

The English Sparrow, like other tramps, used empty freight cars in its journey westward. It is now common about the railroad yards and in the stock-pens of nearly every town, though held in check in the farming country by that hardy native son, the House Finch. In winter, too, it has to compete with the bands of Nuttall or Gambel Sparrows that feed along the roadsides or in truck gardens. The city streets, where the motor car has so largely superseded the horse, no longer offer the English Sparrow abundant and easy pickings of grain, but its coarse, insistent *cheep* is nevertheless a too familiar sound from the cornices of city buildings where the male with drooping wings and tail spread hops about the indifferent female. In spring the male utters a note like the syllables *fee-léep*, with a persistence worthy of a better cause. The chunky figure and unstreaked white breast of the female, and the black throat of the male will serve to identify the English Sparrow to any one who is so fortunate as to be unacquainted with it.

$5\frac{1}{2}$–$6\frac{1}{4}$

Ad. ♂. — Top of head gray; *a patch of chestnut behind eye;* back brown streaked with black; wing-bars white; a stripe of chestnut on the wing; *throat and upper breast black;* rest of upper parts gray or whitish. Bill black; feet brown. **Ad.** ♀. — Head grayish brown; back streaked with black and buff; under parts whitish; breast washed with grayish brown.

Dist. — *Cal.*, *Ore.*, *Wash.* Common R. in many cities and even small towns, particularly along railroads.

FINCHES, etc.: *Subfamily Carduelinæ*

EVENING GROSBEAK. *Hesperiphona vespertina* subsp.

City parks in Washington and Oregon occasionally attract in winter roving flocks of stout, chunky birds, whose contrasting colors of *yellow and black*, *light-colored swollen bills* and surprising fearlessness easily distinguish them as Evening Grosbeaks. They feed in winter on the small berries and haws that still cling to ornamental trees and shrubs, or on the seeds of box-elders and maples. In summer campers in the high mountains come upon pairs of these unmistakable birds feeding on the seeds of pines; the female, though much less yellow than the male, is easily recognized by the *black and white in her wings and tail*, and by her light-colored bill. The ordinary note of the Evening Grosbeak is a shrill whistled *tsée-a.* In the breeding season the male's attempt at song consists of the ordinary sharp *tseé-a,* followed by a lower harsh *grrree.* The flight is undulating like a Goldfinch's. When the bird is perched, the white patches in the wing meet on the back; the wing-patches and the light-colored bill are good recognition marks in flight. The bird often picks up seeds that have fallen to the ground, hopping clumsily like a sparrow. After the breeding season Evening Grosbeaks wander irregularly to lower levels and to the southward, occasionally reaching southern California. They are at all times tame and easily approached.

WESTERN EVENING GROSBEAK (♂)

$6\frac{1}{2}$–$7\frac{1}{3}$

Ad. ♂. — Top of head, wings and tail black; conspicuous *white patch in wing;* tail deeply forked; forehead, *line over eye, shoulders, lower back and belly yellow;* neck, hind-head and breast smoky brown. *Bill swollen, greenish yellow;* feet brown. **Ad.** ♀ **and Im.** — General color brownish gray, darkest on head; yellowish wash on sides of neck and lower back; wings black, feathers edged with white; tail black with white tips; belly whitish.

Dist. — California Evening Grosbeak. [*H. v. californica.*]

Cal. Fairly common R. locally in the forests of the higher mountains from the Yosemite to Mt. Shasta, and in the Warner Mts. (Modoc Co.); wandering widely but irregularly in winter west of the Sierras.

Ore. } Common R. locally in forested regions east; less com-
Wash. } mon west, wandering irregularly in winter.

Note. Subspecific status of the breeding birds of Ore. and of Wash. not yet worked out.

British Columbia Evening Grosbeak. [*H. v. brooksi.*]

Wash. W.V. but to what extent not yet known.

Nest, of sticks, rootlets, etc., in trees at a moderate height. *Eggs,* 3–4, bluish green, sparingly blotched with pale brown.

California Purple Finch. *Carpodacus purpureus californicus*

The advantage of knowing intimately the notes of birds is well illustrated by the confusion in a beginner's mind between the California Purple Finch and the House Finch or Linnet. The presence or absence of streaking on the flanks, and the depth of the notch in the tail are emphasized in many books as distinctive marks. One syllable, however, heard from either bird, no matter how far off, instantly distinguishes it. The Purple Finch repeats in flight a single *pit, pit,* very sharp and emphatic and never varied. When a Purple Finch is perched and calling to a mate or to other members of the flock, it utters a call like the syllables *che-wée,* very sweet in tone with none of the coarse English Sparrow quality so often present in the calls of the House Finch. To distinguish the songs of the two birds is harder for a beginner. Let his ear become thoroughly familiar with the Linnet's song, endlessly repeated from the ridgepole, from the vines on the porch, or from the telephone wires. Let him mark the introduction of single notes, finally running into a rather broken series of wavy lines of song and ending with a low *churr* and perhaps an upward *whee.* Then from the blossoming willows or the sycamores just coming into leaf where the canyon stream comes into the plain, from the moss-draped oaks in cool canyon woods or from conifers he will hear a song that suggests the Linnet's but differs in pitch and in the rapidity with which the notes are rippled forth. It is distinctly lower and there is no hesitation; there are no single introductory notes and the undulations of the song are less marked. It is a single burst of melody, the notes rolling over and over to the end. In the conifers of the Sierras and the Cascades, the Purple Finch and the Cassin Finch are often found in the same localities. For an account of the Cassin's song see the next species. In winter and spring Purple Finches come into orchards; in Oregon and Washington they are widely distributed but in California they are found in the hills and mountains, in oaks and conifers, shunning habitations in the breeding season as much as Linnets seek them. They are restless birds, constantly moving to and fro high overhead, making their presence known by the sharp *pit, pit* described above. They often feed in winter with Goldfinches on the balls that hang in strings from the sycamore.

The darker gray of the female Purple Finch and the dark patch on the cheek bordered above by a light line distinguish her from the female House Finch. The absence of marked streaking on the flanks and the deeply notched tail distinguish the male Purple Finch from the male Linnet. For the distinctions between the Purple and the Cassin Finches see the next species.

$5\frac{1}{2}$–6

Ad. ♂. — *Head, rump and breast rose red,* deepest on head; back streaked with brown and tinged with red; wings and tail brown; tail rather deeply notched; belly whitish. Bill somewhat swollen, gray; feet brown. **Ad.** ♀. — Upper parts grayish brown, streaked with dusky and tinged with olive, brightest on rump; *dark patch back of eye,* bordered above and below with light gray. Bill as in male but darker; feet brown. **Im.** ♀ **in first breeding season.** — Like ♀.

Dist. — *Cal.* Common R. of coniferous forests and cool canyons west of the Sierras, widely distributed over wooded lowlands in winter.

Ore.
Wash. } Fairly common R. west, less common in winter.

Nest, a fairly compact structure of twigs, on a horizontal limb, often high. *Eggs,* 4–5, bluish green, spotted with black.

Cassin Purple Finch. *Carpodacus cassini*

A company of medium-sized birds, some red, some gray, are often seen feeding on the ground under the tall yellow pines that clothe the eastern

HOUSE FINCH ♂ AND ♀ CALIFORNIA PURPLE FINCH ♂ AND ♀
CASSIN PURPLE FINCH ♂ AND ♀ SIERRA ROSY FINCH ♂ AND ♀

slopes of the Cascades, the Sierras and the high mountains of southern California. Their general appearance at once suggests the House Finch, but a close observation of the red males shows that the deep red on the top of the head is sharply separated from the brownish back of the neck. When Cassin Finches are startled they fly to the trees, uttering in flight a note suggesting the syllables *tee-dee-yip*, run together almost as two syllables. The song of the male is a rolling, vibrating warble with the vigor of the Purple Finch but suggesting the House Finch by a somewhat looser construction and by often ending with a *churr*. The Cassin Purple Finch shares the restlessness of the family, starting for no apparent reason on long flights from one feeding place or perch to another. It is chiefly resident, moving after the breeding season to slightly lower levels, occasionally appearing in winter in numbers even on the coast. The greater size, the *crimson crown-patch clearly marked off from the back of the neck,* and the paler tone of the under parts distinguish the male Cassin Finch from the California Purple Finch, which it most closely resembles and with which it is associated on the western border of its range. The female may be distinguished by a trained observer from the female Purple Finch by a difference in the streaking of the breast: in the Cassin the streaks are clearly defined leaving white areas between them; in the California Purple Finch the streaks are broader and more run together, so that there is less contrast of white and dusky. The female Cassin may be distinguished from the female House Finch, where they occur together, by the dusky gray patch on the sides of the head and the light streak over the eye.

6–6½

Ad. ♂. — *Top of head crimson, sharply defined from back of neck* and back, which are brown, streaked with dusky; rump pale rose; wings and tail dark brown; throat and breast suffused with faint rose, fading to white on belly and sides. Bill large; dark gray above, light gray below; feet brown. **Ad.** ♀. — Upper parts gray, tinged with greenish yellow in strong light and streaked with dusky; under parts white sharply streaked with dusky; sides of head dark with light streak over eye.

Dist. — *Cal.* Common R. of the mountains, chiefly east of the Sierran divide, but west as far as the Yosemite; wanders irregularly in winter.

Ore., *Wash.* } S.V. to open timbered country east; some winter at lower levels.

Nest, chiefly of rootlets and grasses, on a horizontal branch often in a pine tip at varying heights. *Eggs*, 4–5, bluish green, lightly spotted with purplish gray and black.

House Finch; Linnet. *Carpodacus mexicanus* subsp.

A pair of birds burst from the vines on the porch as the front door is opened, and with harsh protests fly to the nearest tree. The female is grayish brown, heavily streaked on the under parts, the male is bright crimson on head and breast. As you watch them, he bursts into a rapid, joyous succession of notes ending generally in the syllables *chwee, whurr*. If you find the same pair and their brood later taking toll of your apricots, figs and strawberries, you will feel perhaps that though the presence of so much color and song throughout the year is a delight, you are paying handsomely for it. Be thankful, however, that there is ample compensation for the damage in color and melody; in the East you would have instead the plain appearance and monotonous calls of the English Sparrow. After the breeding season House Finches assemble in large flocks and feed on the seeds of weeds in fields and along highways. Single birds or small groups are always on the telephone wires, and often all the lines between several posts are occupied by solid rows. The ordinary call notes range from a rather coarse *wheat* to high-pitched calls which vary in pitch. The bird is talkative, calling as it flies. At the height of the breeding season the male hops about the indifferent female with tail up, wings drooping, head up and crest feathers raised, singing and making a sound like a sharp intake of breath. The female in the height of the mating period utters a few notes that suggest the male's song. The plumage of the male varies in the extent and shade of the red, and in many individuals the red is replaced by orange yellow.

The House Finch is the common red bird seen about farms, along highways and generally near civilization. The California Purple Finch, from which it is difficult to distinguish it, is a bird of cool canyons or coniferous forests, but the two are in certain regions found together. For the distinction between them see pp. 301, 302. East of the Sierras and Cascades, House Finches and Cassin Finches often occupy the same or adjoining territory (see preceding species).

$5\frac{1}{2}$

Ad. ♂. — *Fore part of crown*, line over eye and rump *crimson or scarlet* (sometimes orange); rest of upper parts grayish brown; *throat and breast bright crimson or scarlet* (or orange), sharply contrasted with the rest of the under parts, which are dull white; flanks and belly streaked with dusky. Bill swollen, dark gray above, light gray on sides and below; feet dark brown. **Ad.** ♀. — Upper parts grayish brown; under parts white streaked with brown. **Im.** — Similar to ♀, but with buffy edgings on the wings.

Dist. — House Finch. *C. m. frontalis.*

Cal. Abundant R. throughout at lower levels and in open country.

Ore. Fairly common R. in open country east and in the valleys of southern Ore. west.

Wash. Fairly common S.V. (Mar.–Sept.) in lowlands east, southerly; R. in extreme southern portion of range.

San Clemente House Finch. *C. m. clementis.*

On the southern Channel Is.

Nest, a compact structure of plant fibers, grasses, etc., in trees, bushes, vines or artificial structures. *Eggs*, 4–5, pale bluish green, sparingly spotted with dark brown or black.

PINE GROSBEAK. *Pinicola enucleator* subsp.

Eastern bird-lovers look forward to a Grosbeak winter when Pine Grosbeaks invade the northern tier of States in great numbers, delighting every one with their beauty and confiding ways. In most of the Pacific Coast States only a hardy mountain climber will see the handsome red male or hear his sweet whistle. The bird breeds here and there in the higher Sierras and northern Cascades, but nowhere abundantly, so that it is a piece of good fortune to find it. Pine Grosbeaks on their breeding grounds feed among evergreens, working on the cones or flying to the ground to pick up the fallen seeds. In the winter they feed largely on tender buds, on berries and even weed seeds. They are extremely confiding but restless, often flying off with strong undulating flight for no apparent reason. The ordinary call note of the Pine Grosbeak consists of two or three clear whistled notes, somewhat suggestive of the call of the Greater Yellow-legs; they may be written *tée-ti, tée-tee-ti,* the last note lower than the others. They often utter besides a sharp *peer.* When feeding they utter low musical twittering sounds, and when flying up suddenly, a low trilled whistle. The song is described as melodious, rich and varied. Many different stages of plumage are represented in a flock, from the rose or vermilion-red of the adult male to the gray female, through stages where saffron or brick-red is conspicuous on the head and rump. There should be no difficulty in recognizing even the dull-colored female, when the stout conical bill, the deeply forked tail, the white wing-bars and the saffron tinge of the head and rump are noted. The size and the conical bill should distinguish the male from the White-winged Crossbill in regions (central Washington) where the two might occur.

$7\frac{1}{2}$–8

Ad. ♂. — Head, all around, breast and rump (sometimes entire body) rose-red, brightest on head and rump; wings blackish with two white wing-bars; tail blackish, deeply forked; rest of body gray. Bill stout, blackish; feet blackish. **Ad. ♀ and Im.** — General plumage gray tinged on head and rump with saffron or brick-red; wings and tail dusky, wings with two white wing-bars.

Dist. — California Pine Grosbeak. *P. e. californica.*
Cal. R. locally in the central high Sierras.
Rocky Mt. Pine Grosbeak. *P. e. montana.*
Wash. Probably R. in northern Cascades; irregular W.V. (Sept.–Feb.) east.
Alaska Pine Grosbeak. *P. e. alascensis.*
Wash. Casual.
Kadiak Pine Grosbeak. *P. e. flammula.*
Wash. W.V. (Nov.–Feb.) irregularly throughout the State.

Nest, a frail structure of twigs, on limbs of conifer. *Eggs,* 3, greenish blue, spotted with brown and lavender.

Gray-crowned / Hepburn / Sierra Nevada } Rosy Finch. *Leucosticte tephrocotis* subsp.

Above timber line on the rocky summits of high mountains from the high Sierras north through the Cascades, medium-sized gray finches are seen in summer scattered over the snowbanks, hopping rapidly over the surface picking up insects that have dropped congealed on the frozen surface. At other times Rosy Finches feed at the edge of the snow on grassy slopes or among low bushes, picking up seeds, or pursue one another with strong pitching flight and hoarse notes. *The tinge of pink on rump and wings,* the *black crown bordered by light gray behind* and the brown under parts readily distinguish the male; the female is duller colored but still has enough pinkish on wings and rump to distinguish her from any of the brown sparrows. Cassin Finches and Crossbills, which also show red on the rump, rarely come above timber line. In winter Rosy Finches descend to lower levels but may at all times be distinguished from Cassin Finches and Crossbills by the blackish head and dark brown breasts. The Sierra Rosy Finch is described by Mr. Dawson as not songless but 'tuneless'; the song consisting only of a 'high-pitched ecstatic (for him) chirping.' The usual note given in flight is a rough *chee-chee-chi-chi-chi.*

$5\frac{1}{2}$–$6\frac{1}{2}$

Ad. ♂ in breeding season. — Top of head black, bordered behind and on the sides with ash; sides of head, throat and breast brown; central portion of wings, rump and belly rose-red. Bill black; feet black. **Ad. ♂ in fall and winter.** — Bill yellow. **Ad. ♀.** — Similar but body chiefly brown, a little rose on bend of wing and rump.

Dist. — Gray-crowned Rosy Finch. *L. t. tephrocotis.*

Ore. } *Wash.* } Rare W.V. (Nov.–Mar.) in extreme eastern Ore. and Wash. Occurs in mountains of Wallowa Co., Ore., in summer, probably breeding, and in small numbers in winter at lower levels with the following.

Hepburn Rosy Finch. *L. t. littoralis.*

Ore. } *Wash.* } Fairly common S.V. (May–Sept.) at or about timber line on the higher peaks of the Olympics and Cascades; common in winter (Oct.–Mar.) in the lowlands east; rarely west.

Sierra Rosy Finch. *L. t. dawsoni.*

Cal. Common R. at or above timber line on the high Sierras from Olancha Pk. to Nevada Co., also sparingly on the higher peaks of the White Mts., Inyo Co.

Nest, a cup of grasses or moss, in a niche in a cliff or under a boulder of a rock slide. *Eggs,* 4–5, white.

Redpoll. *Acanthis linaria linaria*

In the open country of eastern Washington and Oregon in winter a flock of small brown birds with streaked breasts, with varying amounts of crimson on the head and breast, feed briskly among weeds or fly off with a rattling call. The common note of the Redpoll when perched is a sweet call, almost identical with that of the Goldfinch and Siskin, but the rattling call given by flocks when in flight, like the syllables *tshu, tshu, tshu,* is unlike the *ti-di-di* of the Goldfinch or the husky *chee-ee* of the Siskin. The *crimson crown and small chin-patch of black* readily distinguish the more brightly colored individuals from the Siskins, which are also streaked above and below; an immature Redpoll without red on the breast can be told from a Siskin by the black chin and inconspicuous *whitish* instead of yellowish *wing-bars.*

$4\frac{1}{3}$–$5\frac{1}{3}$

Ad. ♂. — *Crown crimson;* back streaked with gray and brown; *whitish wing-bars;* rump sometimes tinged with rose; *throat black;* breast and upper belly sometimes suffused with rose; sides streaked with brown. Bill usually yellow with dusky tip and edges; feet blackish. **Ad.** ♀. — Rump and under parts lacking the red of the male. **Im.** — Lacks red on crown.

Dist. — Irregular, sometimes abundant W.V. (Oct.–Mar.) to the open country of eastern Wash. and Ore., less common in western Wash. One winter record for northeastern Cal.

GOLDFINCH. *Astragalinus tristis* subsp.

Over the willow thickets in the stream beds of southern California and commonly in the valleys of Oregon and Washington, a small yellow bird with black wings and tail flies in summer with a pitching flight, uttering a sweet cheerful twitter. In the breeding season the male with even wing-strokes flutters in wide circles above the brooding female. As he flies he pours forth a continual twittering song which she answers from time to time by a low *tee-dee-dee*. Ordinarily the Goldfinch flies in deep undulations; after a stroke or two has carried the bird upward the wings are held close to the body and the bird dips downward. In early spring companies of males gather in the willow tops, all singing and twittering in concert. When a single bird is separated from the flock, it utters a long sweet canary-like call *chi-ee;* in flight both sexes utter a call *ti-di-di* with none of the minor quality or the variations of the Green-backed Goldfinch.

WILLOW GOLDFINCH (♂, Breeding)

Young birds when about to leave the nest and for some time after they are out following their parents about utter a monotonous *te-wée, te-wée.* In winter Willow Goldfinches join the House Finches and Green-backed Goldfinches and feed on the weed patches in dry fields; they are particularly fond of the seeds of composites — bachelor's-buttons, dandelions, etc.

In summer the plumage of the Willow Goldfinch is a clear yellow, of the same shade on the under parts as on the back; the black cap is confined to the fore part of the head just behind the bill and shows in marked contrast to the yellow back. Female Willow Goldfinches are larger and lighter colored on the back than female Green-backed Goldfinches, but the females of the two species are much less easily distinguished than the males. In winter the male Willow Goldfinch loses his black cap and his yellow is replaced by a rich brown, but the black and white of the wings are retained.

$4\frac{1}{4}$–5

Ad. ♂ **in breeding season.** — *Forehead black;* wings black with white bars;

tail black, outer feathers broadly tipped with white; rest of plumage bright yellow. Bill orange, tipped with black; feet brown. **Ad. ♂ in winter.** — Like female, but wings black and white. **Ad. ♀.** — Head and back brownish olive; wings and tail dusky with grayish bars; under parts yellowish, brightest on throat. Bill light colored; feet brown. **Im.** — Similar to winter adults but browner; wing-bars buffy. Bill and feet dusky.

Dist. — Willow Goldfinch. *A. t. salicamans.*

Cal. Common R. locally in valleys west of the Sierras and desert divides throughout.

Ore. Common R. west of the Cascades, less common in winter.

Wash. Fairly common S.V. (Apr.–Sept.) along the coast, in the Sound region and in Cowlitz Valley; a few winter.

Pale Goldfinch. *A. t. pallidus.*

Ore., *Wash.* } Common R. in plains and foothills east.

Nest, a neat cup of plant fibers, in tall bushes or low trees. *Eggs*, 4–5, pale bluish or bluish white.

Green-backed Goldfinch. *Astragalinus psaltria hesperophilus*

In any weedy border of neglected fields small birds with *yellow under parts and white patches in their wings* fly off when disturbed, with a little shivering note like the jarring of a cracked piece of glass. Much of the time even in winter Green-backed Goldfinches keep in pairs, the male's black cap contrasting with his yellow under parts and the white showing even in the closed wing. The spring flocks gather in trees near their feeding ground and keep up a concert of twittering song. When a pair are nesting the male utters, either from an upper spray or from the air, a series of sweet twittering notes that suggest the song of a canary. The ordinary flight of a Goldfinch is undulating, each stroke of the wings bearing the bird upward, and alternating with an instant of downward drop while the wings are closed. Green-backed Goldfinches can always be identified by their calls. These include a plaintive *tee-yee,* both notes on the same pitch, a *tee ee,* the second note higher, and a single plaintive *tee* and the jarring notes mentioned above. There is more variety in the calls of the Green-backed Goldfinch than in those of the Willow Goldfinch, and a plaintive quality which the latter lacks. Young birds, just before leaving the nest or when following their parents in early summer, utter continually a single sharp *tsi.*

GREEN-BACKED GOLDFINCH (♂)

It takes considerable practice to distinguish Green-backed from Willow Goldfinches except in the case of breeding males. The student should bear in mind that the back of a Green-backed Goldfinch is never either clear yellow or chestnut-brown; it has always an olive-green tint. The male has a black cap that occupies the whole top of the head.

4

Ad. ♂. — *Whole top of head black;* back greenish; *wings* blackish *with white patch;* tail blackish, with white spots in the middle of the outer feathers, tips blackish; under parts greenish yellow. Bill dusky above, lighter on sides and below; feet brownish. **Ad.** ♀. — Upper parts, including top of head, greenish gray; white wing-patch smaller (sometimes almost lacking); white spots on outer tail feathers near the middle of the feather; under parts light olive yellow. **Im.** — Like ♀ but tinged above with buffy brownish, under parts duller.

Dist. — *Cal.* Abundant R. at lower levels west of the Sierras; local in the deserts and less numerous in the humid coast belt.
Ore. Common in valleys as far north as Portland.

Nest, a neat small cup of plant fibers and grasses, in low bushes or trees. *Eggs*, 4–5, pale bluish green.

Lawrence Goldfinch. *Astragalinus lawrencei*

Birds are as a rule so regular in their habits that a student can find year after year a pair of birds which may have traveled a thousand miles or more to and from their winter home and yet returned to the same spot to breed. It is interesting, therefore, and puzzling to find a few birds like the Lawrence Goldfinch which are more gypsy-like. A valley in southern California may be filled with the black-chinned gray-bodied birds one summer and the next year contain not one. As a rule the Lawrence Goldfinch is found in hotter, drier portions of the State than either the Willow or Green-backed Goldfinches. It is a bird of the foothills or mountain valleys, particularly from Los Angeles Co. southward. A male can be easily recognized by the arrangement of the black about the base of the bill; the other two species have black only on the top of the head, but the flesh-colored bill of the Lawrence Goldfinch as he faces the observer is encircled by black, giving the bird almost a hooded appearance.

LAWRENCE GOLDFINCH (♂)

The black about the bill shows even in the winter plumage. The general color of the female is grayish brown; both sexes show *yellow across the wings.* The notes of the Lawrence Goldfinch bear a general resemblance to those of the other Goldfinches but among its call notes is a harsh *kee-yerr*, unlike any note of the other two. The song is lower in pitch and rougher, with occasional harsh phrases.

4–4½

Ad. ♂. — *Chin, face and top of head black;* sides of head and rest of upper parts gray; *broad yellow and black bars across wing* and *yellow patch on gray breast;* rump yellow; tail black with large white areas not reaching to the tip. Bill flesh-colored; feet brown. **Ad.** ♀. — Resembles the ♂ but lacks the black on the head and shows duller yellow and less white in tail. Bill dusky above, paler on sides and below.

Dist. — S.V. (Apr.–Sept.) to central and southern Cal. chiefly west of the Sierras, local and irregular in distribution; commoner from Los Angeles Co. southward. Winters irregularly as far north as Santa Barbara.

Nest, a neat cup of grasses, weed stalks, etc., in tall weeds, bushes or trees. *Eggs*, 4–5, white.

PINE SISKIN. *Spinus pinus*

At the edges of extensive coniferous forests in Washington and Oregon and along the Sierras, the Siskin is as confiding and attractive as the Goldfinch in cultivated regions. The high-pitched wheezy call note

PINE SISKIN

ke-seé-i, is constantly heard as the birds fly overhead in jerky undulations. As soon as dandelions mature, Siskins feed on the ground, opening the ripening heads; in spring they frequent the willows and alders for the ripening catkins. Siskins are very talkative, calling with a twittering note *ti-di-di*, or if one is separated from the flock uttering a sweet *tee-ee*, very similar to the 'canary' note of the Goldfinch but a little hoarser. In April, May and June, the males in song again suggest Goldfinches but mingle with their twittering a curious *whee-ee-ee*, like the sound made by blowing through a comb covered with thin paper. This note once learned is unmistakable, and serves, like the hoarse call used by the bird in flight, to identify a Siskin as far off as it can be heard. In the height of the breeding season the male Siskin sings on the wing like the Goldfinch, circling about with constant easy strokes. In winter Siskins often move in great numbers into the foothills as far south as southern California, feeding with Goldfinches and Purple Finches on the balls of the sycamore along stream beds or on roadside weeds. They may be readily identified at any season by the streaking above and below. The yellow in the wing shows at each stroke but is not noticeable when the wing is closed.

$4\frac{1}{4}$–5

Everywhere streaked, above with dusky and brown, below with dusky and whitish; *a small yellow area* in the wings and yellow in the outspread tail. Bill light brown; feet dark brown.

Dist. — *Cal.* Locally common R. in conifers in the mountains, also along the northern coast from Monterey Co. north; in winter wandering irregularly to lower levels. Common R. in parts of the San Francisco Bay region.

Ore. } *Wash.* } Common R. in coniferous forests, wandering irregularly in winter.

Nest, of twigs, rootlets, etc., generally in conifers. *Eggs,* 3–5, pale greenish blue, speckled chiefly around the larger end with black and reddish brown.

Red Crossbill. *Loxia curvirostra* subsp.

A vigorous *kip, kip, kip,* generally given in threes, twos or singly from a little flock of birds flying overhead or perched among the cones in the tops of a pine or fir, is generally the first intimation that Crossbills are about. When we look the flock over, we find stout chunky birds of medium size varying in color from *brick-red to yellow,* olive and gray, but all with the *rump* of a *brighter shade* or deeper color than the rest of the back. With a good glass one can make out the crossed tips of the mandibles, which enable the bird to pry out the seeds from the unopened cones. Crossbills are regular inhabitants of the deep coniferous forests on all the high mountains from the San Bernardinos northward, but are always more or less erratic in their habits. In some seasons, perhaps when the cones are not abundant enough in the mountains, they move in the autumn to the lowlands. They often feed on the ground, either under trees to pick up the seeds that have fallen from the cones, or in clearings. At such times they are very tame and sometimes allow a person actually to stand among them. Like many of the finches, they are restless; a flock will often for no apparent reason leave the tree in which it is feeding and fiy off to a distance. The song, given either from the top of a pine or fir or while the male is flying, resembles the syllables *too-tée, too-tée, too-tée, tee tee tee.* The chunky appearance of the Crossbill, the stout head and bill and the uniform red of the male will help to distinguish the bird from the Purple Finch. The *kip* of the Crossbill is louder and more energetic than the *pit* of the Purple Finch. The saffron-yellow rump of the gray females and young is a good field mark.

$5\frac{1}{2}$–$6\frac{1}{4}$

Ad. ♂. — Entire body dull vermilion-red, brightest on head and rump; wings and tail blackish. Bill blackish, the mandibles crossed near the tips; feet black. **Ad.** ♀. — Dull greenish gray, brighter and more yellowish on head and rump; wings and tail dusky. Young males are often seen with patches of gray, olive and dusky reddish, or with orange instead of red. **Im.** — Streaked with gray and dusky above and below.

Dist. — American Crossbill. *L. c. minor.*
Cal. Irregular W.V. in northern Cal., casual south.
Ore. Common R. of coniferous forests west, wandering irregularly in winter.
Wash. Common R. in coniferous forests chiefly in the mountains, wandering irregularly to lower levels in winter.
Sierra Crossbill. [*L. c. bendirei.*]
Cal. Fairly common R. of the higher mountains throughout; wandering irregularly to lower levels in winter.
Ore. R. in the mountains east, wandering to lower levels in winter.
Wash. Casual east.
Mexican Crossbill. *L. c. stricklandi.*
Cal. Santa Cruz I.

Nest, of plant fibers in conifers. *Eggs*, 3–4, dull white, spotted with brown and dark gray.

White-winged Crossbill. *Loxia leucoptera*

White-winged Crossbills occasionally appear in flocks in winter along the Canadian border, often with American Crossbills. The White-winged Crossbill is readily distinguished from the American Crossbill by the *rose*, not brick-red, of its plumage and by the *two broad white wing-bars.* Its call note is a sweet monosyllable *peet*, less emphatic than the *kip* of the American Crossbill; in flight it utters a chattering call. Its song as described by Townsend is 'delivered with great vigor and abandon, constantly swelling and dwindling, at times a low sweet warbling, then a rough rattling, then a loud, all-pervading *sweet, sweet, sweet,* recalling exactly a Canary bird.'

Ad. ♂. — *Head, rump and under parts rose-red;* middle of back black, streaked with rose; wings and tail black; *two broad bars of white across the wing.* Bill black, tips of mandibles crossed; feet black. **Ad. ♀ and Im.** — Red of ♂ replaced by gray, tinged with olive-yellow and streaked with black; rump yellow; wing-bars as in male. **Im. ♂.** — Often shows many stages between the plumages of ♂ and ♀, with patches of reddish.

Dist. — Irregular S.V. in Cascades, probably breeding; irregular W.V. (Dec.–May) in Sound region.

Nest, of small twigs, plant fibers, etc., in conifers. *Eggs*, pale blue, spotted with black and lilac.

TOWHEES, SPARROWS, BUNTINGS, etc: *Subfamily Emberizinæ*

Green-tailed Towhee. *Oberholseria chlorura*

A cat-like call, *pee-you-wee* is often heard in summer from the low bushes on open mountain-sides or high sage-brush plains east of the Sierras or Cascades. Presently a bird with *reddish brown cap* mounts to the top of some bush and utters a lively song. The singer has a *white throat,* which shows like a bit of cotton when the notes are poured forth. The Green-tailed Towhee is an active bird, slipping in and out of the sage or deer-brush, inquisitive about intruders and not shy. Most of its time is spent on or near the ground, but it does not scratch with both feet after the manner of the larger Towhees. In migration it associates with Gambel Sparrows in the bushes in the deserts of southeastern California, rarely appearing on the west side of the Coast Range. The song varies greatly in different individuals and even the same bird frequently changes his song after a few repetitions. It suggests the Bewick Wren and the Fox Sparrow, and is about intermediate in richness between the two. The song generally begins with a phrase like the syllables *wee churr*, followed by some high clear notes and ending with a feebler trill. One or two examples were written down, *wée chee chí-wi chí-wi, chit a-chit,* or *chip cheér burr-chip-chip-chip*. There is almost always a rough burr in the middle of the song which helps to distinguish it from the song of the Fox Sparrow.

GREEN-TAILED TOWHEE

$6\frac{1}{4}$–7

Ad. — *Crown reddish brown*, forehead dark gray, bordered by two short white lines; rest of upper parts grayish brown, tinged in strong light with yellowish green; edge of wing bright yellow; tail dusky, tinged with yellowish green; *throat white*, bordered by black stripes; breast ashy; belly whitish; region under base of tail buffy. Bill black above, gray below; feet light gray. **Im.** — Lacks the reddish brown crown; back brown. In early summer streaked with dusky.

Dist. — *Cal.* Common S.V. (Apr.–Sept.) chiefly on the eastern slopes of the mountains and eastward; common M. east of the Sierras and casually to the coast.
Ore. Common S.V. east.
Wash. Perhaps regular S.V. to extreme southeastern Wash.

Spotted Towhee. *Pipilo maculatus* subsp.

As soon as the winter rains start the first ferns from the mould, the song of the Spotted Towhee sounds with monotonous persistence from a perch in a tree or from brushy thickets, *bree*, long drawn out and with a suggestion of an *l* as well as the *r*. Throughout the year the Towhee utters a cat-like call *quee*, higher than the song or a drawled *chee ee*, but often its presence is first indicated by the loud rustle of dry leaves as the bird scratches vigorously in the thicket. A rarer note is a sibilant *zeee*. The *black head and neck*, sharply contrasting with the white belly, the *clear reddish brown along the flanks*, and the *white spots in the tail* make identification easy. The fiery red eye of the bird, his active movements and challenging call give a suggestion of vigor and energy. The female is much like to the male, but has a browner head and less white in the wings.

SPOTTED TOWHEE

7–8¼

Ad. ♂. — *Head, neck and upper parts black,* wings flecked and barred with *white; outer tail feathers tipped with white,* the next with large white spots near the tips; throat and breast black, sharply marked off from the white belly; *flanks reddish brown.* Bill dusky above, paler on sides and below; iris red; feet brown. **Ad.** ♀. — Like ♂, but head brownish black. **Im. in summer.** — Upper parts dark brown; under parts light brown, streaked with dusky.

Dist. — San Diego Towhee. *P. m. megalonyx.*
Cal. Common R. along the coast north to San Luis Obispo Co., and east to southern Kern Co.
San Clemente Towhee. *P. m. clementæ.*
Cal. San Clemente Is. and Santa Catalina.
Sacramento Towhee. *P. m. falcinellus.*
Cal. Common R. of the Sacramento Valley north to the Oregon line, of parts of the San Joaquin Valley and both slopes of the Sierras.
Rocky Mountain Towhee. *P. m. montanus.*
Cal. Panamint Mts.
San Francisco Towhee. *P. m. falcifer.*
Cal. Common R. of the coast belt from Monterey Co. to Humboldt Co.
Nevada Towhee. *P. m. curtatus.*
Cal. Common R. (?) in the Warner Mts. and probably in the desert ranges southeast; W.V. along the lower Colorado R.
Ore. / *Wash.* } Probably R. east.

Oregon Towhee. *P. m. oregonus.*
Cal. Rare straggler.
Ore. }
Wash. } Common R. west, less common in winter.

Nest, of shreds of bark and plant fibers, on the ground or in bushes. *Eggs*, 3–5, dull white, heavily spotted with reddish brown.

BROWN TOWHEE. *Pipilo crissalis* subsp.

Can even a bird-lover become enthusiastic over a Brown Towhee — a plain brown bird that hops stolidly in and out of brush heaps about farm buildings, with no bright colors, no attractive song and no tricks or manners of especial interest? The bird is a rustic with the stolidity of the peasant, and like a rustic it apparently lives its entire life near the spot where it was born. It is a stout brown bird with a longish tail, next to the House Finch and Brewer Blackbird the commonest and most obvious bird about gardens, ranch buildings and roadside brush. When startled it flies with a jerky flight, spreading its short broad wings and its dusky tail to the full just before it reaches a landing on a wood-pile or in the brush. When feeding it scratches, sparrow-fashion, with both feet, and often jerks its tail in a nervous fashion. Sooner or later a bird will show the *reddish brown area under the base of the tail;* on close view the throat appears tinged with reddish brown, and faintly streaked with black. The commonest note is a rather emphatic *chip.* The song is a feeble imitation of the Wren-tit's fine crescendo performance. It suggests the syllables *tsip tsip tsip tsip, churr, churr, churr,* given without much animation, and not freely uttered even in the height of the breeding season. Two or more birds often squabble and utter a succession of squeaking and gurgling notes.

BROWN TOWHEE

$8\frac{1}{2}$–10

Ad. — Upper parts grayish brown; tail dusky; eyelids and throat tinged with cinnamon-brown, the latter narrowly streaked with dusky; breast and upper belly pale grayish brown; lower belly and *area under tail* pale cinnamon deepening into *bright cinnamon.* Bill dusky above, light brownish gray below; feet light brown. **Im.** — Breast and belly streaked with dusky.

Dist. — Anthony Brown Towhee. *P. c. senicula.*
Cal. Common R. of brushy and cultivated country west of the desert divides north to San Luis Obispo and Amador Cos.

California Brown Towhee. *P. c. crissalis.*
Cal. Common R. of the coast belt from San Luis Obispo Co. to Humboldt Co.
Northern Brown Towhee. [*P. c. carolæ.*]
Cal. Fairly common R. locally in the interior of northern Cal.
Ore. R. locally in southwestern Ore.
Nest, of weed stalks and grasses in bushes. *Eggs*, 3–4, bluish white, marked chiefly with black.

Abert Towhee. *Pipilo aberti*

When one goes south from Banning, California, and reaches the head of Gorgonio Pass, guarded by the snow-capped San Bernardinos on one side and San Jacinto on the other, the desert and a new world open before one. The stony hillsides and the sandy desert floor are sparsely clothed with low shrubs among which the white-spined cactus clumps are prominent. Here with almost a clear line of demarcation a new association of life begins. A number of birds that have been common cease as suddenly as the vegetation with which they were associated, and a new set which come no farther north take their place. The familiar Brown Towhee, which has skulked in every brush pile along the road, is found no farther south than Palm Springs, but a bird very similar in appearance, habits and notes replaces it. In the tall weeds (arrow-weed and salt-bush) that line the ditches, the paler Abert Towhee skulks and chips, and quarrels with others of its kind with the same noisy scolding splutter that the Brown Towhees give. There is a small black area entirely circling the base of the bill of the Abert Towhee which a beginner should note to verify his assumption that the boundary mark between the two species has been passed. The song is very similar to the Brown Towhee's, perhaps a little more musical. The Abert Towhee is extremely shy and retiring, an adept at concealing itself in the rank growth in which it makes its home.

8–9

Ad. — Upper parts grayish brown, tinged with cinnamon; *base of bill encircled with black all around;* under parts pale cinnamon-brown, deepening on throat, which is narrowly streaked with black, and under the base of the tail. Bill and feet light brown.
Nest and eggs similar to Brown Towhee's.

Lark Bunting. *Calamospiza melanocorys*

In winter in the southeastern desert of southern California a flock of grayish brown birds a little smaller than Red-winged Blackbirds may fly from the weeds along the road-side, some of them showing a *broad white patch in the wing*. In April many of the males are wholly black, except for a conspicuous white wing-patch; others show considerable black in the wings and tail. When they fly Lark Buntings utter a sweet call, like the syllables *whoo͡-ee;* in spring the males, generally hidden in or under bushes, suddenly begin a chorus of sweet notes and trills, often interspersed with harsh notes. The white patch in the extended wing distinguishes a Lark Bunting in flight in any plumage; at close range the swollen bluish bill is noticeable.

LARK BUNTING (Adult ♂, winter)

6–7

Ad. ♂ in late spring. — Wholly black, except a large white patch in the wing and white tips of tail feathers. Bill swollen, dusky above, pale bluish gray below; feet brown. **Ad. ♀ and Im.** — Upper parts brown; cheek-patch brown, bordered above and below by whitish lines; wing-patch white or pale buff; all but middle tail feathers tipped with white; under parts white, thickly streaked with brown. **Ad. ♂ in winter.** — Similar to ♀, but wings blackish. Toward spring individuals in a flock show varying amounts of brown and black.

Dist. — *Cal.* Irregular W.V. in southeastern Cal. from the Salton Sea to to the Colorado R.; more common in migration, occurring as far north as Antelope Valley, Los Angeles Co.

Savannah Sparrow. *Passerculus sandwichensis* subsp.

In the grassy meadows of western Oregon and Washington or in the sage-brush country from eastern California northward, a small brown sparrow starts from underneath our feet and hastens off with jerky flight, pitching down in a moment into cover. In winter Savannah Sparrows are common in dry weedy fields, alfalfa or wheat land; their small brown forms are often ranged along fence wires or perched on posts or tall weeds. The song of the Savannah Sparrow consists of two or three preliminary chirps, followed by two long insect-like trills, the second pitched a little lower than the first, *tsip, tsip, tsip, tseeeeeeee tseer*. The rarer Grasshopper Sparrow, local in California, has a shriller song, less musical, and with no change of pitch. The ordinary call note of the Savannah Sparrow is a slight *tsip;* it also utters when alarmed, particularly about the nest, a heavier *tsup*. The Savannah Sparrow's breast is streaked and blotched

WESTERN SAVANNAH SPARROW

as in a Song Sparrow; but a close examination of the head when the bird faces us shows *a narrow whitish line through the middle of the crown* and white or yellowish lines over the eyes. The tail is shorter than the Song Sparrow's, the feet pinker and the bird rarely takes refuge in the thickets in which the Song Sparrow delights. Along the edges of salt marshes in southern California the Savannah Sparrow may mingle with Belding Sparrows. A trained eye can distinguish it from the latter by the lighter color of its upper parts and much lighter streaking below and by the well-defined line through the crown.

$4\frac{1}{2}$–$5\frac{3}{4}$

Ad. — Upper parts brown, streaked with blackish; a yellow or whitish line over the eye; *a narrow whitish stripe through crown;* breast and sides narrowly streaked; dark spot in center of breast not so prominent as in Song Sparrow; tail short. Bill dusky above, flesh-color below; legs flesh-color.

Dist. — Aleutian Savannah Sparrow. *P. s. sandwichensis.*
Cal. *Ore.* *Wash.* } W.V. in Washington and Oregon and occasional as far south as Merced Co., Cal.

Eastern Savannah Sparrow. *P. s. savanna.*
Cal. *Ore.* *Wash.* } Rare M. and in Cal. W.V.

Western Savannah Sparrow. *P. s. alaudinus.*
Cal. *Ore.* *Wash.* } Common M. throughout west of the Sierras and Cascades, and in Cal. common W.V. (Oct.–May).

Nevada Savannah Sparrow. *P. s. nevadensis.*
Cal. *Ore.* *Wash.* } Common S.V. east of the Sierras; W.V. on the deserts of southern Cal. and north to Los Angeles Co.

Brooks Savannah Sparrow. [*P. s. brooksi.*]
Cal. *Ore.* *Wash.* } Common S.V. in western Wash. and Ore.; M. and W.V. in Cal.

Bryant Savannah Sparrow. *P. s. bryanti.*
Cal. R. in the salt marshes about San Francisco Bay and Watsonville, and about Humboldt Bay.

Nest, in a depression in the ground, of grass. *Eggs*, 4–6, greenish or bluish white, spotted and clouded with reddish brown.

Belding Sparrow. *Passerculus beldingi*

In the tidal marshes from Santa Barbara to San Diego, a fleshy plant called pickle-weed (*Salicornia*) covers acres of the muddy saline flats. These marshes are the home of dark brown sparrows which fly up as one walks through the tangled growth, uttering a faint *tsip*, and perch by twos or threes on the tops of the plants beyond to watch the intruder. The birds have the short tail and the characteristic nervous flight of the group to which the Savannah Sparrow belongs. The general tone is dark grayish brown and the breast is heavily streaked with blackish. A close view of the bird shows a faint pale line through the middle of the crown and broader gray lines over the eye, which show a little yellow near the bill. If the marshes adjoin the ocean beach, the Belding Sparrows spend much time about the piles of kelp at the high-tide line. They are wary, hiding when alarmed behind the kelp, or running rapidly to the next heap. In early spring the salicornia is dotted here and there with males guarding their breeding station, and singing constantly a fine-drawn, wheezy song, *tsip tsip tsip tsrree, tsick-a-tsee,* differing from the Savannah Sparrow's song in the emphatic ending.

BELDING SPARROW

Both the Western Savannah Sparrow and the Large-billed Sparrow may be found along with the Belding Sparrow, the former in the drier grassier portions of the marsh, the latter near the shore. Even a trained observer needs considerable practice to distinguish the three species. The Belding Sparrow is more heavily and darkly streaked than the Savannah and the line through the forehead is usually less clearly defined. For the distinction between the Belding and the Large-billed Sparrow see the next species.

$4\frac{1}{3}$–$5\frac{1}{2}$

Ad. — Upper parts dark brown streaked with black; a very indistinct light stripe through crown and another over eye, the latter ending in front in yellowish; *under parts whitish heavily streaked with black.* Bill dusky above, flesh-color on the sides and below; feet light brown. **Im.** — No yellow between eye and bill.

Dist. — *Cal.* Common R. in salt marshes from San Diego to Morro, San Luis Obispo Co.

Nest, on the ground under protecting growth, of grasses and weed stems. *Eggs,* 3–5, greenish or bluish white, speckled and spotted with brown.

Large-billed Sparrow. *Passerculus rostratus* subsp.

Among the piles of lumber on some wharf or on the ground under the pier one finds from San Diego to Santa Barbara, from August to April, a brown sparrow about the size of a linnet with a noticeably heavy bill. When startled the bird often flies to the ridgepole of a warehouse like an English Sparrow. At the same time a careful search in the marshes near by will reveal, besides the dark Belding Sparrows, a few of the paler Large-billed Sparrows perching on the tops of the low plants, or slipping into the tangled growth for shelter. The tail, as in the Savannah and Belding Sparrows, is short in proportion to the length of the bird, but the back is not noticeably streaked; there is no well-defined yellow streak above the eye, and the breast is lightly streaked with brown. The characteristic by which the Large-billed Sparrow is definitely identified is, however, the *heavy bill,* which shows particularly when the bird is seen in profile. When the Large-billed and the Belding Sparrows are seen together, the lighter *unstreaked brown* of the back and wings,

LARGE-BILLED SPARROW

and the pale *brown streaking* on the breast serve to distinguish the Large-billed from the Belding.

$5\frac{1}{2}$

Ad. — Upper parts brown, very indistinctly streaked with dark brown, no line through crown or over eye; cheek-patch and line bordering throat dark brown; under parts white, throat unstreaked, rest of under parts lightly streaked with brown. *Bill large and swollen* (making a continuous line from top of head to tip of bill) dusky above, flesh-color on sides and below; feet pale brown.

Dist. — Large-billed Sparrow. *P. r. rostratus.*

Cal. Common W.V. (Oct.–Apr.) along the coast north to Santa Barbara.

San Lucas Large-billed Sparrow. *P. r. guttatus.*

Cal. Occurs occasionally with the preceding; indistinguishable in the field.

Western Grasshopper Sparrow. *Ammodramus savannarum bimaculatus*

Only a sharp ear catches from some dry weedy field a shrill insect-like trill, almost a buzz. The singer crouches on a weed stalk or fence post or even on the ground, throwing up his head at intervals and uttering his fine dry trill. When the Grasshopper Sparrow flies from his perch, he flutters off with curiously feeble flight. The *unstreaked under parts* distinguish the Grasshopper Sparrow from a Savannah Sparrow. Its song might easily be mistaken for a Savannah's but is composed of one long dry trill without a change of pitch at the end. The song may be written *tsick tsick tsurrrrrrr.* The call note consists of two notes *tillic*, almost run together as one.

GRASSHOPPER SPARROW

$4\frac{1}{4}$–5

Ad. — Upper parts streaked with black, rich chestnut and gray; buffy line through crown; *under parts buffy unstreaked.* Bill, horn-color above, yellow below; feet stout, flesh-color. **Im.** — Streaked with blackish on the breast.

Dist. — *Cal.* R. locally in the valleys west of the Sierras north to Sacramento and Mendocino Cos.; more widely distributed in winter.

Wash. Rare S.V. (May–Aug. or Sept.) in eastern Wash., in bunch-grass country or in wheat fields.

Nest, of grasses heavily arched. *Eggs*, 4–6, marked with reddish brown.

Vesper Sparrow. *Poœcetes gramineus* subsp.

In the open 'prairies' of western Oregon and Washington, or in the miles of gray sage-brush east of the Cascades, a brown sparrow flies from some post or bush on the roadside, showing *two white outer tail feathers* when the tail is spread. If undisturbed, the male sings from his lowly perch a song suggesting the Song Sparrow's, but opening with two sweet notes, held longer than the brisk opening notes of the Song Sparrow.

After sunset when many birds have ceased singing, these pensive opening notes of the Vesper Sparrow and the runs that follow are a characteristic sound of the summer twilight. In most of California the Vesper Sparrow is a winter visitant or migrant flying up from weedy fields or grassy hillsides, consorting with Savannah Sparrows or Lark Sparrows. If pursued, it runs among the low herbs or stands quietly behind a tuft of grass. It rarely perches higher than the top wire of a fence. The Vesper Sparrow may be distinguished from any other sparrow by the white outer tail feathers. The Lark Sparrow has the whole tail deeply edged with white; the Junco, which has white outer tail feathers, has no streaking or spotting on the breast, and is rarely found in as open country as the Vesper Sparrow.

WESTERN VESPER SPARROW

5–6¼

Ad. — Upper parts brown, streaked with dusky; side of head brown, unstreaked; wings and tail dusky, bend of wing chestnut (not easily made out); *two outer tail feathers nearly or entirely white;* under parts white, streaked with dusky on the flanks, streaks uniting to form a dusky spot in the middle of the breast. Bill dusky above, flesh-colored below; feet light brown.

Dist. — Western Vesper Sparrow. *P. g. confinis.*

Cal. Common S.V. (Mar.–Sept.) in the sage-brush country of northeastern Cal. Common W.V. west of the Sierras from the San Joaquin Valley and Santa Barbara south.

Ore. / *Wash.* } Common S.V. (Mar.–Sept.) on the plains east.

Oregon Vesper Sparrow. *P. g. affinis.*

Cal. W.V. west of the Sierras south to Los Angeles Co.
Ore. / *Wash.* Fairly common S.V. (Apr.–Sept.) in the prairies and grassy fields west.

Nest, of grass on the ground. *Eggs*, 4–5, white, speckled and clouded with reddish brown.

Western Lark Sparrow. *Chondestes grammacus strigatus*

As one drives through the less fruitful agricultural regions, where dry hillsides or cattle ranges border the road, a brown bird larger than the House Finch often flies from the road to the fence or telephone wires, showing in flight, especially just before alighting, a *rounded tail,* all but the central feathers of which are conspicuously *edged with white*, the whole white margin set off by a black inner border. When the Lark Sparrow faces the observer a *small dark spot* is evident *in the middle of the breast,* and a *white stripe through the middle of the forehead.* A side view of the head shows a very marked pattern made up of a brown cheek-patch bordered above and below with white, and a black line running off from each side of the throat. In winter Lark Sparrows gather in small flocks and frequent the lawns of residences near the foothills, or gather in trees and keep up a chorus of broken bits of song. The song just lacks considerable beauty, but it is never free and flowing; trills and sweet notes are interrupted by a rather unmelodious *churr*. In the breeding season the Lark Sparrow sings on the wing and then gives its finest performance. The call note is a weak *tsip*, relatively faint for the size of the bird. The flight of the Lark Sparrow is vigorous and inclined to pitch in rather long but shallow sweeps. If the general brown tone of the bird, its size between a House Finch and a Towhee, the striking markings about the head, and the deep white edging of the rounded tail are all taken into account, there should be no confusion between the Lark Sparrow and any other bird.

WESTERN LARK SPARROW

$5\frac{1}{2}$–$6\frac{3}{4}$

Ad. ♂. — *Crown chestnut* with a *narrow white stripe through the center;* rest of upper parts brownish gray; wings with indistinct buffy bars; *tail* long, rounded, blackish brown, all but the central feathers *broadly tipped with white;* a *chestnut patch on the side of the head,* bordered above and below with white stripes; narrow line on side of throat and *spot on breast black;* rest of under parts white. Bill dark brown above, paler below; feet pale brown. **Ad.** ♀. — Similar but colors of head duller. **Im. in summer.** — Chestnut replaced by grayish brown; top of head and breast streaked.

Dist. — *Cal.* Common R. of open country, scarce in the humid coast belt; more widespread in winter.

Ore. Common S.V. (Apr.–Sept.) east, and in the southern valleys west.

Wash. Common S.V. in open country east.

Nest, on the ground or in low bushes, of grasses, weed stems, etc. *Eggs,* 4–5, white or bluish white, spotted or scrawled about the larger end with dark purple or brown.

Fox Sparrow. *Passerella iliaca* subsp.

In winter where a trail leads through chaparral-covered hillsides or along cool canyons, if an observer is walking quietly, he will see a large sparrow scratching vigorously in the dry leaves, jumping forward and kicking back with both feet at once. When everything else is quiet, the sound of a Fox Sparrow's feet in the dry leaves will announce its presence even when it is hidden in the bushes. When disturbed, the Fox Sparrow flies with a metallic *chick* into thick cover, giving a glimpse of a reddish tail as it flies. Careful observation of wintering birds even in the field shows two well-marked types, one with much light gray on the head and back and gray spots on the breast, the other with brown head and breast and dark brown spots on the breast. The gray birds have often very large yellowish bills; the dark birds have smaller and darker bills. This distinction is practically all that a field observer can make among the fifteen or more subspecies that occur in the Coast States.

VALDEZ FOX SPARROW

The gray Fox Sparrows with the heavy yellowish bills breed in summer on the high mountains from San Jacinto north along the Sierras and far up into eastern Washington and Oregon. Their rich and powerful song rings from the open mountain-sides where low masses of 'deer brush' offer a safe retreat to the shy singer. The song varies greatly, even in the same individual, but once heard is unmistakable; it includes as one of the opening phrases a pair of loud sweet notes, *swee chew* or *wee chee* followed by trills and runs. The only song with which it can be confused is that of the Green-tailed Towhee, which is often found on the same open brushy mountain-sides, particularly on the eastern slopes; the Fox Sparrow's song is richer, louder and sweeter, and lacks the *burr* or *chirr* included in the Towhee's song. Besides the heavier *chick* or *chuck*, the Fox Sparrow has a light *tsip* of alarm. Only one of the dark brown types of Fox Sparrow breeds in the Coast States, the Sooty Fox Sparrow of the coast of northwestern Washington.

A Fox Sparrow may be distinguished from the Hermit Thrush, which also has a reddish brown tail, by the conical sparrow-like bill. The Fox Sparrow never raises its tail slowly when excited after the manner of the Hermit Thrush, and the latter never scratches vigorously like a Fox Sparrow. In winter both may be found in brush, but in summer the Hermit Thrush keeps to the deep shade of forests, the Fox Sparrow to more open clearings.

$6\frac{1}{2}$–$7\frac{1}{4}$

Ad. — Upper parts varying from reddish brown to dark grayish brown, rump and tail reddish brown; under parts heavily marked with arrowy markings which vary from reddish brown to dark brown. Bill dusky above, yellowish below; feet brown.

Dist. — Eastern Fox Sparrow. *P. i. iliaca.*
Cal. Casual W.V. chiefly along the coast southerly.
Ore. Probably casual.
Wash. Casual M. and W.V.

Alberta Fox Sparrow. [*P. i. altivagans.*]
Cal. Fairly common W.V. (Sept.–Mar.)
Ore. Probably regular M. east.
Wash. Casual fall M. east (two records).

Shumagin Fox Sparrow. *P. i. unalaschcensis.*
Cal. Not common M. chiefly inland; W.V. chiefly in southern Cal.
Ore. M. and probably W.V.
Wash. M. and common W.V. west.

Kadiak Fox Sparrow. *P. i. insularis.*
Cal. Fairly common M. and W.V., chiefly along the coast south.
Ore. } *Wash.* } Not common M. and perhaps W.V.

Valdez Fox Sparrow. [*P. i. sinuosa.*]
Cal. } *Ore.* } *Wash.* } Common M. and W.V.

Yakutat Fox Sparrow. [*P. i. annectens.*]
Cal. M. and W.V. chiefly along the coast in central Cal.
Ore. } *Wash.* } M. and probably W.V. along the coast.

Townsend Fox Sparrow. *P. i. townsendi.*
Cal. W.V. on the northern coast.
Ore. } *Wash.* } Not common M. and W.V. (Oct.–Apr.) on or near the coast.

Sooty Fox Sparrow. *P. i. fuliginosa.*
Cal. Not common M. and W.V., chiefly north of San Francisco Bay.
Ore. Not common M. and perhaps W.V. along the coast.
Wash. Common M. and W.V.; S.V. on islands off the north coast and perhaps on adjacent mainland.

Slate-colored Fox Sparrow. *P. i. schistacea.*
Cal. M. and W.V. (Sept.–Apr.).
Ore. M. east.
Wash. Common S.V. (May–Sept.) and M.

Warner Mountains Fox Sparrow. [*P. i. fulva.*]
Cal. S.V. in extreme northeastern Cal.
Ore. S.V. in the mountains of central and eastern Ore.

Thick-billed Fox Sparrow. *P. i. megarhyncha.*
Cal. Summer home unknown; common W.V. to Pacific slope of southern Cal.

Yolla Bolly Fox Sparrow. [*P. i. brevicauda.*]
Cal. S.V. in mountains of north central Cal.; common W.V. near coast of central and southern Cal.

White Mountains Fox Sparrow. [*P. i. canescens.*]
Cal. S.V. in the White Mts.; casual W.V. south.

Mono Fox Sparrow. [*P. i. monoensis.*]
Cal. S.V. on east slope of Sierras; W.V. west and south.

Yosemite Fox Sparrow. [*P. i. mariposæ.*]
Cal. Common S.V. in the central Sierras; a few winter south.

STEPHENS FOX SPARROW

Stephens Fox Sparrow. *P. i. stephensi.*
Cal. Common S.V. in the higher mountains of southern Cal.
Nest, bulky, of twigs, lined with grasses, low in bushes. *Eggs*, 3–5, greenish gray, spotted or blotched with reddish brown.

DESERT SPARROW. *Amphispiza bilineata deserticola*

One of the first sounds heard at dawn among the thorny bushes of the deserts of southern California is the tinkle of the Desert Sparrow. The little fellow sits on the top of some bush, his *black throat* swelling with the simple but cheerful melody, *tsee tsi tsi tsi tsee*, or *weet weet wee*, the last note held and almost trilled. The whole performance suggests the song of the Bewick Wren, a form of which often occurs in the same region, but the Desert Sparrow utters a far simpler song, without the distinct division into parts and the distinct musical trill at the end. When he has sung his fill, the singer flies to the ground, but always near or under the protecting bushes, to scratch and feed. If disturbed, the Desert Sparrow shows the same wariness in keeping behind a bush that characterizes many species of the desert. When it flies, the *blackish tail* is conspicuous, often showing no white unless widely spread, when the white tips become visible.

DESERT SPARROW

The only bird that might be confused with the Desert Sparrow would be a migrating Black-throated Gray Warbler. The Warbler's manner of feeding as it gleans among twigs and its slender bill should enable even a beginner to distinguish the two birds. Moreover, the Sparrow's head and cheek-patch are dark gray, the Warbler's black.

5

Ad. — Top and sides of head dark gray; a white stripe from bill above and behind eye; rest of upper parts grayish brown; *tail blackish*, outer feathers edged with white, both first and second feathers tipped with white; lores (area between bill and eye), *chin and throat black*, separated from the sides of the neck by a white stripe; rest of under parts white. Bill dusky; feet black. **Im. in summer.** — Without markings on head, throat white.

Dist. — *Cal.* Common R. in the deserts, north through Owens Valley, and in Modoc Co.; casual on the Pacific slope of southern Cal.
Ore. Probably R. in extreme southeastern Ore.

Nest, of plant fibers in low bushes, cactus, etc. *Eggs*, 3–4, white.

BELL SPARROW. *Amphispiza belli*

In broken country where chaparral covers the hillsides, a small gray bird with a dark tail flies from the ground to the top of some bush and perches, nervously jerking its tail. When the bird faces the observer, a dark blotch shows in the center of its white breast. When feeding, the Bell Sparrow is very wary; it runs from the shelter of one bush to the next, keeping always in the shadow. Even on the ground it jerks its tail from time to time. The alarm and call note is a light *kik, kik, kik*, suggesting the Junco's chitter. The song is a modest performance in a rather thin high voice, like the syllables *tsit tsit, tsi you, tee a-tee*, the third note high and accentuated.

BELL SPARROW

If the marks on the sides of the throat are seen in conjunction with the black breast-spot, the Bell Sparrow could hardly be confused with any other species except the Lark Sparrow. The Bell Sparrow is a smaller bird and shows almost no white on the tail even in flight; the Lark Sparrow shows a conspicuous border of white on the tail. The best field character of the Bell Sparrow, when taken together with its markings, is its habit of flipping its tail as it sits on the tops of bushes.

5–5½

Ad. — Top and sides of head gray; spot before eye and eye-ring white; rest of upper parts grayish brown; a *black line from bill back and down*, separating a white area above from the white throat, and continued in broken black streaks along sides of breast; *black spot in center of breast;* rest of under parts brownish white. Bill and feet (apparently black) grayish blue. **Im.** — More streaked below.

Dist. — *Cal.* Locally common R. on brushy slopes, as far north along the coast as Sonoma and Marin Cos. and in the foothills bordering the interior valleys as far as Amador and Eldorado Cos.

Nest, of weed stalks, in bushes. *Eggs*, 3–4, white, speckled with reddish brown.

Sage Sparrow. *Amphispiza nevadensis* subsp.

In appearance, habits and notes the Sage Sparrow closely resembles the Bell Sparrow, but the range of the two species is distinct. The Bell Sparrow is confined to the brush-covered foothills; the Sage Sparrow is found in dry, open plains, often alkaline, where a variety of low bushes (*Artemisia*, *Atriplex* and *Chrysothamnus*) are all locally known as sage. In winter the California and Nevada Sage Sparrows occur together on the deserts of southern California; they are practically indistinguishable in the field.

CALIFORNIA SAGE SPARROW

$5\frac{1}{2}$–6

Ad. — Similar to the preceding species but paler and with sides of throat bordered by an *interrupted chain of dark streaks.*

Dist. — California Sage Sparrow. *A. n. canescens.*

Cal. Common S.V. in the belt of sage, salt-bush, etc., from the San Bernardino Mts. north to the south end of the San Joaquin Valley and to Owens L.; W.V. from the Mexican border to the south end of the San Joaquin Valley.

Nevada Sage Sparrow. *A. n. nevadensis.*

Cal. Common S.V. in the sage-brush from Mono L. east of the Sierras to the Warner Mts. (Modoc Co.); winters on the Mohave and Colorado deserts.

Ore. Common S.V. (Mar.–Sept.) in the sage-brush east; less common in winter.

Wash. Common S.V. (Mar.–Sept.) in sage and bunch-grass east.

Nest and *eggs* as in preceding species.

Rufous-crowned Sparrow. *Aimophila ruficeps* subsp.

On dry grassy or brushy slopes from central California southward an inconspicuous brown bird may fly from the ground and perch for a moment on some low rock or bush, showing a *reddish brown crown-patch* and at close range narrow black lines bordering the throat. When startled the bird frequently drops to the ground and makes off through the grass or bushes. The song of the Rufous-crowned Sparrow is short, with little carrying power, and is not given freely; it suggests a somewhat feeble Song Sparrow. The reddish brown crown distinguishes the Rufous-crowned Sparrow from any other sparrow except the Chipping Sparrow and the immature White-crowned (Gambel or Nuttall) Sparrows. The lack of a black line through the eye distinguishes it from the Chipping Sparrow, and the lack of a pale stripe through the center of the crown distinguishes it from the immature White-crown. The black stripes bordering the throat are distinctive

RUFOUS-CROWNED SPARROW

of the Rufous-crowned. The common call note of the Rufous-crown has been described as a musical '*dear, dear*' (Myers).

5

Ad. — *Top of head reddish brown,* separated from sides by a dull buffy line; back grayish brown, streaked with rufous; whitish *chin bordered by narrow black stripes;* rest of under parts gray or buffy. Bill dark above, lighter below; feet light brown. **Im.** — Narrowly streaked below; crown like back.

Dist. — Rufous-crowned Sparrow. *A. r. ruficeps.*
Very local R. on dry hillsides, among grass, old-man sage and other low bushes west of the Sierras, from Los Angeles Co. to Sutter and Marin Cos.
Southern California Rufous-crowned Sparrow. [*A. r. canescens.*]
Cal. San Diego Co.
Santa Cruz I. Rufous-crowned Sparrow. [*A. r. obscura.*]
Santa Cruz I.

Nest, of grass on the ground. *Eggs,* 3–4, white.

Slate-colored Junco. *Junco hyemalis hyemalis*

A careful search among the flocks of wintering Juncos occasionally reveals one which has a uniform slate-gray head, breast and back, showing no brown or chestnut in the back. In nearly all cases the Slate-colored Junco has been found with flocks of some form of the Oregon Junco. Its habits and notes are almost identical with those of the latter.

$5\frac{1}{2}$–$6\frac{1}{4}$

Ad. ♂. — *Head, back and breast slate-gray,* sharply defined from the white belly; two outer tail feathers on each side wholly white, next pair partly white. Bill flesh-colored, feet brown. **Ad.** ♀. — Upper parts browner; under parts paler.

Dist. — *Cal.* Rare M. and W.V.
Ore. Casual.
Wash. Casual W.V. (Sept.–Apr.) both east and west of the Cascades.

Cassiar Junco. [*J. h. connectens.*]
A subspecies breeding in northern British Columbia. The male has 'a fairly distinct blackish head; the female has a brownish back and pinkish sides' (Swarth). (See p. 329.)
Cal. *Ore.* *Wash.* } Distribution in the Coast States not yet worked out, but the form is known to occur in winter as far south as Santa Barbara, Cal., and is probably a regular W.V. in Ore. and Wash., particularly east.

Oregon / Sierra / Point Pinos } Junco. *Junco hyemalis* subsp.
[*Junco oreganus* subsp.]

The Juncos with black heads and brown backs are placed in the A.O.U. Check-List of 1910 under *Junco hyemalis.* In most of the Pacific Coast publications they are considered forms of *Junco oreganus.*

To any camper among the Sierra pines or to the dwellers among the red firs of western Washington and Oregon, the *black heads* and *white outer tail feathers* of Juncos are among the most familiar sights. The birds feed and nest on the ground, hopping about in open spaces or flying when startled into the low branches of a near-by tree, displaying in flight the white V formed by the outer tail feathers. When they feed at the observer's feet, the *chestnut or brown* back shows in contrast to the blackish head; when they face the observer, the *light-colored bill* is set off by the dark head and breast. All through the pine forests the bright jingle of the Junco's song is a familiar sound in spring and early summer.

SIERRA JUNCO (♂)

The singer perches on a stub or branch well up and greets the dawn with the repetition of a single rather metallic note, running the notes rapidly into almost a trill. The song is difficult to distinguish from that of the Chipping Sparrow but to a trained ear is slightly more musical. In winter Juncos move in little flocks from the mountains to the foothills and valleys, and winter along roadsides and bushy places, in cool canyons or even near dwellings where there is shrubbery. Besides their song Juncos utter a *tsup* when excited, a smacking note, a musical *pew pew pew*, and a light twitter when a flock flies off. When Juncos feed, they hop actively over open ground, accompanying each movement with a partial opening of the tail which shows the white outer feathers. They do not scratch for their food like the larger sparrows but pick up the seeds from the bare surface.

5–6

Ad. ♂. — Head, neck and breast black, sharply divided from rest of plumage ; back and wings brown; tail black, *two outer feathers on each side white;* black of breast sharply divided from the white of the rest of the under parts. Bill whitish; feet light brown. **Ad.** ♀. — Head and chest dark gray; brown of back paler. Bill pink, dusky at tip; feet light brown. **Im. in summer.** — Whole body streaked. Bill blackish.

Dist. — Oregon Junco. *J. h. oreganus* [*J. o. oreganus.*]

Cal. W.V. along the coast as far south as San Francisco Bay.

Ore., *Wash.* Common W.V. (end of Sept.–early Apr.) west.

Shufeldt **Junco.** *J. h. connectens* of the A.O.U Check-List (1910) [*J. o. shufeldti*]. (Coues's *J. h. connectens*, described from Colorado, was identified in the Check-List (apparently erroneously) with *J. h. shufeldti* of Coale. Swarth, who discovered its breeding grounds, shows it to be a separate form, which he calls the Cassiar Junco (1922). See p. 328.)

Cal. Irregular W.V. in central Cal.

Ore. }
Wash. } Common R. throughout, breeding in timbered country, moving in winter to lower levels.

Sierra Junco. *J. h. thurberi* [*J. o. thurberi.*]

Cal. Common S.V. in the mountains throughout except from Monterey to San Francisco Bay; common W.V. (Oct.–Apr.) at lower levels.

Ore. Common S.V. in southern Ore.

Point Pinos Junco. *J. h. pinosus* [*J. o. pinosus.*]

Common R. on the Monterey Peninsula, sparingly from San Mateo Co. to Big Creek, Monterey Co., and about San Francisco Bay.

Nest, generally on the ground (often in tin cans), but occasionally in trees or on beams, of grasses and plant stems. *Eggs*, 4–5, bluish white, spotted with lavender or brown.

Gray-headed Junco. *Junco phæonotus caniceps*

A few individuals of the Gray-headed Junco have strayed into southern California. The reddish brown back, the *ash-gray head*, and the lack of pinkish on the flanks distinguish the bird from the common Sierra Junco.

Western Tree Sparrow. *Spizella monticola ochracea*

The Tree Sparrow, so familiar in winter in the Middle West, migrates southward chiefly east of the Coast States, barely brushing eastern Washington and Oregon with the fringe of its great hosts. It frequents sheltered spots where food and cover can be found, old fields grown up to weeds and the edges of marshy ground. The birds are found scattered over the feeding ground, reaching up for seeds, jumping for them, or lighting on the taller plants and bending them down with their weight. While feeding, the flock keep up a constant twitter, each bird repeating the syllables *teel-wit* in a lively cheerful tone. The call note is a slight *tsip*. The song, heard toward spring, is sweet and fairly loud, beginning with long-drawn notes, suggesting the beginning of a Fox Sparrow's song, but not so rich and powerful. The Tree Sparrow may be distinguished from any other wintering sparrows by the combination of *white wing-bars and a dusky spot in an otherwise unstreaked breast.*

$5\frac{1}{2}$–6

Ad. — Crown reddish brown; back brownish, streaked with black; wing-bars white; under parts pale gray; *a dusky spot in the center of the breast;* sides washed with reddish brown. Bill blackish above, yellowish below; feet brown.

Dist. — *Cal.* One record (1879).

Ore. }
Wash. } More or less regular W.V. (Sept.–Apr.) to plains east; casual west.

Western Chipping Sparrow. *Spizella passerina arizonæ*

In the east the Chipping Sparrow has become a bird of the dooryard and orchards, but in the Coast States its slim, brown form and chestnut cap is associated with open groves of yellow pine or park-like forests of Douglas fir. Its slight *tsip* and dry monotonous trill become a humble part of the woodland sounds, and are passed over with a certain indifference by the student who is puzzling over the more baffling Warblers and Flycatchers. In southern California it is found regularly in the orchards in the lower valleys and in northern California in the humid coast belt; it is absent from the foothills but occupies the mountains almost to the timber line.

WESTERN CHIPPING SPARROW

Chipping Sparrows spend much of their time on the ground, picking up food in open spaces instead of scratching for it, and flying when startled, not into thick bushes like Song Sparrows but to the lower limbs of neighboring trees. Their song is a succession of dry chips on the same pitch, difficult to distinguish from the trill of a Junco; the trained ear detects in the latter a little more vigor and musical quality. The *reddish brown crown, unstreaked gray breast,* slender form and long notched tail distinguish the Chipping Sparrow readily from most other sparrows. The much rarer Rufous-crowned Sparrow also has a reddish brown crown, but the Chipping Sparrow's crown is set off sharply from the gray sides of the head by a white or whitish stripe and a black line below it, while the Rufous-crown's reddish brown is bordered by a line only slightly more buffy than the buffy cheek. The Chipping Sparrow, moreover, is a bird of orchards and forests, the Rufous-crowned of dry rocky slopes covered with grass or low bushes. The Brewer Sparrow, with which the Chipping Sparrow is often associated in migration, lacks the reddish brown crown-patch. Young Chipping Sparrows in summer and fall also lack the bright crown-patch and might be easily mistaken for Brewer sparrows.

$5–5\frac{1}{3}$

Ad. — Crown reddish brown, a whitish or gray line over the eye, a *black line through it;* cheek gray; back brown, streaked with black; rump ashy gray; under parts ashy gray; tail long, slender, rather deeply notched. Bill black (cinnamon-brownish in winter); feet black. **Im. in late summer.** — Breast streaked; crown-patch lacking. **Im. in winter.** — Crown brown, streaked with black; black line through eye not well marked. Bill dusky above, flesh-color beneath; feet dusky brown.

Dist. — *Cal.* Common S.V. (Mar.–Aug.) in orchards in the valleys and in the forested regions of the mountains to timber line; winters sparingly in the San Joaquin Valley, along the coast from Santa Barbara south and commonly in the Imperial Valley and along the lower Colorado R.

Ore. } *Wash.* } Common S.V. (Apr.–Sept.), less common toward the coast.

Nest, of rootlets, grasses, etc., in bushes or trees. *Eggs,* 3–5, light greenish blue, speckled with black, dark brown, or lavender.

Brewer Sparrow. *Spizella breweri*

In the gray sage-brush that extends for miles in the plains and higher valleys east of the Sierras and Cascades, a small brown bird with a long slender tail sings in summer a series of trills and runs, which if they had more volume would rank as one of the noteworthy bird songs. When disturbed the Brewer Sparrow slips into the cover of a bush or flits ahead from one bush to the next. It feeds on the ground under the bushes, always keeping warily close to shelter. In fall companies pass south chiefly east of the mountains; many pass the winter on the deserts of southern California or in the weed patches or alfalfa fields of the Imperial Valley. In spring companies passing north are already singing in chorus. The call note is a weak *tsip*. The slender figure of the Brewer Sparrow, very like that of the Chipping Sparrow, its long, rather deeply notched tail and its streaked head and back distinguish it from any other desert sparrow. It might be confused in late summer and winter with an immature Chipping Sparrow which has not acquired the chestnut crown.

BREWER SPARROW

5

Ad. — Upper parts brown streaked with black on back and *very finely streaked on top of head;* sides of head grayish brown unstreaked; tail slender, dusky, notched; under parts gray, unstreaked. Bill dusky above and at tip, pale flesh on sides and below; feet light brown. **Im.** — Breast and sides streaked.

Dist. — *Cal.* Common S.V. in sage (*Artemisia* or *Chrysothamnus*), local from San Jacinto north to Kern Co., commoner northeast. Winters sparingly as far north as Fresno Co. and commonly in the Colorado desert and the Imperial Valley.

Ore., *Wash.* } Fairly common S.V. (Apr.–Aug.), chiefly in sage, east.

Nest, of twigs and rootlets in sage-brush. *Eggs*, 4, light greenish blue, speckled with reddish brown.

Black-chinned Sparrow. *Spizella atrogularis*

From the brush-covered mountain slopes of southern California, particularly in the belt of chamise (*Adenostoma*), one hears in summer a sweet plaintive song, beginning with several liquid notes in a minor key followed by a long run which descends the chromatic scale; the song often ends with a rough trill. The Black-chinned Sparrow is shy, hiding for the most part in the thick chaparral, flying off when approached with a faint *tsip* and rarely giving an observer a good view of its *black chin, flesh-colored bill* and *reddish brown back.*

BLACK-CHINNED SPARROW (♂)

5–5½

Ad. ♂. — Head, sides, back of neck and rump ashy gray; an area around bill, including *chin, black; middle of back reddish brown;* under parts, except chin, ashy gray. Bill flesh-colored; feet brown. **Ad.** ♀. — Black replaced by dark gray. **Im.** — Black replaced by light gray. Bill duller.

Dist. — *Cal.* Fairly common S.V. in the chaparral of mountain-sides north to San Luis Obispo Co. and to Owens Valley.

Nest, of grasses, weeds, etc., in bushes. *Eggs*, 3–4, bluish, unmarked or speckled with reddish brown.

White-crowned Sparrow. *Zonotrichia leucophrys leucophrys*

If one has fought mosquitoes while casting for trout around some willow-bordered lake in the high Sierras, and has an open ear for bird music, the song of the White-crowned Sparrow is definitely bound up with his memory of the scene. From the first streaks of dawn till late in the evening and occasionally through the night the same wheezy syllables, *tee tsee tseetsi tsee,* follow each other in the same lyrical cadence. The White-crowned Sparrow differs from the Gambel and the Nuttall Sparrows in having the black line back of the eye extend through the eye to the base of the bill. (See the cut.) Great care and a favorable opportunity are necessary to establish the presence of the black 'lores.'

WHITE-CROWNED SPARROW

$5\frac{3}{4}$–$6\frac{3}{4}$

Ad. — Crown black with a white stripe through the middle; *lores* (area between bill and eye) *black;* white stripe from just above eye back, meeting its fellow and making a white area on the hind-head; upper back grayish brown; lower back and tail unstreaked; two white wing-bars; under parts clear ashy gray, paling to whitish on chin and belly. Bill light brown, tinged with flesh-color, darker at tip; feet light brown. ♀ very similar to ♂ but usually duller. **Im.** — Black of head replaced by rich brown, and white by pale brown; gray of under parts tinged with brownish.

Dist. — *Cal.* Common S.V. to the high mountains; M. chiefly east of the Sierras.

Ore. S.V. (Apr.–Aug.) to mountains of eastern Ore.

Nest, of twigs, rootlets and grasses, on the ground or in low bushes, often willows in alpine meadows. *Eggs,* 3–5, pale bluish green, spotted with brown.

Gambel Sparrow. *Zonotrichia leucophrys gambeli*

Throughout the winter from the borders of fields flocks of brown sparrows, a little larger than House Finches, make when startled a hurried dive for the nearest bushes, slipping farther and farther into concealment, and reappearing only after a cautious interval. When they are in good view, the head is seen to be marked by *lines over the eye and through the crown.* These are white and black in the adult Gambel Sparrows, reddish brown and gray in the immature. All winter, from their arrival in October to their departure in April, their rather wheezy but cheerful song is heard. It is made up of one or two long opening notes, then two or three quicker, higher notes, and then a closing note lower in pitch. One form suggests the syllables *twee, tsweet-si, tweetsi-si, twee,* but individual songs vary greatly. The call note is a faint *tsip.* When individuals of the flock disagree about a resting place they utter little confused squabbling notes, and just at dusk, when birds settle in thick trees for the night, and at dawn, they repeat for several minutes the alarm note, a metallic *pink.*

No other bird can be confused with an adult sparrow of the White-crowned group, if the markings of the head are seen. Immature birds might be mistaken by a beginner for several other birds with reddish brown on the crown. (See under Rufous-crowned and Chipping Sparrows.) When there are adults with the immature birds, the resemblance in the pattern of the head markings is obvious. It is very difficult even for a trained observer to distinguish the Gambel Sparrow from the White-crowned or the Nuttall Sparrows. Except in migration along the eastern border of California the Gambel and the White-crowned Sparrows rarely occur together; the Gambel and the Nuttall Sparrows occur together in winter and in migration. For the distinctions between the last two see the following species.

$5\frac{3}{4}$–$6\frac{1}{2}$

Ad. — Similar to the preceding species but *lores* (area between eye and bill) not black, the white stripe over eye uninterrupted.

Dist. — *Cal.* Common M. (Apr.–May; Sept.–early Nov.) in brushy country west of the Sierras except along the north coast; winters from the Sacramento Valley southward, commoner from Los Angeles Co. south.

Ore. Common M. (Apr.–May; Sept.–Nov.) and W.V. in brushy country east.

Wash. Common M. (Apr.–May; Sept.–Nov.) in brushy country east, occasionally west; winters casually on east side southerly.

Nuttall Sparrow. *Zonotrichia leucophrys nuttalli*

Along the coast from Puget Sound as far south as San Luis Obispo, California, a white-crowned sparrow breeds abundantly. Its habits are similar to those of the Gambel Sparrow, cautious of open places, feeding on the ground always near shelter and as much in the shade as possible. Its song is perhaps a little more leisurely than those of the other two subspecies, and begins with two drawled notes, the first either higher or lower than the second. The form noted at Carmel and at Morro is like the syllables *chee chee, tsid-i, tsid-i, tsee.* A typical Nuttall Sparrow may be distinguished by a trained observer by noting the greater amount of brownish wash on the breast and neck of the former, and the yellow at the base of the bill. The white line through the crown is generally not broader than the black line bordering it. In winter, however, many individuals are seen that cannot be definitely assigned to one or the other subspecies. In summer, of course, any white-crowned sparrow found near the seacoast from California to Washington is the Nuttall; moreover, even in winter the Nuttall does not move far inland.

NUTTALL SPARROW
(Adult)

$5\frac{1}{2}$–$6\frac{3}{4}$

Ad. — Similar to preceding subspecies, but white stripe through crown narrower than black stripe bordering it; general tone of coloration browner. *Bill yellowish,* especially toward base.

Dist. — *Cal.* Common R. of a narrow belt along the coast from Santa Barbara Co. (where not common) northward (inland in the San Francisco Bay region to Berkeley); winters south to Los Angeles and inland to the north end of the San Joaquin Valley.
Ore. Common S.V. (Apr.–Sept.) west; a few may winter.
Wash. Common S.V. (Apr.–Oct.) in clearings and prairies west and casual east; casual in winter west.

Nest, a well-built cup of grasses, weed stems, etc., on the ground, in bushes or small trees. *Eggs*, 3–5, like those of the White-crowned Sparrow.

GOLDEN-CROWNED SPARROW. *Zonotrichia coronata*

From chaparral-covered slopes, or from the tangled growth along streams and in canyons, there comes in winter a plaintive whistled song of three notes, to the tune of 'Three Blind Mice,' more poetically rendered, 'Oh, dear me!' each note an interval lower in pitch than the preceding. When the birds venture forth from the cover to feed, they look much like Gambel or Nuttall Sparrows without the white through the crown. The head is blackish, and when seen from in front shows a crown of dull orange-brown. The Golden-crowned Sparrow is even shyer than the White-crown, and keeps farther from civilization. If a garden or lawn is near the foothills, one occasionally sees the Golden-crown among its relatives the White-crowns. In the canyons and among the hills, flocks are made up of Golden-crowns alone or with only a few White-crowns.

GOLDEN-CROWNED SPARROW (Adult)

Care must be taken not to mistake the immature Nuttall or Gambel Sparrows for the Golden-crown. The latter has only the orange or brownish yellow patch in the middle of the crown with no lines over the eyes, while the immature Nuttall and Gambel have a buffy stripe through the crown and buffy lines over the eyes.

6–7

Ad. — Sides of head black; a dull yellow patch extending from the bill through the crown; upper parts grayish brown, streaked on the back with black; two white wing-bars; under parts grayish brown, fading on the belly. Bill blackish above, yellowish at base; feet pale brown. **Im.** — Head brown with only a trace of yellow on the forehead.

Dist. — *Cal.* Common W.V. (Oct.–early May) chiefly west of the Sierran divides.
Ore., *Wash.* Common M. (Apr.–May; Sept.–Oct.) both east and west; commoner on the west side. Common in winter as far north as Tillamook Co., Ore.; rarer in winter northward.

WHITE-THROATED SPARROW. *Zonotrichia albicollis*

The White-throated Sparrow is a regular but very rare winter visitant to the Pacific Coast. A few birds straggle across the mountains in migration, and spend the winter in natural brushy cover or in plantations

WHITE-THROATED SPARROW

of bushes. They are generally found with Golden-crowned or Gambel Sparrows, scratching on the ground for food and flying when disturbed into the nearest bushes. The *square white throat* set off by gray is distinctive, but the beginner should note that Gambel and Nuttall Sparrows have a nearly white chin. Toward spring a wintering bird occasionally utters the clear whistled 'pea-body' notes. Its ordinary call notes are a rather heavy *tseet*, and a *chink* similar to that of the White-crowned Sparrow.

6–6½

Ad. — Crown black, with a white stripe through middle; a broad white stripe over eye, ending in *a yellow line before eye;* back and wings rich reddish brown; tail brown; wing-bars white; a square, clearly defined *white throat-patch* bounded by ashy gray; breast pale gray; belly white; sides brownish. Bill dark above, paler below; feet brown. **Im.** — Crown dark brown; stripe through middle faint; line over eye dull buffy; yellow before eye dull; throat patch grayish white.

Dist. — *Cal.* Rare but regular W.V. (Oct.–end of Feb.) in brushy places west of the Sierras; many records.

Ore., *Wash.* One record for each State. (Oct.)

Song Sparrow. *Melospiza melodia* subsp.

Song Sparrows are birds of the brushy borders of streams or stream beds, or the tall weedy growths of irrigated land. From the protection of these bushes and weeds issues their metallic *tschük*, or the bird itself, when startled from the ground at the edge of the cover, flips back into concealment, punctuating its flight with jerks of its long tail. When a Song Sparrow faces an observer, the blotch on the middle of the breast and the brown lines at the sides of the throat offer characteristic field marks. The brown of these markings and the brown of the back varies from light reddish brown to almost black in the different subspecies, but the streaks are always rather coarse and set off by gray lines about the head and throat. At almost any season, but particularly after the winter rains, the brisk little jingle of the male is heard from bushes or from a perch in a small tree. It begins generally with several short high notes *chit, chit, chit,* followed by a higher *to-whée*, which is held an instant and then passes into trills and runs. When the male pursues the female in the mating season, one or both utter a bat-like twitter, and the male often flutters with wings spread. Where the Vesper Sparrow is absent, as in most of California, there is no song with which the Song Sparrow's could be confused, except that of the Bewick Wren. (See p. 243.) There are two birds with which

RUSTY SONG SPARROW

the Song Sparrow might be confused in appearance, the Lincoln Sparrow and the Savannah Sparrow. (See pp. 338 and 317.)

5–6½

Upper parts brown, varying from rusty to grayish brown; under parts white streaked with rusty, dark brown or pale reddish brown; a faint gray line over eye; a dark stripe down side of throat, dark spot in middle of breast. Bill dusky; feet brown.

Dist. — Desert Song Sparrow. *M. m. fallax.*
[*M. m. saltonis.*]
Cal. Common R. from the Colorado R. north to Needles, west to Mecca.
San Diego Song Sparrow. *M. m. cooperi.*
Cal. Common R. chiefly west of the desert divide north to Santa Barbara.
San Clemente Song Sparrow. *M. m. clementæ.*
Cal. R. on many of the Channel Is.
Santa Barbara Song Sparrow. *M. m. graminea.*
Cal. R. on Santa Barbara I.
Heermann Song Sparrow. *M. m. heermanni.*
Cal. Common R. in the southern part of the San Joaquin Valley.
Santa Cruz Song Sparrow. [*M. m. santæcrucis.*]
Cal. Common R. in fresh water marshes from San Luis Obispo Co. north to the San Francisco Bay region.
Alameda / Salt Marsh } Song Sparrow. *M. m. pusillula.*
Cal. Common R. on salt marshes on south arm of San Francisco Bay.
Modesto Song Sparrow. [*M. m. maillardi.*]
Cal. Common R. from Stanislaus Co. to Shasta Co.
Suisun Song Sparrow. *M. m. maxillaris.*
Cal. Common R. on marshes around Suisun Bay.
Samuels Song Sparrow. *M. m. samuelis.*
Cal. Common R. on salt marshes chiefly on the north side of San Francisco Bay.
Marin Song Sparrow. [*M. m. gouldi.*]
Cal. Common R. on fresh-water marshes and streams, chiefly in Marin and Sonoma Cos.
Mendocino Song Sparrow. *M. m. cleonensis.*
Cal. Common R. on the coast from Mendocino Co. to Del Norte Co.
Modoc Song Sparrow. [*M. m. fisherella.*]
Cal. Common R. in northeastern Cal.; common W.V. locally south to Colusa and Glenn Cos. and to the southeastern deserts.
Ore. Common R. in southeastern Ore.
Wash. Possibly S.V. in southeast Wash.
Merrill Song Sparrow. *M. m. merrilli.*
Cal. W.V. in northern Cal., east of the coast belt, south to Glenn and Colusa Cos.; casual farther south.
Ore. / *Wash.* } Common R. east, M. and W.V. west.
Mountain Song Sparrow. *M. m. montana.*
[*M. m. fallax.*]
Ore. S.V. in northeastern Ore.
Wash. Casual east.
Rusty Song Sparrow. *M. m. morphna.*
Cal. Fairly common W.V. along the coast south to the San Francisco Bay region; casual farther south.

Ore. }
Wash. } Common R. west.
Yakutat Song Sparrow. *M. m. caurina.*
Cal. }
Ore. } Rare W.V. on the coast.
Wash. }
Kenai Song Sparrow. *M. m. kenaiensis.*
Ore. }
Wash. } Rare W.V. on the coast.

Nest, on the ground, in low bushes or in trees, of twigs, weed stems and grasses. *Eggs*, 3–5, greenish white, spotted with reddish brown.

Lincoln Sparrow. *Melospiza lincolni* subsp.

In the weedy borders of low ground, a small dark sparrow slips in and out in winter as shyly as a mouse. If an observer waits motionless, the trim little figure appears and feeds with nervous active movements, always near shelter and ready to take instant alarm. A beginner might pass the bird as a Song Sparrow, but close observation shows a darker general coloration, and when the bird faces one a *wash* of *buff* across the *narrowly streaked breast*. A trained observer can tell a Lincoln Sparrow from a Song Sparrow by the proportions; the shorter tail gives the bird a daintier, trimmer figure. When startled, a Lincoln Sparrow raises the crest slightly. In summer the Lincoln Sparrow is common in the wet meadows of the high mountains, among the rank growth of hellebore and the tall flowers of the shooting star. Here its song is constantly poured forth by some male perched on a low tree or bush at the edge of the meadow. The song is made up of parts, with short intervals between, with very rapid bubbling notes suggesting both the House Wren and the Purple Finch. It is a vigorous, joyous outburst, surprisingly loud for such a shy and diminutive singer. The alarm note varies from a light *tsip* to a heavier *tsup*. A beginner should be sure of the *buffy* wash across the breast before identifying a Lincoln Sparrow.

LINCOLN SPARROW

$4\frac{3}{4}$–$5\frac{3}{4}$

Ad. — Upper parts dark brown and olive gray, narrowly streaked with black; throat light gray, with a few streaks of black, bordered by dark lines down the sides; *breast washed with buff*, narrowly streaked with black; dark spot in the middle of the breast. Bill dark above, paler below; feet light brown.

Dist. — Lincoln Sparrow. *M. l. lincolni.*
Cal. Common S.V. (Apr.–Sept.) in wet meadows in the higher mountains; common M. throughout and W.V. north to the San Joaquin Valley.
Ore. }
Wash. } Common S.V. (May–Sept.) in moist meadows in the higher mountains; M. in the lowlands.
Forbush Lincoln Sparrow. *M. l. striata.*
Cal. Fairly common W.V. in the coast belt south to Monterey Co.; casual south to San Diego.

Ore. } Probably not uncommon M. and perhaps W.V. (Sept.–
Wash. } Apr.) west.

Nest, on the ground of grasses. *Eggs,* 4–5, bluish white, heavily marked with reddish brown.

Snow Bunting. *Plectrophenax nivalis nivalis*

Occasionally in eastern Oregon and Washington one sees a flock of Snow Buntings whirling over the prairies in mid-winter with strong undulating flight, the sun shining through the white patches in their wings. Snow Buntings often associate in winter with Horned Larks, feeding on weed seeds in waste ground, on open prairies or even among the outbuildings of ranches. The great amount of white in the plumage easily distinguishes the bird, particularly on the wing. Its notes are a high, sweet and slightly mournful *tee* or *tée-oo,* a sweet rolling whistle, and a harsh *bzz.*

6–7

Ad. in winter. — *Head and under parts white,* washed on the head and sides of breast with rusty brown; the black feathers of the back veiled with gray and brown; *wings and tail black and white.* Bill yellow, tipped with dusky; feet black. Towards spring the plumage becomes gradually black and white. **Im.** — Brown on the crown and sides of head deeper; black of wings and tail not so clear, and white less pure.

Dist. — *Cal.* One record.
Ore. } Irregular and uncommon W.V. (Oct.–Mar.) both east
Wash. } and west, commoner east.

INDEX